A-Level Mathematics

for AQA Statistics 2

The Complete Course for AQA S2

Contents

Introduction

Chapter 1

Discrete Random Variables

Chapter 2

The Poisson Distribution

Chapter 3

Continuous Random Variables

Chapter 4

Estimation and Hypothesis Testing

Chapter 5

Chi-Squared Contingency Table Tests

Reference

About this book

In this book you'll find...

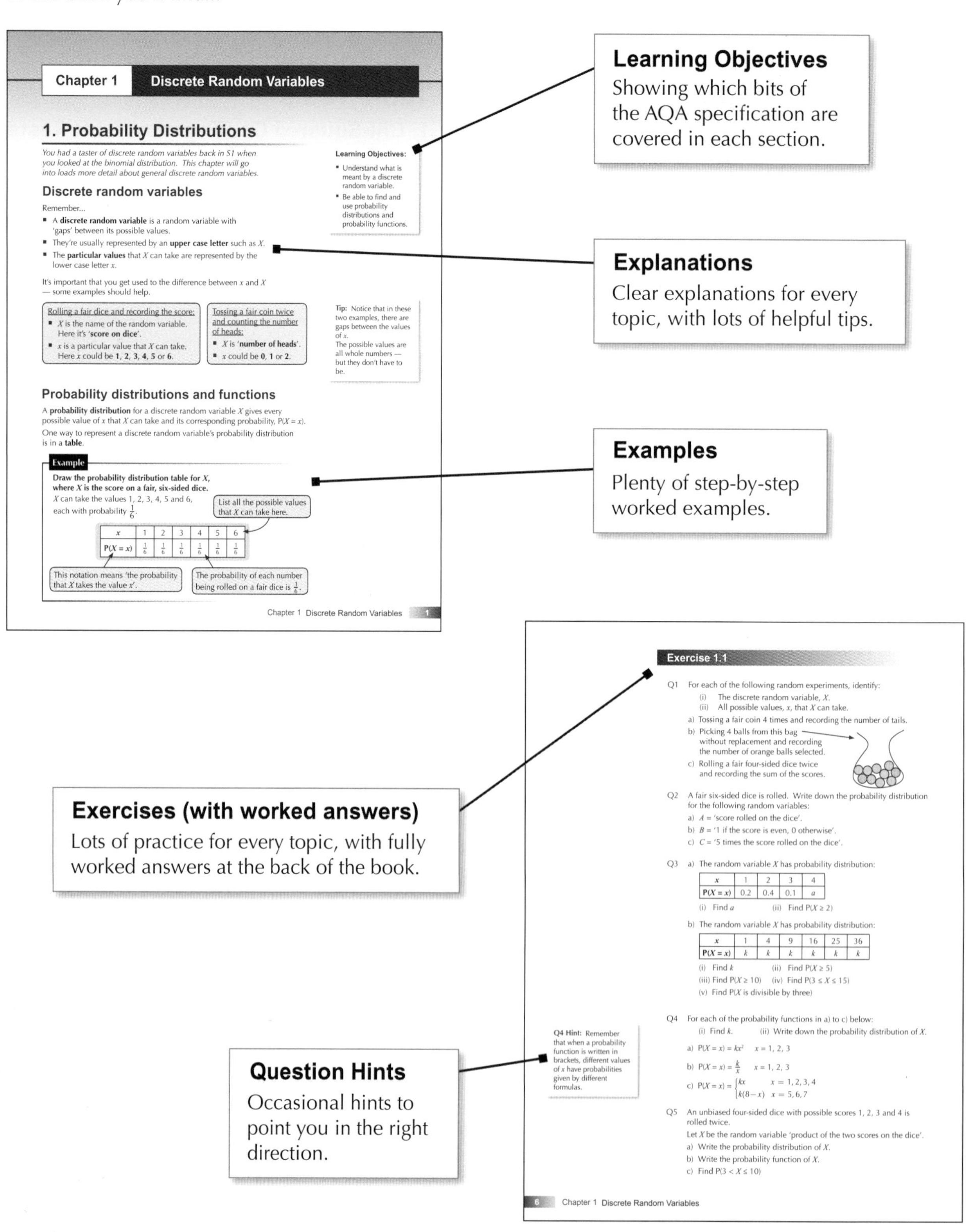

Review Exercise — Chapter 1

Q1 The probability distribution of Y is:

y	0	1	2	3
$P(Y = y)$	0.5	k	k	$3k$

a) Find the value of k. b) Find $P(Y < 2)$.

Q2 A discrete random variable X has the probability function:

x	1	2	3
$P(X = x)$	0.6	0.3	0.1

a) Find $E(X)$ b) Find $Var(X)$ c) Find $E\left(\frac{3}{X}\right)$ d) Find $Var\left(\frac{3}{X}\right)$

Q3 A discrete random variable X has the probability distribution shown in the table, where k is a constant.

x_i	1	2	3	4
p_i	$\frac{1}{6}$	$\frac{1}{2}$	k	$\frac{5}{24}$

a) Find k b) Find $E(X)$ and show that $Var(X) = \frac{63}{64}$ c) Find $E(2X - 1)$ and $Var(2X - 1)$

Q4 A discrete random variable X has the probability distribution shown in the table.

x_i	1	2	3	4	5	6
p_i	0.1	0.2	0.25	0.2	0.1	0.15

a) Find $E(X)$ b) Find $Var(X)$

Q5 a) The random variable X is given by the probability distribution:

x	8	10	15	20
$P(X = x)$	0.2	0.3	0.1	0.4

(i) Find $E(X)$ and $Var(X)$.
(ii) $Y = 4X + 3$. Find $E(Y)$ and $Var(Y)$.
(iii) $Z = 50 - 2X$. Find $E(Z)$ and $Var(Z)$.

b) The random variable X is given by the probability distribution:

x	−4	−1	0	2	5	6
$P(X = x)$	$\frac{1}{2}$	$\frac{1}{4}$	$\frac{1}{8}$	$\frac{1}{16}$	$\frac{1}{32}$	$\frac{1}{32}$

(i) Find $E(X)$ and $Var(X)$.
(ii) $Y = 7 - 2X$. Find $E(Y)$ and $Var(Y)$.
(iii) $Z = 7 + 2X$. Find $E(Z)$ and $Var(Z)$.

16 Chapter 1 Discrete Random Variables

Review Exercises

Mixed questions covering the whole chapter, with fully worked answers.

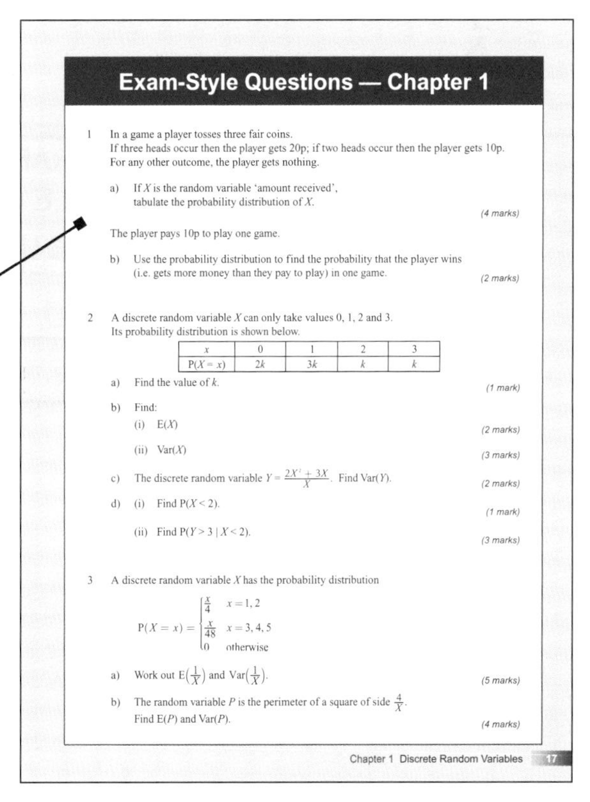

Exam-Style Questions — Chapter 1

1 In a game a player tosses three fair coins.
If three heads occur then the player gets 20p; if two heads occur then the player gets 10p.
For any other outcome, the player gets nothing.

a) If X is the random variable 'amount received', tabulate the probability distribution of X. *(4 marks)*

The player pays 10p to play one game.

b) Use the probability distribution to find the probability that the player wins (i.e. gets more money than they pay to play) in one game. *(2 marks)*

2 A discrete random variable X can only take values 0, 1, 2 and 3.
Its probability distribution is shown below.

x	0	1	2	3
$P(X = x)$	$2k$	$3k$	k	k

a) Find the value of k. *(1 mark)*

b) Find:
(i) $E(X)$ *(2 marks)*
(ii) $Var(X)$ *(3 marks)*

c) The discrete random variable $Y = \frac{2X^2 + 3X}{X}$. Find $Var(Y)$. *(2 marks)*

d) (i) Find $P(X < 2)$. *(1 mark)*
(ii) Find $P(Y > 3 \mid X < 2)$. *(3 marks)*

3 A discrete random variable X has the probability distribution

$$P(X = x) = \begin{cases} \frac{x}{4} & x = 1, 2 \\ \frac{x}{48} & x = 3, 4, 5 \\ 0 & \text{otherwise} \end{cases}$$

a) Work out $E\left(\frac{1}{X}\right)$ and $Var\left(\frac{1}{X}\right)$. *(5 marks)*

b) The random variable P is the perimeter of a square of side $\frac{4}{X}$.
Find $E(P)$ and $Var(P)$. *(4 marks)*

Chapter 1 Discrete Random Variables 17

Exam-Style Questions

Questions in the same style as the ones you'll get in the exam, with worked solutions and mark schemes.

Formula Sheet and Statistical Tables

Containing all the formulas and statistical tables you'll be given in the S2 exam.

Glossary

All the definitions you need to know for the exam, plus other useful words.

Practice Exam Papers (on CD-ROM)

Two printable exam papers, with fully worked answers and mark schemes.

A-Level
Mathematics
for AQA
S2
Exam Practice Papers
& Worked Answers
CGP

Published by CGP

Editors:
Ali Palin, Andy Park, Charlotte Whiteley.

Contributors:
Michael Coe, Claire Creasor, Anna Gainey, Dave Harding,
Claire Jackson, James Nicholson, Janet West.

ISBN: 978 1 84762 799 5

With thanks to Mona Allen and Glenn Rogers for the proofreading.

Groovy website: www.cgpbooks.co.uk

Printed by Elanders Ltd, Newcastle upon Tyne.
Jolly bits of clipart from CorelDRAW®

1. Probability Distributions

You had a taster of discrete random variables back in S1 when you looked at the binomial distribution. This chapter will go into loads more detail about general discrete random variables.

Learning Objectives:
- Understand what is meant by a discrete random variable.
- Be able to find and use probability distributions and probability functions.

Discrete random variables

Remember...
- A **discrete random variable** is a random variable with 'gaps' between its possible values.
- They're usually represented by an **upper case letter** such as X.
- The **particular values** that X can take are represented by the lower case letter x.

It's important that you get used to the difference between x and X — some examples should help.

Rolling a fair dice and recording the score:
- X is the name of the random variable. Here it's '**score on dice**'.
- x is a particular value that X can take. Here x could be **1**, **2**, **3**, **4**, **5** or **6**.

Tossing a fair coin twice and counting the number of heads:
- X is '**number of heads**'.
- x could be **0**, **1** or **2**.

Tip: Notice that in these two examples, there are gaps between the values of x. The possible values are all whole numbers — but they don't have to be.

Probability distributions and functions

A **probability distribution** for a discrete random variable X gives every possible value of x that X can take and its corresponding probability, $P(X = x)$.

One way to represent a discrete random variable's probability distribution is in a **table**.

Example

Draw the probability distribution table for X, where X is the score on a fair, six-sided dice.

X can take the values 1, 2, 3, 4, 5 and 6, each with probability $\frac{1}{6}$.

List all the possible values that X can take here.

x	1	2	3	4	5	6
$P(X = x)$	$\frac{1}{6}$	$\frac{1}{6}$	$\frac{1}{6}$	$\frac{1}{6}$	$\frac{1}{6}$	$\frac{1}{6}$

This notation means 'the probability that X takes the value x'.

The probability of each number being rolled on a fair dice is $\frac{1}{6}$.

Tip: You've seen a probability function before, for the binomial distribution:

$P(X = x) = \binom{n}{x} \times p^x \times (1-p)^{n-x}$

Tip: Make sure you're always clear what X represents — here it's the score.

Tip: The probability of X being any other value is zero — it's impossible.

Tip: Even though it's described as a 'formula', the probability function can be just a number.

Tip: This probability function is defined 'piecewise' — there are different formulas for different values of x.

Tip: You can check this rule works for the examples above — just add up the 6 probabilities in part a) (or the 2 probabilities for part b)) and you should get 1.

Tip: So $P(X > k) = 1 - P(X \leq k)$ and $P(X < k) = 1 - P(X \geq k)$

A **probability function** is a formula that generates the probability of X taking the value x, for every possible x. It is written $\mathbf{P(X = x)}$ or sometimes just $\mathbf{p(x)}$. A probability function is really just another way of representing the information in the probability distribution table.

Examples

a) A fair six-sided dice is thrown once and the score, X, is recorded. Write down the probability function of X.

- To write down the probability function, you need to work out the **possible values**, x, that X can take and the **probability** of each value.
  The outcome of throwing the dice can either be 1, 2, 3, 4, 5 or 6, so X can take any of these values.
  The probability of each outcome is $\frac{1}{6}$.
- Now you can write down the probability function:

$$P(X = x) = \frac{1}{6} \quad x = 1, 2, 3, 4, 5, 6$$

List the possible values of x after the 'formula'.

b) A biased coin, for which the probability of heads is $\frac{3}{4}$ and tails is $\frac{1}{4}$, is tossed once and the number of tails, X, is counted. Write down the probability function of X.

- The outcome can either be heads or tails, so X can either be **0** or **1**. The probability of heads, $P(X = 0)$, is $\frac{3}{4}$ and the probability of tails, $P(X = 1)$, is $\frac{1}{4}$.
- This time, the probabilities are **different** for different values of x — so it's best to use two 'formulas', one for each x value. Write the probability function as a bracket like this:

$$P(X = x) = \begin{cases} \frac{3}{4} & x = 0 \\ \frac{1}{4} & x = 1 \end{cases}$$

Put each value of x next to the 'formula' which gives its probability.

And don't forget the important rule about the sum of all the probabilities:

The **probabilities** of **all** the possible values that a discrete random variable can take **add up to 1**.

For a **discrete random variable** X:

$$\sum_{\text{all } x} P(X = x) = 1$$

You can use the fact that all the probabilities add up to 1 to solve problems where **probabilities** are **unknown** or contain unknown factors.

Example

The random variable X has the probability function below:

$$P(X = x) = \begin{cases} \left(\frac{2}{5}\right)\left(\frac{1}{4^x}\right) & x = 1, 2 \\ \frac{k}{8} & x = 3 \end{cases}$$

Find the value of k.

So X has three possible values (x = 1, 2 and 3), and the probability of each is given by the probability function.

It's easier to understand if you write out the probability distribution:

x	1	2	3
P(X = x)	$\left(\frac{2}{5}\right)\left(\frac{1}{4^1}\right) = \frac{1}{10}$	$\left(\frac{2}{5}\right)\left(\frac{1}{4^2}\right) = \frac{1}{40}$	$\frac{k}{8}$

Now just use the rule: $\sum_{\text{all } x} P(X = x) = 1$

Here, this means: $\frac{1}{10} + \frac{1}{40} + \frac{k}{8} = 1$

$\Rightarrow \frac{1}{8} + \frac{k}{8} = 1 \Rightarrow k = 7$

Tip: It'll often help to write down the probability distribution table when solving problems like these — that way you won't miss out any values.

You may be asked to find the probability that X is **greater** or **less** than a value, or **lies between** two values. You just need to identify all the values that X can now take and then it's a simple case of **adding up** all their **probabilities**.

Example

The discrete random variable X has the following probability distribution:

x	0	1	2	3	4
P(X = x)	0.1	0.2	0.3	0.2	a

Find: a) the value of a, b) P(X < 3), c) P(2 ≤ X < 4)

a) Use $\sum_{\text{all } x} P(X = x) = 1$ again.

From the table: $0.1 + 0.2 + 0.3 + 0.2 + a = 1$

$\Rightarrow 0.8 + a = 1 \Rightarrow a = 0.2$

b) The probability that 'X is less than 3' means the probability that 'X is 0, or X is 1, or X is 2'. So just add up the three probabilities:

$P(X < 3) = P(X = 0) + P(X = 1) + P(X = 2) = 0.1 + 0.2 + 0.3 = 0.6$

c) This is asking for the probability that 'X is greater than or equal to 2, but less than 4'. In other words the probability that $X = 2$ or $X = 3$.

Just add up the probabilities:

$P(2 \le X < 4) = P(X = 2 \text{ or } 3)$

$= P(X = 2) + P(X = 3)$

$= 0.3 + 0.2 = 0.5$

The events $X = 2$ and $X = 3$ are mutually exclusive so you can add the probabilities.

Tip: Careful with the inequality signs — you need to include $X = 2$ but not $X = 4$.

When it's not clear what the probability distribution or function should be, it can be helpful to draw a **sample-space diagram** of all the **possible outcomes** and work it out from that.

Example 1

An unbiased six-sided dice has faces marked 1, 1, 1, 2, 2, 3.
The dice is rolled twice.
Let X be the random variable 'sum of the two scores on the dice'.
a) Find the probability distribution of X.

- To find the probability distribution, you need to identify all the possible values, x, that X could take and the probability of each.

  The easiest way to do this is to draw a sample-space diagram showing the 36 possible outcomes of the dice rolls:

Score on roll 1 (columns); Score on roll 2 (rows)

+	1	1	1	2	2	3
1	2	2	2	3	3	4
1	2	2	2	3	3	4
1	2	2	2	3	3	4
2	3	3	3	4	4	5
2	3	3	3	4	4	5
3	4	4	4	5	5	6

- From the diagram you can see that there are only five values that X can take: $x = 2, 3, 4, 5, 6$.

- Since all 36 outcomes are equally likely, you can find the probability of each value by counting how many times it occurs in the diagram and dividing by 36.

  9 out of the 36 outcomes give a score of 2.
  So $P(X = 2) = \frac{9}{36} = \frac{1}{4}$

  12 out of the 36 outcomes give a score of 3.
  So $P(X = 3) = \frac{12}{36} = \frac{1}{3}$

  Similarly,
  $P(X = 4) = \frac{10}{36} = \frac{5}{18}$, $P(X = 5) = \frac{4}{36} = \frac{1}{9}$, $P(X = 6) = \frac{1}{36}$

Tip: See S1 for the equally likely outcomes formula.

Tip: Don't forget to change the fractions into their simplest form.

Tip: You should always check that all the probabilities in your table add up to 1 — if they don't you've done something wrong.

- So the probability distribution is:

x	2	3	4	5	6
$P(X = x)$	$\frac{1}{4}$	$\frac{1}{3}$	$\frac{5}{18}$	$\frac{1}{9}$	$\frac{1}{36}$

b) Find $P(X < 5)$.

This is asking for the probability that X is strictly less than 5, in other words X takes values 2, 3 or 4. Just add the probabilities together.

$P(X < 5) = P(X = 2) + P(X = 3) + P(X = 4) = \frac{1}{4} + \frac{1}{3} + \frac{5}{18} = \frac{31}{36}$

Example 2

A game involves rolling two fair dice. If the sum of the scores is greater than 10 then the player wins 50p. If the sum is between 8 and 10 (inclusive) then they win 20p. Otherwise they get nothing.

a) If X is the random variable 'amount player wins', find the probability distribution of X.

- There are three possible amounts of money to be won, so there are three possible values that X can take: 0, 20 and 50.
- For each x value, you need to find the probability of getting a sum of scores which results in that value of x.

$$P(X = 0) = P(\text{Sum of scores} < 8)$$
$$P(X = 20) = P(8 \leq \text{Sum of scores} \leq 10)$$
$$P(X = 50) = P(\text{Sum of scores} > 10)$$

- To find these probabilities, draw a sample-space diagram showing the 36 possible outcomes of the dice rolls.
  Mark on your diagram all the outcomes that give each value of x.

Score on dice 1 (columns); Score on dice 2 (rows)

+	1	2	3	4	5	6
1	2	3	4	5	6	7
2	3	4	5	6	7	8
3	4	5	6	7	8	9
4	5	6	7	8	9	10
5	6	7	8	9	10	11
6	7	8	9	10	11	12

- 21 out of 36 outcomes give a sum of scores which is strictly less than 8, so $P(X = 0) = P(\text{Sum of scores} < 8) = \frac{21}{36} = \frac{7}{12}$
- 12 out of 36 outcomes give a sum of scores between 8 and 10 inclusive, so $P(X = 20) = P(8 \leq \text{Sum of scores} \leq 10) = \frac{12}{36} = \frac{1}{3}$
- 3 out of 36 outcomes give a sum of scores strictly greater than 10, so $P(X = 50) = P(\text{Sum of scores} > 10) = \frac{3}{36} = \frac{1}{12}$
- Using this information, draw the probability distribution:

x	0	20	50
$P(X = x)$	$\frac{7}{12}$	$\frac{1}{3}$	$\frac{1}{12}$

b) The game costs 15p to play. Find the probability of making a profit.

- A player will make a profit if they win more than 15p — so if they win 20p or 50p.
- So the probability of making a profit is
  $P(X > 15) = P(X = 20) + P(X = 50) = \frac{1}{3} + \frac{1}{12} = \frac{5}{12}$

Exercise 1.1

Q1 For each of the following random experiments, identify:

(i) The discrete random variable, X.

(ii) All possible values, x, that X can take.

a) Tossing a fair coin 4 times and recording the number of tails.

b) Picking 4 balls from this bag without replacement and recording the number of orange balls selected.

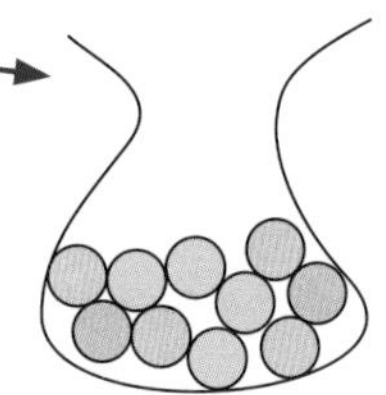

c) Rolling a fair four-sided dice twice and recording the sum of the scores.

Q2 A fair six-sided dice is rolled. Write down the probability distribution for the following random variables:

a) A = 'score rolled on the dice'.

b) B = '1 if the score is even, 0 otherwise'.

c) C = '5 times the score rolled on the dice'.

Q3 a) The random variable X has probability distribution:

x	1	2	3	4
$P(X = x)$	0.2	0.4	0.1	a

(i) Find a (ii) Find $P(X \geq 2)$

b) The random variable X has probability distribution:

x	1	4	9	16	25	36
$P(X = x)$	k	k	k	k	k	k

(i) Find k (ii) Find $P(X \geq 5)$

(iii) Find $P(X \geq 10)$ (iv) Find $P(3 \leq X \leq 15)$

(v) Find P(X is divisible by three)

Q4 For each of the probability functions in a) to c) below:

(i) Find k. (ii) Write down the probability distribution of X.

Q4 Hint: Remember that when a probability function is written in brackets, different values of x have probabilities given by different formulas.

a) $P(X = x) = kx^2 \quad x = 1, 2, 3$

b) $P(X = x) = \frac{k}{x} \quad x = 1, 2, 3$

c) $P(X = x) = \begin{cases} kx & x = 1, 2, 3, 4 \\ k(8-x) & x = 5, 6, 7 \end{cases}$

Q5 An unbiased four-sided dice with possible scores 1, 2, 3 and 4 is rolled twice.

Let X be the random variable 'product of the two scores on the dice'.

a) Write the probability distribution of X.

b) Write the probability function of X.

c) Find $P(3 < X \leq 10)$

2. Expected Values, Mean and Variance

All discrete random variables have a mean (expected value) and variance. They are theoretical values based on the probability distribution — what you'd expect the mean and variance to be if you took lots of readings. You've used formulas for finding the mean and variance of a binomial distribution, but now you need to be able to find them for any discrete random variable.

Learning Objectives:

- Be able to calculate the mean and variance of discrete random variables.
- Be able to calculate the expected value and variance of functions of discrete random variables.

The expected value

The expected value of X, E(X)

Every **discrete random variable**, X, has an '**expected value**' (or **mean**) **E(X)**. In theory, it's what you'd **expect** the mean of the data to be if you took lots of readings. In practice, the mean is unlikely to be exactly E(X), but it should be pretty close.

If the discrete random variable X can take values $x_1, x_2, x_3, ...$ then the expected value of X is:

$$\text{Mean} = \text{Expected Value } \mathrm{E}(X) = \sum x_i \mathrm{P}(X = x_i) = \sum x_i p_i$$

So all you do is **multiply** each **x-value** by its **probability** and **add** all the results together.

Tip: Remember that x_i is just notation for all the different x-values, x_1, x_2 etc.

So $\sum x_i \mathrm{P}(X = x_i)$
$= x_1 \mathrm{P}(X = x_1)$
$+ x_2 \mathrm{P}(X = x_2) + ...$

And p_i is just short for $\mathrm{P}(X = x_i)$.

Example 1

The probability distribution of X, the number of daughters in a family of 3 children, is shown in the table. Find the expected number of daughters.

x_i	0	1	2	3
p_i	$\frac{1}{8}$	$\frac{3}{8}$	$\frac{3}{8}$	$\frac{1}{8}$

Just add up all the $x_i p_i$'s:

$$\mathrm{E}(X) = \sum x_i p_i = \left[0 \times \frac{1}{8}\right] + \left[1 \times \frac{3}{8}\right] + \left[2 \times \frac{3}{8}\right] + \left[3 \times \frac{1}{8}\right]$$
$$= 0 + \frac{3}{8} + \frac{6}{8} + \frac{3}{8} = \frac{12}{8} = 1.5$$

So the expected number of daughters is 1.5.

Tip: The expected value (or mean) of a random variable is sometimes labelled μ.

Tip: It sounds a bit weird to expect 1.5 daughters — but all it means is that if you check a large number of 3-child families, the mean will be close to 1.5.

Example 2

A discrete random variable, X, has the probability distribution shown in the table. Given that E(X) = 2.7, find a and b.

x_i	1	2	3	4
p_i	0.2	0.3	a	b

- There are two unknowns to find, so you'll need **two** bits of information. The first is given in the question, **E(X) = 2.7**.

$$\mathrm{E}(X) = \sum x_i p_i = [1 \times 0.2] + [2 \times 0.3] + 3a + 4b$$
$$\Rightarrow 2.7 = 0.8 + 3a + 4b$$
$$\text{So} \quad 1.9 = 3a + 4b$$

- It might not be obvious what the second bit of information is — nothing else is given in the question. But there is something that is true for every discrete random variable — all the probabilities must add up to 1.

$$\sum p_i = 1$$

So $0.5 + a + b = 1$ so $a + b = 0.5$

- Now you just need to solve the simultaneous equations

(1) $a + b = 0.5$ and (2) $3a + 4b = 1.9$

(1) gives $a = 0.5 - b$ and substituting this into (2) gives:

$$3(0.5 - b) + 4b = 1.9$$
$$1.5 - 3b + 4b = 1.9$$
$$1.5 + b = 1.9$$
$$b = 0.4$$

Substituting $b = 0.4$ into (1) gives $a = 0.1$

Tip: This is the 'substitution' method of solving simultaneous equations. In general it means isolating one of the variables (getting a or b on its own) and substituting it into the other equation. You can also solve simultaneous equations using the 'elimination' method (which involves adding or subtracting them to get rid of one unknown).

The expected value of X^2, E(X^2)

It is sometimes useful to work out the expected value of 'X^2', **E(X^2)** — for example, when calculating the **variance** of X (see p10). You can work out a **probability distribution** for X^2, just as you can for X, and then calculating the expected value is easy.

Tip: You'll be using E(X^2) to work out the variance a lot in this chapter so make sure you get comfortable with it here.

Example 1

Here's the probability distribution from Example 1 on the previous page:

x_i	0	1	2	3
p_i	$\frac{1}{8}$	$\frac{3}{8}$	$\frac{3}{8}$	$\frac{1}{8}$

Find the probability distribution of X^2.

The probability distribution table for X^2 is similar to the one for X. You just need to square the x_i values and keep the probabilities the same.

The distribution of X^2 is:

These are just the x_i values squared.

x_i^2	0	1	4	9
$P(X^2 = x_i^2)$	$\frac{1}{8}$	$\frac{3}{8}$	$\frac{3}{8}$	$\frac{1}{8}$

The probabilities don't change, which means $\mathbf{P(X^2 = x_i^2) = P(X = x_i) = p_i}$.

If the discrete random variable X can take values $x_1, x_2, x_3, \ldots$ then the expected value of X^2 is:

$$E(X^2) = \sum x_i^2 P(X = x_i) = \sum x_i^2 p_i$$

Tip: You'll see in a few pages that you can find the expected value of any function of X (p13).

Example 2

For the discrete random variable defined in Example 1 on the previous page, find the value of E(X^2).

Using the formula:

$$E(X^2) = \sum x_i^2 p_i = \left[0 \times \frac{1}{8}\right] + \left[1 \times \frac{3}{8}\right] + \left[4 \times \frac{3}{8}\right] + \left[9 \times \frac{1}{8}\right]$$

$$= 0 + \frac{3}{8} + \frac{12}{8} + \frac{9}{8} = \frac{24}{8} = 3$$

Tip: Notice that E(X^2) is not the same as $[E(X)]^2$.

Exercise 2.1

Q1 Find E(X) for each of the following discrete random variables.

a) $P(X = x) = 0.2 \quad x = 0, 1, 2, 3, 4$

b) $P(X = x) = \frac{x^2}{14} \quad x = 1, 2, 3$

c) $P(X = x) = \begin{cases} 0.1 & x = 2 \\ 0.4 & x = 3 \\ 0.5 & x = 1 \end{cases}$

d) $P(X = x) = \begin{cases} 0.1 & x = -2 \\ 0.2 & x = -1, 1, 2 \\ 0.3 & x = 0 \end{cases}$

e) $P(X = x) = k(x + 2) \quad x = 1, 2, 3, 4, 5$

f) $P(X = x) = \frac{k}{x} \quad x = 1, 2, 3, 4, 5$

Q1 Hint: You might want to write out the probability distribution to help you find E(X) — but you don't need to.

Q1 Hint: For parts e) and f), you'll need to work out the value of k first.

Q2 Each table below shows the probability distribution of a discrete random variable, X. Use the information given to find the required values.

a)

x	2	5	6	p
P(X = x)	0.2	0.3	0.1	0.4

If E(X) = 6.5 find the value of p.

b)

x	4	8	p	15
P(X = x)	0.5	0.2	a	0.2

If E(X) = 7.5 find the values of a and p.

Q2 b) Hint: Find a first.

Q3 Each table below shows the probability distribution of a discrete random variable, X. Use the information given to find a and b for each.

a)

x	1	2	3	4
P(X = x)	0.2	a	0.1	b

where E(X) = 2.5

b)

x	3	7	8	12
P(X = x)	0.1	a	b	0.1

where E(X) = 7.8

Q4 In parts a)-c), the tables show the probability distribution for a discrete random variable, X. For each part, find: (i) E(X) (ii) E(X^2)

a)

x	1	2	3	4	5
P(X = x)	0.2	0.1	0.25	0.25	0.2

b)

x	–3	–2	–1	0	1
P(X = x)	0.2	0.1	0.25	0.25	0.2

c)

x	3	4	5	7	9
P(X = x)	0.1	0.25	0.15	0.3	0.2

Variance

Just like you can find the **mean** (μ) of a discrete random variable, you can also find its **variance**. This measures the **spread** of the random variable's distribution about its mean. Again, it's a theoretical value — it's the '**expected variance**' of a large number of readings.

The graphs below show the probability distributions of two **discrete random variables**, X and Y:

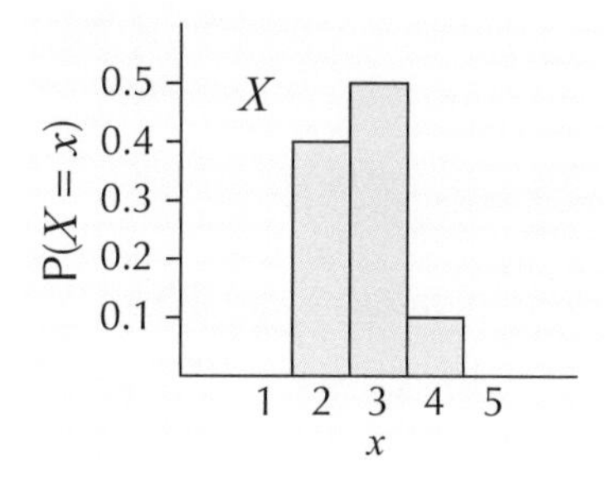

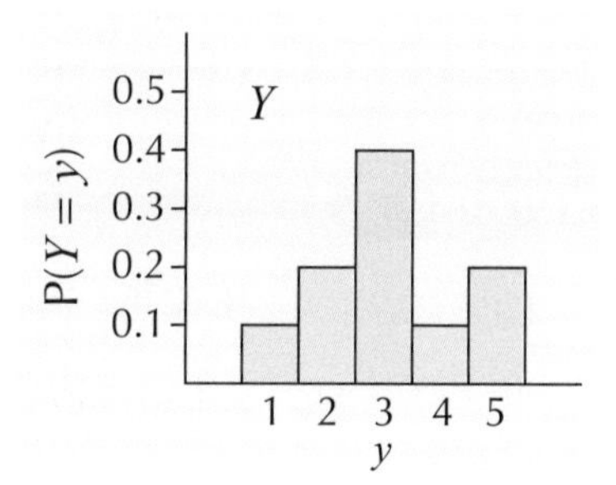

If you were to collect a large number of readings of both X and Y, you'd expect the readings of X to be **less spread out** than the readings of Y.

But... even if you **don't** collect any actual readings of X or Y, you can still work out the variance of X and Y based on their probability distributions. And you'd expect the variance of X to be **smaller** than that of Y.

Now then... suppose a **discrete random variable** X can take values $x_1, x_2, x_3,$...
The variance of X is 'the expected squared deviation from the mean (μ)' — in other words: $\text{Var}(X) = E[(X-\mu)^2] = \sum(x_i-\mu)^2 p_i$ (see Tip above).

But there's a different way to write the formula for the variance that's much **easier to use**:

$$\text{Var}(X) = E(X^2) - [E(X)]^2 = \sum x_i^2 p_i - [\sum x_i p_i]^2$$

In fact, the formula for the variance can be written in various ways.
For example, on the formula sheet you'll get in the exam, it's written as:

$$\text{Var}(X) = \sigma^2 = \sum(x_i-\mu)^2 p_i = \sum x_i^2 p_i - \mu^2 = E(X^2) - \mu^2$$

But these formulas are all **equivalent** — they'll always give the same answers. And you can always take one of these formulas and 'turn it into' any of the others — just by rearranging it, and using the definitions on the left.

For example:

$$\begin{aligned}\text{Var}(X) &= E[(X-\mu)^2] \\ &= E[X^2 - 2\mu X + \mu^2] && \text{(multiplying out the brackets)} \\ &= E(X^2) - 2\mu E(X) + \mu^2 && \text{(see the bottom Tip for more info)} \\ &= E(X^2) - 2[E(X)]^2 + [E(X)]^2 && \text{(using the definition } \mu = E(X)) \\ &= E(X^2) - [E(X)]^2\end{aligned}$$

The **standard deviation** of a discrete random variable X is just the square root of its variance: $\text{Standard deviation} = \sqrt{\text{Variance}} = \sqrt{\text{Var}(X)}$

Tip: The variance of a data set is given by

$$\text{variance} = \frac{\sum(x-\bar{x})^2}{n}$$

— so the variance is 'the average squared deviation from the mean'.

Tip: $E[(X-\mu)^2] = \sum(x_i-\mu)^2 p_i$ because to work out an expected value, you always:

(i) swap the random variable in the expression for each of its possible values — so here you need to find $(x_i-\mu)^2$ for the various possible values x_i,

(ii) multiply each of those values by the probability (p_i) of x_i,

(iii) sum the results.

Tip: You can remember the variance formula as:

'mean of the squares minus the square of the mean.'

Tip: Remember...

(i) $P(X = x_i) = p_i$

(ii) $E(X) = \mu = \sum x_i p_i$

(iii) $E(X^2) = \sum x_i^2 p_i$

Tip: You'll see on p13 that $E(aX + b) = aE(X) + b$

This tells you that you can 'break apart' an expected value involving addition, or multiplication by a **number** (not by another variable, though). This means you can write $E[X^2 - 2\mu X + \mu^2]$ as $E(X^2) - 2\mu E(X) + \mu^2$.

Example 1

X has the probability function $P(X = x) = k(x + 1)$ $\quad x = 0, 1, 2, 3, 4$.
Find the mean and variance of X.

- First you need to find k.
  Work out all the probabilities and remember they add up to 1:

$$P(X = 0) = k \times (0 + 1) = k$$

Similarly, $P(X = 1) = 2k$

$$P(X = 2) = 3k$$
$$P(X = 3) = 4k$$
$$P(X = 4) = 5k$$

So $k + 2k + 3k + 4k + 5k = 1$, i.e. $15k = 1$, and so $k = \frac{1}{15}$

- Now use the formulas — find the **mean, E(X),** first:

$$E(X) = \sum x_i p_i$$
$$= \left[0 \times \tfrac{1}{15}\right] + \left[1 \times \tfrac{2}{15}\right] + \left[2 \times \tfrac{3}{15}\right] + \left[3 \times \tfrac{4}{15}\right] + \left[4 \times \tfrac{5}{15}\right]$$
$$= \frac{40}{15} = \frac{8}{3}$$

- For the **variance** you also need **E(X^2)**:

$$E(X^2) = \sum x_i^2 p_i$$
$$= \left[0^2 \times \tfrac{1}{15}\right] + \left[1^2 \times \tfrac{2}{15}\right] + \left[2^2 \times \tfrac{3}{15}\right] + \left[3^2 \times \tfrac{4}{15}\right] + \left[4^2 \times \tfrac{5}{15}\right]$$
$$= \frac{130}{15} = \frac{26}{3}$$

- And finally:

$$\text{Var}(X) = E(X^2) - [E(X)]^2 = \frac{26}{3} - \left[\frac{8}{3}\right]^2 = \frac{14}{9}$$

Tip: Work out the variance in steps to avoid making mistakes.

You know E(X), so now find E(X^2).

Then put them both into the formula for variance.

Example 2

The discrete random variable X has the following probability distribution:

x	1	4	p	8
P($X = x$)	0.2	a	0.5	0.2

If E(X) = 5.2, find the values of a and p and the standard deviation of X.

- First find the value of a. Use the fact that the sum of the probabilities must be 1:

$$0.2 + a + 0.5 + 0.2 = 1$$
$$\Rightarrow 0.9 + a = 1$$
$$\Rightarrow a = 0.1$$

- Now use E(X) = 5.2 to find the value of p:

$$E(X) = [1 \times 0.2] + [4 \times 0.1] + [p \times 0.5] + [8 \times 0.2]$$
$$= 2.2 + 0.5p$$

$a = 0.1$

So $5.2 = 2.2 + 0.5p$

$\Rightarrow \quad 3 = 0.5p \quad \Rightarrow \quad p = 6$

- Now work out $E(X^2)$ so you can calculate the variance.

$$E(X^2) = [1^2 \times 0.2] + [4^2 \times 0.1] + [6^2 \times 0.5] + [8^2 \times 0.2]$$
$$= [1 \times 0.2] + [16 \times 0.1] + [36 \times 0.5] + [64 \times 0.2] = 32.6$$

So $\text{Var}(X) = E(X^2) - [E(X)]^2 = 32.6 - 5.2^2 = 32.6 - 27.04 = 5.56$

- Standard deviation $= \sqrt{\text{Variance}} = \sqrt{\text{Var}(X)}$

So standard deviation $= \sqrt{5.56} =$ 2.36 (3 sig. fig.)

Exercise 2.2

Q1 For each of the following probability distributions, calculate the mean and variance of X.

a)

x	1	2	3	4	5
p(x)	0.2	0.1	0.2	0.1	0.4

b)

x	1	3	6	8	9	10
p(x)	$\frac{1}{2}$	$\frac{1}{4}$	$\frac{1}{8}$	$\frac{1}{16}$	$\frac{1}{32}$	$\frac{1}{32}$

c)

x	–2	–1	0	1	2
p(x)	0.2	0.1	0.2	0.1	0.4

Q2 Each of the probability functions below defines a discrete random variable, X. Calculate the mean and variance of X.

a) $P(X = x) = \frac{1}{5}$ $x = 1, 2, 3, 4, 5$ b) $P(X = x) = \frac{x^2}{30}$ $x = 1, 2, 3, 4$

Q3 For each of the probability distributions below:
(i) Find a. (ii) Find the mean, variance and standard deviation of X.

a)

x	1	2	3	4
P($X = x$)	0.2	a	0.4	0.1

b)

x	–3	–2	–1	0
P($X = x$)	a	0.3	a	0.1

Q4 Each of the probability distributions below describes a discrete random variable, X.

a)

x	3	4	6	p
P($X = x$)	0.2	0.3	0.1	0.4

If $E(X) = 5.2$, find:
(i) the value of p, (ii) the standard deviation of X.

b)

x	1	4	p	9
P($X = x$)	0.2	a	0.4	0.3

If $E(X) = 5.7$, find the values of a and p and the variance of X.

Q5 Each of the probability functions below describes a discrete random variable, X. For each: (i) Find k (ii) Find $E(X)$ (iii) Find $\text{Var}(X)$

a) $P(X = x) = kx^2$ $x = 3, 4, 5$ b) $P(X = x) = \frac{k}{x}$ $x = 3, 4, 5, 6$

Expected value and variance of a function of X

On p8, you saw that you can find $E(X^2)$ by replacing x_i with x_i^2 in the formula for $E(X)$. Well... you can actually do this with any function of X.

- A **function** of a random variable, X, is an expression that 'does something' to X. For example, $g(X) = \frac{12}{X}$ or $f(X) = X^4 + 5$.
- A function of a random variable is a random variable too, so you can calculate the mean and variance.

If X is a random variable and $g(X)$ is a function of X, then:

$$E(g(X)) = \sum g(x_i)p_i$$

Tip: You can use this formula, and the formula for variance on p10, to find the variance of a function of X, as you'll see in the examples.

Examples

A discrete random variable X has the probability function $P(X = x) = \frac{x}{10}$, for $x = 1, 2, 3, 4$. Find:

a) $E\left(\frac{1}{X}\right)$

$g(X) = \frac{1}{X}$, so $E\left(\frac{1}{X}\right) = \sum \frac{1}{x_i} \times p_i$

$$= \left(\frac{1}{1} \times \frac{1}{10}\right) + \left(\frac{1}{2} \times \frac{2}{10}\right) + \left(\frac{1}{3} \times \frac{3}{10}\right) + \left(\frac{1}{4} \times \frac{4}{10}\right)$$

$$= \frac{1}{10} + \frac{1}{10} + \frac{1}{10} + \frac{1}{10} = \frac{4}{10} = \frac{2}{5}$$

b) $E\left(\frac{1}{X^2}\right)$

Now $g(X) = \frac{1}{X}$, so $E\left(\frac{1}{X^2}\right) = \sum \frac{1}{x_i^2} \times p_i$

$$= \left(\frac{1}{1^2} \times \frac{1}{10}\right) + \left(\frac{1}{2^2} \times \frac{2}{10}\right) + \left(\frac{1}{3^2} \times \frac{3}{10}\right) + \left(\frac{1}{4^2} \times \frac{4}{10}\right)$$

$$= \frac{1}{10} + \frac{1}{20} + \frac{1}{30} + \frac{1}{40} = \frac{5}{24}$$

The formula for the variance of a discrete random variable on p10 just involves two expected values.

Example

A discrete random variable X has the probability function $P(X = x) = \frac{x}{10}$, for $x = 1, 2, 3, 4$. Find $\mathrm{Var}\left(\frac{1}{X}\right)$.

- Just put $\frac{1}{X}$ into the formula for variance on p10:

From example above.

$$\mathrm{Var}\left(\frac{1}{X}\right) = E\left(\left(\frac{1}{X}\right)^2\right) - \left[E\left(\frac{1}{X}\right)\right]^2 = E\left(\frac{1}{X^2}\right) - \left[E\left(\frac{1}{X}\right)\right]^2 = \frac{5}{24} - \left(\frac{2}{5}\right)^2$$

$$= \frac{5}{24} - \frac{4}{25} = \frac{29}{600}$$

Tip: To find a variance, you just need to find two expected values — here, you've already found them in the example above.

If the function of X is **linear** (of the form $\boldsymbol{aX + b}$, where a and b are any numbers), the formula above gives these two really useful rules:

$$E(aX + b) = aE(X) + b \qquad \mathrm{Var}(aX + b) = a^2\mathrm{Var}(X)$$

Tip: You **won't** get these formulas on the formula sheet in your exam, but you **need to know** them. Commit them to memory — they'll get you easy marks.

Example 1

If E(X) = 3 and Var(X) = 7, find:
a) E($2X + 5$) b) Var($2X + 5$) c) E($2 - 4X$) d) Var($2 - X$)
e) Var$\left(\frac{X}{2}\right)$ f) The standard deviation of $\left(\frac{X}{2}\right)$

a) The function of X is $2X + 5$, so let $a = 2$ and $b = 5$ and use the formula for E($aX + b$):

E(X) = 3

$$E(2X + 5) = 2E(X) + 5 = (2 \times 3) + 5 = 11$$

b) The function of X is $2X + 5$, so let $a = 2$ and $b = 5$ and use the formula for Var($aX + b$):

Var(X) = 7

$$Var(2X + 5) = 2^2Var(X) = 4 \times 7 = 28$$

c) The function of X is $2 - 4X$. Don't get confused about it being the wrong way round — it's just the same as $-4X + 2$.
So let $a = -4$ and $b = 2$:

$$E(2 - 4X) = -4E(X) + 2 = (-4 \times 3) + 2 = -10$$

d) The function of X is $2 - X$, so let $a = -1$ and $b = 2$:

$$Var(2 - X) = (-1)^2\,Var(X) = Var(X) = 7$$

e) The function of X is $\frac{X}{2}$. This is just the same as $\frac{1}{2}X + 0$, so let $a = \frac{1}{2}$ and $b = 0$:

$$Var\left(\frac{X}{2}\right) = \left(\frac{1}{2}\right)^2 Var(X) = \frac{1}{4} \times 7 = \frac{7}{4}$$

f) Standard deviation of $\frac{X}{2} = \sqrt{Var\left(\frac{X}{2}\right)} = \sqrt{\frac{7}{4}} = 1.32$ (to 3 sig. fig.)

Example 2

The discrete random variable X has the following probability distribution:

x	2	3	4	5	6
$P(X = x)$	0.1	0.2	0.3	0.2	k

Find: a) k b) E(X^2) c) Var(X^2) d) E($3X^2 - 1$) e) Var($3X^2 - 1$)

a) Using the fact that the probabilities add up to 1 —
$0.1 + 0.2 + 0.3 + 0.2 + k = 1$, and so $k = 0.2$

b) Now you can use the formula to find E(X^2):

$$E(X^2) = \sum x_i^2 p_i = [2^2 \times 0.1] + [3^2 \times 0.2] + [4^2 \times 0.3] + [5^2 \times 0.2] + [6^2 \times 0.2] = 19.2$$

c) Next work out E(X^4) (= E[(X^2)^2]) so you can use it to find the variance:

$$E(X^4) = \sum x_i^4 p_i = [2^4 \times 0.1] + [3^4 \times 0.2] + [4^4 \times 0.3] + [5^4 \times 0.2] + [6^4 \times 0.2] = 478.8$$

Then the variance of X^2 is easy:

$$Var(X^2) = E(X^4) - [E(X^2)]^2 = 478.8 - 19.2^2 = 110.16$$

Tip: Remember...
$Var(X^2)$
$= E[(X^2)^2] - [E(X^2)]^2$
$= E[X^4] - [E(X^2)]^2$

d) Using the formula for $E(aX + b)$:

$E(3X^2 - 1) = 3E(X^2) - 1 = 3 \times 19.2 - 1 = 56.6$

$3X^2 - 1$ is just a linear function of X^2.

e) $Var(3X^2 - 1) = 3^2Var(X^2) = 9 \times 110.16 = 991.44$

Tip: This might make more sense if you let $Y = X^2$ and use the formulas from page 13:

$E(aY + b) = aE(Y) + b$

$Var(aY + b) = a^2Var(Y)$

Exercise 2.3

Q1 X is a discrete random variable with probability distribution:

x	1	2	3	4
$P(X = x)$	0.2	0.3	0.4	0.1

a) Find $E(X^2)$ b) Find $E(2X^2 - 3)$

c) Find $Var(X^2)$ d) Find $Var(2X^2 - 3)$

Q1 b) Hint: $2X^2 - 3$ is a linear function of X^2, and you already know $E(X^2)$.

Q2 A discrete random variable X has the probability function:

$$P(X = x) = \frac{x}{k} \text{ for } x = 3, 4, 5.$$

a) Show that $k = 12$ b) Find $E(3X^2 + 2)$ c) Find $Var(3X^2 + 2)$

Q3 X is a discrete random variable with the following probability distribution, where $a > 0$:

x	0	1	2	a	6
$P(X = x)$	0.1	0.1	0.3	0.2	0.3

a) Find a when $E(X^2) = 17.1$. b) For this value of a, evaluate $Var(3X^2)$.

Q4 X is a discrete random variable with $E(X) = 4$ and $Var(X) = 3$.
Write down the mean and variance of the following random variables:

a) $Y = X + 3$ b) $Z = 5X$ c) $W = 2X - 7$ d) $V = 7 - 2X$

Q5 X is a discrete random variable with probability distribution:

x	1	2	3	4	5
$P(X = x)$	0.1	0.2	0.3	0.2	0.2

$E(X) = 3.2$ and $Var(X) = 1.56$.

For each of the random variables in a)-d) below, find:

(i) the probability distribution,
(ii) the mean and variance directly from the probability distribution,
(iii) the mean and variance using the values of $E(X)$ and $Var(X)$ given.

a) $Y = 3X + 4$ b) $Z = 3X - 4$ c) $V = 20 - 3X$ d) $W = 20 + 3X$

Q5 Hint: The probability distribution of a function of X is easy to find — just apply the function to the values of x, but keep the probabilities the same (just like we did with X^2 on p8).

Q6 The random variable X is given by the probability distribution:

x	10	12	13	15	16
$P(X = x)$	0.2	0.3	0.1	0.3	0.1

a) Find $E(X)$ and $Var(X)$.

b) $Y = 26 - mX$. If $E(Y) = 0$, find m and $Var(Y)$.

c) $Z = 3X - c$. If $E(Z) = 30$, find c and $Var(Z)$.

Q6 Hint: Don't get confused by the letters m and c in this one — just treat them as numbers when working out the expected values.

Review Exercise — Chapter 1

Q1 The probability distribution of Y is:

y	0	1	2	3
$P(Y = y)$	0.5	k	k	$3k$

a) Find the value of k. b) Find $P(Y < 2)$.

Q2 A discrete random variable X has the probability function:

x	1	2	3
$P(X = x)$	0.6	0.3	0.1

a) Find $E(X)$ b) Find $Var(X)$ c) Find $E\left(\frac{3}{X}\right)$ d) Find $Var\left(\frac{3}{X}\right)$

Q3 A discrete random variable X has the probability distribution shown in the table, where k is a constant.

x_i	1	2	3	4
p_i	$\frac{1}{6}$	$\frac{1}{2}$	k	$\frac{5}{24}$

a) Find k b) Find $E(X)$ and show that $Var(X) = \frac{63}{64}$ c) Find $E(2X - 1)$ and $Var(2X - 1)$

Q4 A discrete random variable X has the probability distribution shown in the table.

x_i	1	2	3	4	5	6
p_i	0.1	0.2	0.25	0.2	0.1	0.15

a) Find $E(X)$ b) Find $Var(X)$

Q5 a) The random variable X is given by the probability distribution:

x	8	10	15	20
$P(X = x)$	0.2	0.3	0.1	0.4

(i) Find $E(X)$ and $Var(X)$.

(ii) $Y = 4X + 3$. Find $E(Y)$ and $Var(Y)$.

(iii) $Z = 50 - 2X$. Find $E(Z)$ and $Var(Z)$.

b) The random variable X is given by the probability distribution:

x	−4	−1	0	2	5	6
$P(X = x)$	$\frac{1}{2}$	$\frac{1}{4}$	$\frac{1}{8}$	$\frac{1}{16}$	$\frac{1}{32}$	$\frac{1}{32}$

(i) Find $E(X)$ and $Var(X)$.

(ii) $Y = 7 - 2X$. Find $E(Y)$ and $Var(Y)$.

(iii) $Z = 7 + 2X$. Find $E(Z)$ and $Var(Z)$.

Exam-Style Questions — Chapter 1

1 In a game a player tosses three fair coins.
If three heads occur then the player gets 20p; if two heads occur then the player gets 10p.
For any other outcome, the player gets nothing.

a) If X is the random variable 'amount received', tabulate the probability distribution of X.
(4 marks)

The player pays 10p to play one game.

b) Use the probability distribution to find the probability that the player wins (i.e. gets more money than they pay to play) in one game.
(2 marks)

2 A discrete random variable X can only take values 0, 1, 2 and 3.
Its probability distribution is shown below.

x	0	1	2	3
$P(X = x)$	$2k$	$3k$	k	k

a) Find the value of k.
(1 mark)

b) Find:

(i) $E(X)$
(2 marks)

(ii) $Var(X)$
(3 marks)

c) The discrete random variable $Y = \frac{2X^2 + 3X}{X}$. Find $Var(Y)$.
(2 marks)

d) (i) Find $P(X < 2)$.
(1 mark)

(ii) Find $P(Y > 3 \mid X < 2)$.
(3 marks)

3 A discrete random variable X has the probability distribution

$$P(X = x) = \begin{cases} \frac{x}{4} & x = 1, 2 \\ \frac{x}{48} & x = 3, 4, 5 \\ 0 & \text{otherwise} \end{cases}$$

a) Work out $E\left(\frac{1}{X}\right)$ and $Var\left(\frac{1}{X}\right)$.
(5 marks)

b) The random variable P is the perimeter of a square of side $\frac{4}{X}$.
Find $E(P)$ and $Var(P)$.
(4 marks)

4 A discrete random variable X has the probability function:
$P(X = x) = ax$ for $x = 1, 2, 3$, where a is a constant.

a) Show that $a = \frac{1}{6}$. *(1 mark)*

b) Find $E(X)$. *(2 marks)*

c) If $Var(X) = \frac{5}{9}$ find $E(X^2)$. *(2 marks)*

d) Find $E(3X + 4)$ and $Var(3X + 4)$. *(3 marks)*

5 The number of points awarded to each contestant in a talent competition is given by the discrete random variable X with the following probability distribution:

x	0	1	2	3
$P(X = x)$	0.4	0.3	0.2	0.1

a) Find $E(X)$. *(2 marks)*

b) Find $E(6X + 8)$. *(2 marks)*

c) Show that $Var(X) = 1$. *(4 marks)*

d) Find $Var(5 - 3X)$. *(2 marks)*

6 The discrete random variable X is given by the probability distribution:

x	0	1	2	3
$P(X = x)$	a	$5b$	b	0.2

Given that $E(X) = 1.3$:

a) Find a and b. *(5 marks)*

b) Find $E(\frac{10}{13}X + 3)$. *(2 marks)*

c) Show that $Var(X) = 1.01$. *(3 marks)*

d) Find $Var(4 - X)$. *(2 marks)*

Chapter 2 The Poisson Distribution

1. Poisson Distributions

The Poisson distribution is a really common discrete probability distribution. It crops up all over the place when things happen at random — such as when radioactive atoms decay or errors occur in an industrial process.

Learning Objectives:
- Be able to recognise the conditions that give rise to a Poisson distribution.
- Be able to find probabilities for the Poisson distribution using the Poisson probability function.
- Be able to use the additive property of the Poisson distribution.

The Poisson distribution

Like the binomial distribution, the Poisson distribution is a **discrete** probability distribution (and so there are 'gaps' between the possible values that a Poisson random variable can take).

- A random variable X following a Poisson distribution can take only **non-negative integer** values (although there's no upper limit).
- So if X follows a Poisson distribution, then the possible values for X are 0, 1, 2, 3, 4, 5... and so on.

The Poisson distribution occurs quite a lot in everyday life.

- For example, a Poisson distribution can be used to describe:
  - the number of cars that will pass a point in a minute,
  - the number of radioactive atoms that will decay in an hour,
  - the number of misprints that will occur on a page of a book,
  - the number of plants that grow in 1 m^2 of a field,
  - the number of a certain type of cell in 1 cm^3 of blood.

All of the examples above are kinds of **rates**. They tell you **how often** an event **happens** (or **how often** something **is present**) in one minute / in one hour / on one page / in 1 m^2 of field / in 1 cm^3 of blood.

- This rate is the **parameter** of the Poisson distribution — and is usually called λ (the Greek letter 'lambda').
- λ represents the **average** number of events or things that occur/are present in a particular **period** — either a period of **time** (e.g. minute / hour etc.), or a period of **space** (e.g. page / m^2 / cm^3 etc.)
- If X is a random variable that follows a Poisson distribution with parameter λ, then you can write $X \sim \text{Po}(\lambda)$.

Tip: The notation $X \sim \text{Po}(\lambda)$ is similar to $X \sim \text{B}(n, p)$ for a binomial distribution. It gives you all the information you need to define the probability distribution.

There are **three conditions** that need to be met for a random variable to follow a Poisson distribution.

If X represents the number of events that occur in a particular space or time, then X will follow a Poisson distribution as long as:

1) The events occur **randomly**, and are all **independent** of each other.
2) The events happen **singly** (i.e. **'one at a time'**).
3) The events happen (on average) at a **constant rate** (λ).

If $X \sim \text{Po}(\lambda)$, then X can take values 0, 1, 2, 3... with probability:

$$P(X = x) = \frac{e^{-\lambda}\lambda^x}{x!}$$

Tip: The events need to happen at a constant average rate, but this could be a rate in either **time** or **space**.

Tip: This is the Poisson **probability function**. There's lots more about it on page 21.

Examples

Which of the random variables below would follow a Poisson distribution?

a) The random variable X represents the number of sixes thrown in 20 minutes of dice-throwing.

- Sixes will occur **randomly**, **independently** and **singly** and at a **constant rate** (on average), so X will follow a Poisson distribution.

b) The random variable A represents the number of grains of sand in 1 cm^3 of a large beaker full of water. On average, there are 750 grains of sand per litre, but the beaker has been standing for a few minutes.

- This is **not** Poisson, since the grains of sand will all have sunk to the bottom, and so they **won't** be distributed **independently** or **randomly**.

c) The random variable B represents the number of tiny soil particles in 1 cm^3 of a large beaker full of water. On average, there are 750 soil particles per litre, and the water has just been well stirred.

- This is Poisson, since the soil particles will occur **singly** and should be distributed **randomly** and **independently** of each other because of the stirring (i.e. they shouldn't be in large clusters).

Tip: In exam questions, there are usually hints about whether it's reasonable to **assume** something.
For example, this question is about wedding dresses — and these are usually sold one at a time (i.e. singly).

But you **wouldn't** be able to make the same assumption about books (because people often buy more than one book at a time).

Example

A shop sells wedding dresses at an average rate of 1.5 per week. The random variable X represents the number of wedding dresses sold by the shop in a given week. State the probability distribution of X.

- Wedding dresses are likely to be sold **randomly** and **singly**, and you're told they're sold at a constant average rate. So X will follow a Poisson distribution.
- The **parameter** of this distribution is the average number of wedding dresses sold per week — this is 1.5. So $X \sim \text{Po}(1.5)$.

Exercise 1.1

Q1 In each of the following situations, explain whether or not the random variable follows a Poisson distribution. If it does follow a Poisson distribution, state the parameter of its distribution.

a) The number of daisies (D) in 1 m^2 of a field where they grow randomly with an average density of 10 daisies per square metre.

b) The number of randomly scattered flaws (F) in 1 m of a roll of cloth, where on average there are 0.5 flaws per metre.

c) The number of gravel particles (P) in 1 litre of a large container full of water which has been standing for 24 hours, and which contains an average of 40 gravel particles per litre.

d) The number of micro-organisms (M) in 1 litre of a large container full of water which has just been vigorously stirred up, and which contains an average of 40 micro-organisms per litre.

Q2 A farmer keeps 100 sheep in a field of area 7000 m^2. The farmer puts food into the corner of the field at 7 am. The random variable X is the number of sheep in a randomly chosen square metre of field at 7:30 am. Will X follow a Poisson distribution? Explain your answer.

Using the Poisson probability function

Remember... a Poisson distribution has just one parameter: λ.

It appears twice in the **probability function** for the Poisson distribution.

If $X \sim \text{Po}(\lambda)$, then X takes values 0, 1, 2, 3... with probability:

$$P(X = x) = \frac{e^{-\lambda}\lambda^x}{x!}$$

Tip: The Greek letter 'lambda' (λ) is often used for the Poisson parameter.

Examples

If $X \sim \text{Po}(2.8)$, find:

a) $P(X = 0)$

- Use the formula:

$$P(X = 0) = \frac{e^{-2.8} \times 2.8^0}{0!} = e^{-2.8} = 0.06081... = 0.0608 \text{ (to 3 sig. fig.)}$$

Tip: Remember...
- $0! = 1$
- $a^0 = 1$, for any number a.

b) $P(X = 1)$

- Again, just use the formula:

$$P(X = 1) = \frac{e^{-2.8} \times 2.8^1}{1!} = e^{-2.8} \times 2.8 = 0.17026... = 0.170 \text{ (to 3 sig. fig.)}$$

c) $P(X = 2)$

- And again...

$$P(X = 2) = \frac{e^{-2.8} \times 2.8^2}{2!} = \frac{e^{-2.8} \times 2.8^2}{2 \times 1} = 0.23837... = 0.238 \text{ (to 3 sig. fig.)}$$

You might need to do a little bit more than just plug numbers into a formula.

Examples

If $X \sim \text{Po}(2.8)$, find:

a) $P(X < 3)$

- A Poisson distribution allows only whole-number values. So $P(X < 3)$ is the same as $P(X \le 2)$.

$$\begin{aligned} P(X < 3) &= P(X \le 2) \\ &= P(X = 0) + P(X = 1) + P(X = 2) \\ &= 0.06081... + 0.17026... + 0.23837... \\ &= 0.4694... = 0.469 \text{ (to 3 sig. fig.)} \end{aligned}$$

Tip: Use the probability function to find the probabilities $P(X = 0)$, $P(X = 1)$ and $P(X = 2)$ (see the previous Examples), and then add the results together.

b) $P(X \ge 3)$

- All the normal probability rules still apply.

$$\begin{aligned} P(X \ge 3) &= 1 - P(X < 3) = 1 - 0.4694... \\ &= 0.5305... = 0.531 \text{ (to 3 sig. fig.)} \end{aligned}$$

Tip: Remember... if X is a discrete random variable: $P(X \ge k) = 1 - P(X < k)$

Example

The number of wedding dresses (X) sold in a week by a particular shop follows the Poisson distribution Po(1.5).

a) Find the probability that in a particular week the shop sells 2 dresses.

- Use the formula with $\lambda = 1.5$ and $x = 2$.

$$P(X = 2) = \frac{e^{-\lambda}\lambda^x}{x!} = \frac{e^{-1.5} \times 1.5^2}{2!} = 0.25102... = 0.251 \text{ (to 3 sig. fig.)}$$

b) Find the probability that in a particular week the shop sells fewer than 2 dresses.

- $P(X < 2) = P(X \leq 1) = P(X = 0) + P(X = 1)$

$$P(X < 2) = P(X = 0) + P(X = 1) = \frac{e^{-1.5} \times 1.5^0}{0!} + \frac{e^{-1.5} \times 1.5^1}{1!} = 0.22313... + 0.33469... = 0.55782... = 0.558 \text{ (to 3 sig. fig.)}$$

Exercise 1.2

Give your answers to 3 significant figures in this exercise.

Q1 The random variable X has distribution $X \sim \text{Po}(2)$. Find:

a) $P(X = 1)$ b) $P(X = 0)$ c) $P(X = 4)$

Q2 The random variable X has distribution $X \sim \text{Po}(3)$. Find:

a) $P(X = 4)$ b) $P(X \leq 1)$ c) $P(4 \leq X \leq 6)$

Q3 If $X \sim \text{Po}(3.8)$, find:

a) $P(X = 3)$ b) $P(X < 3)$ c) $P(X \geq 3)$

Q4 For the random variable $X \sim \text{Po}(1.4)$, find $P(X > 3)$.

Q5 Flaws occur randomly in a length of fabric at an average rate of 0.2 flaws per metre.

a) State an appropriate statistical model to represent the random variable X, the number of flaws in a given metre of fabric. Explain your answer.

b) In a randomly chosen metre of fabric, find the probability of obtaining:

(i) no flaws,

(ii) fewer than 2 flaws.

Q6 Telephone calls arrive at a switchboard at an average rate of 12 per minute. In a randomly chosen minute, find the probability of receiving:

a) exactly 12 phone calls,

b) between 10 and 13 calls inclusive.

Mean and variance of a Poisson distribution

For a Poisson distribution, the **mean** and the **variance** are the same — they both equal λ, the Poisson parameter.

If $X \sim \text{Po}(\lambda)$: **Mean ($\mu$) of X = E(X) = λ**
Variance (σ^2) of X = Var(X) = λ

This means that the **standard deviation** (σ) is given by: $\sigma = \sqrt{\lambda}$

Examples

If $X \sim \text{Po}(7)$, find:

a) E(X)

- It's Poisson, so E(X) equals λ.

$E(X) = \lambda = 7$

b) Var(X)

- It's Poisson, so Var(X) also equals λ.

$\text{Var}(X) = \lambda = 7$

c) The standard deviation of X.

- Take the square root of the variance to find the standard deviation.

$$\text{Standard deviation of } X = \sqrt{\text{Var}(X)} = \sqrt{\lambda} = \sqrt{7}$$

Examples

If $X \sim \text{Po}(1)$, find:

a) $P(X \le \mu)$

- $\mu = \lambda = 1$.

$$P(X \le \mu) = P(X \le 1) = P(X = 0) + P(X = 1)$$
$$= \frac{e^{-1} \times 1^0}{0!} + \frac{e^{-1} \times 1^1}{1!}$$
$$= e^{-1} + e^{-1}$$
$$= 0.735758... = 0.736 \text{ (to 3 sig. fig.)}$$

b) $P(X \le \mu - \sigma)$

- $\sigma^2 = \lambda = 1$. So $\sigma = 1$ too.
- So $\mu - \sigma = 0$.

$$P(X \le \mu - \sigma) = P(X \le 0)$$
$$= P(X = 0)$$
$$= \frac{e^{-1} \times 1^0}{0!}$$
$$= 0.367879... = 0.368 \text{ (to 3 sig. fig.)}$$

Example

The number of injuries each week (x) during a school's PE lessons was recorded. After 33 weeks, the following results had been obtained:

$$\sum x = 16 \qquad \sum x^2 = 24$$

a) Calculate the mean number of injuries per week.

- Use the formula for the mean.

$$\bar{x} = \frac{\sum x}{n} = \frac{16}{33} = 0.484848...$$
$$= 0.485 \text{ (to 3 sig. fig.)}$$

b) Calculate the variance of the number of injuries per week.

- The variance is the mean of the squares $\left(\frac{\sum x^2}{n}\right)$ minus the square of the mean $\left(\frac{\sum x}{n}\right)^2$.

$$\frac{\sum x^2}{n} - \left(\frac{\sum x}{n}\right)^2 = \frac{24}{33} - \left(\frac{16}{33}\right)^2$$
$$= 0.492194...$$
$$= 0.492 \text{ (to 3 sig. fig.)}$$

Tip: Whenever you come across a distribution where the mean and the variance are the same (or very nearly the same), then think Poisson.

c) Explain why this data supports the choice of a Poisson distribution as a model for the number of injuries (X) per week.

- For this data, the mean and the variance are almost equal.
- Since the mean and variance of a Poisson distribution are equal, this suggests that this data may follow a Poisson distribution.

Tip: You choose the parameter λ by using the mean of your data.

d) If $X \sim \text{Po}(\lambda)$, what value should be chosen for λ?

- The parameter of a Poisson distribution equals the mean for a given period.

Since X is the number of injuries per week, $X \sim \text{Po}(0.485)$.

e) Find the probability of there being at least 1 injury in a given week.

- Use the Poisson probability function.

$$P(X > 0) = 1 - P(X = 0)$$
$$= 1 - \frac{e^{-0.485} \times 0.485^0}{0!}$$
$$= 1 - 0.61569...$$
$$= 0.384 \text{ (to 3 sig. fig.)}$$

Exercise 1.3

Q1 For each of the following random variables, state:

(i) the mean

(ii) the variance

a) $X \sim \text{Po}(9)$ b) $Y \sim \text{Po}(12)$ c) $M \sim \text{Po}(4.3)$

Q2 The discrete random variable $X \sim \text{Po}(9)$.

a) State the mean (μ) and variance (σ^2) of X.

b) Find the standard deviation (σ) of X.

c) Find $P(X = \mu + \sigma)$

Q3 A discrete random variable X follows a Poisson distribution with $\lambda = 16$.

a) State the mean (μ) and variance (σ^2) of X.

b) Find the standard deviation (σ) of X.

c) Find $P(X \leq \sigma)$. Give your answer to 4 decimal places.

Q4 A company rents out video cameras. In their current shop, the weekly rentals (X) occur at an average rate of 10 per week, and follow a Poisson distribution.

The owners decide to open a new shop in a nearby town and assume that the rentals will also follow a Poisson distribution. During the first year, the weekly rentals were as follows:

Rentals per week (x)	5	6	7	8	9	10	11	12	13
Frequency (f)	4	6	3	8	16	9	3	2	1

a) Calculate the mean and variance of this data

b) Comment on the assumption that the sales follow a Poisson distribution.

Additive property of the Poisson distribution

The Poisson parameter is **additive**. That sounds complicated, but there are just two things you need to know. This is the **first** one:

> If X represents the number of events in **1 unit** of time or space (e.g. 1 minute / hour / m^2 / m^3), and $X \sim \text{Po}(\lambda)$, then the number of events in ***t*** **units** of time or space follows the distribution $\text{Po}(t\lambda)$.

That sounds trickier than it really is.
Think of it this way:

- If X describes the number of events in a day, and $X \sim \text{Po}(4)$, then...
- ...this means that the event happens 4 times a day, on average...
- ...so in a week, the event will happens 28 times, on average...
- ...and so the number of events per week (Y) follows $Y \sim \text{Po}(28)$.

Tip: If X follows a Poisson distribution, then you know the events happen randomly, singly and at a constant rate.

But Y is just describing the same events, so Y must also follow a Poisson distribution — only with the parameter $\lambda = 28$.

Example 1

Sunflowers grow singly and randomly in a field with an average of 10 sunflowers per square metre. What is the probability that a randomly chosen area of 0.25 m² contains no sunflowers?

- The number of sunflowers in 1 m^2 follows the distribution Po(10).
- So the number of sunflowers in 0.25 m^2 must follow the distribution Po(2.5).
- This means $\text{P(no sunflowers)} = \frac{e^{-2.5} \times 2.5^0}{0!}$

$= 0.08208... = 0.0821$ (to 3 sig. fig.).

Tip: Here $t = 0.25$, as $0.25 \text{ m}^2 = 1 \text{ m}^2 \times 0.25$.

So the number of sunflowers in 0.25 m^2 will follow $\text{Po}(10 \times 0.25) = \text{Po}(2.5)$

Example 2

The number of radioactive atoms that decay per second follows the Poisson distribution Po(5). If the probability of no atoms decaying in t seconds is 0.5, verify that $t \approx 0.1386$.

- If the random variable X represents the number of radioactive atoms that decay in t seconds, then $X \sim \text{Po}(5t)$.
- This means $\text{P}(X = 0) = \frac{e^{-5t}(5t)^0}{0!} = e^{-5t} = 0.5$.
- This equation is satisfied by $t = 0.1386$, since $e^{-5 \times 0.1386} = e^{-0.693} = 0.500$ (to 3 d.p.).

This is the **second** thing you need to know about the Poisson parameter being additive:

> If X and Y are independent variables with $X \sim \text{Po}(\lambda)$ and $Y \sim \text{Po}(\mu)$, then $X + Y \sim \text{Po}(\lambda + \mu)$.

Tip: If X represents the number of events in 1 unit of time or space, and $X \sim \text{Po}(\lambda)$...

...then the number of events in 2 units of time or space is $X + X$, which (from the formula on the right) follows $\text{Po}(\lambda + \lambda) = \text{Po}(2\lambda)$.

This is exactly the same as the formula from p25 with $t = 2$.

Example

The random variables D and C both follow Poisson distributions, and represent the number of claims per week to one insurance company against policies for dogs and cats respectively. D and C are independent random variables. The average numbers of claims per week are 5 for dogs and 8 for cats.

a) State the distribution for the total number (T) of claims against 'dog policies' and 'cat policies'.

- You know the average numbers of claims per week for dogs and cats are 5 and 8 respectively.

  D and C are independent and $D \sim \text{Po}(5)$ and $C \sim \text{Po}(8)$.

- The total number of claims equals the number of 'dog claims' added to the number of 'cat claims'.

  $T = D + C \sim \text{Po}(5 + 8)$
  i.e. $T \sim \text{Po}(13)$

b) Find the probability that the total number of claims for dogs and cats in a randomly chosen week is between 10 and 12 (inclusive).

- Use the Poisson probability function:

$$\begin{aligned}\text{P}(10 \le T \le 12) &= \text{P}(T = 10) + \text{P}(T = 11) + \text{P}(T = 12) \\ &= \frac{e^{-13} \times 13^{10}}{10!} + \frac{e^{-13} \times 13^{11}}{11!} + \frac{e^{-13} \times 13^{12}}{12!} \\ &= 0.08587... + 0.10148... + 0.10993... \\ &= 0.297 \text{ (to 3 sig. fig.)}\end{aligned}$$

Exercise 1.4

Q1 At a particular time, bacteria occur randomly and singly on a piece of glass at an average rate of 600 bacteria per square centimetre.

a) State the distribution followed by the random variable X, where X is the number of bacteria on 1 cm^2 of the glass.

b) State the distribution followed by the random variable Y, where Y is the number of bacteria on 1 mm^2 of the glass.

c) Find the probability that there are exactly 3 bacteria on a random 1 mm^2 of the glass.

Q2 Potholes occur randomly and singly on a stretch of road at an average rate of 3 per kilometre. Find the probability that in a randomly chosen 8 km stretch of this road, there are between 20 and 22 potholes (inclusive).

Q3 Louise and Hannah each receive text messages randomly, singly and independently of each other throughout the day. Louise receives an average of 4 texts per day and Hannah receives an average of 2 per day.

a) Find the probability that the total number of text messages the two girls receive on a randomly chosen day is equal to 5.

b) Find the probability that the total number of text messages the two girls receive in a randomly chosen week is equal to 44.

Q4 A bookshop sells wizard books at an average rate of 20 per day and celebrity biographies at an average rate of 15 per day.
If sales of both types of books occur randomly, singly and independently of each other, find the probability that the shop sells a total of 40 of these books in a day.

2. Using Poisson Tables

Learning Objectives:

- Be able to use Poisson tables to find probabilities.
- Be able to use Poisson tables to find values for a random variable given a probability.

Just like for the binomial and normal distributions, there are tables for the Poisson distribution that make it relatively easy to find probabilities. You use them in a similar way to the binomial tables, so some of this section might seem familiar.

Using tables to find probabilities

Suppose weeds grow singly and randomly in a garden with an average of 8 weeds per square metre, and you need to find the probability that a randomly chosen square metre contains **no more than 6 weeds**.

You *could* do this using the Poisson probability function. If the random variable X represents the number of weeds in one square metre, then you'd need to work out $P(X = 0) + P(X = 1) + \ldots + P(X = 5) + P(X = 6)$ using Po(8).

But it's quicker to use a table of the **Poisson cumulative distribution function**. The Poisson cumulative distribution function for Po(λ) shows the probabilities $P(X \leq x)$, for different values of λ and x.

- In the weeds example, $X \sim$ Po(8), so you need to find $\lambda = 8$ across the top of the table — any probabilities you need will be in this column.
- Then you need to look up a value of x. Here, you need to find $P(X \leq 6)$, so find $x = 6$ down the left-hand side of the table, and read across to the column for $\lambda = 8$.

Tip: Remember... the cumulative distribution function of a discrete random variable X gives $P(X \leq x)$ — the probability that X takes any value less than or equal to x for each value of x.

Tip: This is just an extract from the Poisson tables — the full tables are given on p127.

Poisson Cumulative Distribution Function
Tables show $P(X \leqslant x)$, where X~Po(λ)

① $\lambda = 8$

② $x = 6$

λ / x	6.0	6.5	7.0	7.5	8.0	8.5	9.0	9.5	10.0	11.0	12.0	13.0	14.0	15.0
0	0.0025	0.0015	0.0009	0.0006	0.0003	0.0002	0.0001	0.0001	0.0000	0.0000	0.0000	0.0000	0.0000	0.0000
1	0.0174	0.0113	0.0073	0.0047	0.0030	0.0019	0.0012	0.0008	0.0005	0.0002	0.0001	0.0000	0.0000	0.0000
2	0.0620	0.0430	0.0296	0.0203	0.0138	0.0093	0.0062	0.0042	0.0028	0.0012	0.0005	0.0002	0.0001	0.0000
3	0.1512	0.1118	0.0818	0.0591	0.0424	0.0301	0.0212	0.0149	0.0103	0.0049	0.0023	0.0011	0.0005	0.0002
4	0.2851	0.2237	0.1730	0.1321	0.0996	0.0744	0.0550	0.0403	0.0293	0.0151	0.0076	0.0037	0.0018	0.0009
5	0.4457	0.3690	0.3007	0.2414	0.1912	0.1496	0.1157	0.0885	0.0671	0.0375	0.0203	0.0107	0.0055	0.0028
6	0.6063	0.5265	0.4497	0.3782	0.3134	0.2562	0.2068	0.1649	0.1301	0.0786	0.0458	0.0259	0.0142	0.0076
7	0.7440	0.6728	0.5987	0.5246	0.4530	0.3856	0.3239	0.2687	0.2202	0.1432	0.0895	0.0540	0.0316	0.0180
8	0.8472	0.7916	0.7291	0.6620	0.5925	0.5231	0.4557	0.3918	0.3328	0.2320	0.1550	0.0998	0.0621	0.0374
9	0.9161	0.8774	0.8305	0.7764	0.7166	0.6530	0.5874	0.5218	0.4579	0.3405	0.2424	0.1658	0.1094	0.0699
10	0.9574	0.9332	0.9015	0.8622	0.8159	0.7634	0.7060	0.6453	0.5830	0.4599	0.3472	0.2517	0.1757	0.1185
11	0.9799	0.9661	0.9467	0.9208	0.8881	0.8487	0.8030	0.7520	0.6968	0.5793	0.4616	0.3532	0.2600	0.1848

- So if $X \sim$ Po(8), then $P(X \leq 6) = 0.3134$.

The next few examples will look fairly familiar — because they're showing the same ideas as you've already seen for binomial tables.

Examples

When cloth is manufactured, faults occur randomly in the cloth at a rate of 8 faults per square metre. Use the Poisson tables to find:

a) The probability of 7 or fewer faults in a square metre of cloth.

- Use the column for $\lambda = 8$.
- Then read across from $x = 7$. $\qquad P(X \leq 7) = 0.4530$

b) The probability of more than 4 faults in a square metre of cloth.

- Remember...
  $P(X > 4) = 1 - P(X \leq 4)$

$$P(X > 4) = 1 - P(X \leq 4) = 1 - 0.0996 = 0.9004$$

Tip: The faults occur randomly, singly and at a constant rate (= 8 faults per square metre).

So if X represents the number of faults in a square metre, then $X \sim$ Po(8).

c) **The probability of exactly 10 faults in a square metre of cloth.**

- Remember...
  $P(X = 10) = P(X \leq 10) - P(X \leq 9)$

$$P(X = 10) = P(X \leq 10) - P(X \leq 9) = 0.8159 - 0.7166 = 0.0993$$

d) **The probability of at least 9 faults in a square metre of cloth.**

- Remember...
  $P(X \geq 9) = 1 - P(X < 9) = 1 - P(X \leq 8)$

$$P(X \geq 9) = 1 - P(X \leq 8) = 1 - 0.5925 = 0.4075$$

e) **The probability of exactly 4 faults in 0.75 m^2 of cloth.**

- For this one, you need to use the additive property of the Poisson distribution.

Let the random variable Y represent the number of faults in 0.75 m^2 of cloth.

Since the number of faults in 1 m^2 of cloth ~ Po(8), then $Y \sim Po(0.75 \times 8) = Po(6)$.

- $P(Y = 4)$ equals P(exactly 4 faults in 0.75 m^2 of cloth).

$$P(Y = 4) = P(Y \leq 4) - P(Y \leq 3) = 0.2851 - 0.1512 = 0.1339$$

Tip: This time you need to use the column for $\lambda = 6$.

Just like with binomial tables, you can find $P(a < X \leq b)$ by **subtracting** one value from the table from another:

- Use the table to find $\mathbf{P(X \leq b)}$ — the probability that X is less than or equal to the **largest** value satisfying the inequality '$a < X \leq b$'...
- ...**and subtract** $\mathbf{P(X \leq a)}$ to 'remove' the probability that X takes one of the smaller values not satisfying the inequality '$a < X \leq b$'.

Tip: This is the same method that you used in S1 when you used binomial tables.

Examples

If $W \sim$ Po(5.5), then find:

a) $\mathbf{P(3 < W \leq 8)}$

- $W = 8$ is the largest value satisfying $3 < W \leq 8$, so find $P(W \leq 8)$...
- ...and subtract $P(W \leq 3)$, since $W = 3$ **doesn't** satisfy the inequality $3 < W \leq 8$, and neither does any value smaller than 3.

$$P(3 < W \leq 8) = P(W \leq 8) - P(W \leq 3) = 0.8944 - 0.2017 = 0.6927$$

Tip: Use the full Poisson tables on p127.

b) $\mathbf{P(2 \leq W < 7)}$

- Find $P(W \leq 6)$, since $W = 6$ is the largest value satisfying $2 \leq W < 7$...
- ...and subtract $P(W \leq 1)$, since $W = 1$ **doesn't** satisfy the inequality $2 \leq W < 7$, and neither does any value smaller than 1.

$$P(2 \leq W < 7) = P(W \leq 6) - P(W \leq 1) = 0.6860 - 0.0266 = 0.6594$$

Exercise 2.1

Q1 If $X \sim \text{Po}(2)$, use the Poisson tables to find:

a) $P(X \leq 3)$ b) $P(X \leq 7)$ c) $P(X < 5)$

Q2 If $X \sim \text{Po}(7.5)$, use the Poisson tables to find:

a) $P(X > 6)$ b) $P(X = 9)$ c) $P(2 \leq X \leq 8)$

Q3 The random variable X follows a Poisson distribution with mean 6. Use the Poisson tables to find:

a) $P(X > 4)$ b) $P(2 < X \leq 5)$ c) $P(4 \leq X < 9)$

Q4 The random variable X follows a Poisson distribution with mean 5.5. Use the Poisson tables to find:

a) $P(X > 2)$ b) $P(X = 4)$ c) $P(2 \leq X \leq 7)$

Q5 Telephone calls arrive at a switchboard at an average rate of 8 per minute. Find the probability that, in a randomly chosen minute, the switchboard receives:

a) exactly 6 phone calls b) at least 3 phone calls

Q6 The number of tadpoles in a 10 cm^3 sample of water from a stream follows a Poisson distribution with mean 0.1. Use tables to find the probability that a randomly selected litre of water contains:

a) fewer than 7 tadpoles b) more than 15 tadpoles

Using tables 'backwards'

Just like with the binomial tables, sometimes you'll need to use the Poisson tables 'the other way round'. So you might be given a probability, and asked to find a corresponding value of x.

Examples

a) If $X \sim \text{Po}(4)$, then find x such that $P(X \leq x) = 0.8893$.

- Use the column in the Poisson tables for $\lambda = 4$.
- Go down the column until you find 0.8893, then read off the corresponding value of x. This is $x = 6$.

b) If $X \sim \text{Po}(5.5)$, then find x such that $P(X > x) = 0.1905$.

- If $P(X > x) = 0.1905$, then $P(X \leq x) = 1 - 0.1905 = 0.8095$.
- So go down the column for $\lambda = 5.5$ till you reach 0.8095, and read off the corresponding value of x. This is $x = 7$.

c) If $X \sim \text{Po}(8.5)$, then find the maximum value of a with $P(X \leq a) < 0.1$.

- Use the Poisson table with $\lambda = 8.5$.
- You can see that $P(X \leq 4) = 0.0744$ and $P(X \leq 5) = 0.1496$.
- So the maximum value of a with $P(X \leq a) < 0.1$ is $a = 4$.

Tip: Remember... the function $P(X \leq x)$ can only **increase** (or stay the same) as x increases. So there can't be any values of a greater than 4 with $P(X \leq a) < 0.1$.

These questions can also involve real-life situations.

Example

Celebrity Gossip magazine is published weekly. On average, 9 people want to buy the magazine from a particular newsagent each week. What is the minimum number of copies the newsagent should order at the start of the week if she wants the probability of not having enough copies to sell to all the potential customers to be less than 0.05?

- Let the random variable X represent the number of people wanting to buy a copy of Celebrity Gossip from this newsagent in a particular week. Then $X \sim \text{Po}(9)$.
- The newsagent needs to order at least k copies of Celebrity Gossip, where $P(X > k) < 0.05$.
- From the column of the Poisson table for $\lambda = 9$:
  $P(X \leq 13) = 0.9261$, and so $P(X > 13) = 1 - 0.9261 = 0.0739 > 0.05$.
  And $P(X \leq 14) = 0.9585$, and so $P(X > 14) = 1 - 0.9585 = 0.0415 < 0.05$.
- So the minimum number of copies the newsagent needs to order is 14.

Exercise 2.2

Q1 The random variable X follows a Poisson distribution with mean 5.5. Find the values of x such that:

a) $P(X \leq x) = 0.5289$ b) $P(X < x) = 0.9983$

Q2 The random variable Y follows a Poisson distribution with mean 3.4. Find the values of y such that:

a) $P(Y > y) = 0.8532$ b) $P(Y \geq y) = 0.1295$

Q3 If $X \sim \text{Po}(1.8)$, find the largest value of x where the probability of X taking a value less than x is at most 0.25.

Q4 The random variable X follows a Poisson distribution with mean 8. Find the smallest possible value of x where the probability of X taking a value of at least x is less than 0.05.

Q5 A company rents out equipment on a large beach in Spain.
On average it rents out 6 inflatables per hour.
At the end of each hour the inflatables must be returned.
Find the minimum number of inflatables the company should have if it is to be at least 90% certain of meeting demand each hour.

Q6 A photocopier supplier offers a support service to customers.
The supplier knows that a particular type of photocopier breaks down at an average rate of 0.5 times per month.
The supplier offers a deal: if there are more than y breakdowns in a four-month period, the supplier will pay a penalty.
Find the minimum value of y for which the supplier has a probability of less than 0.1 of paying the penalty.

3. Modelling Real Problems

Learning Objective:

- Be able to apply knowledge of the Poisson distribution to real-life situations.

This is the part where you get to use what you've learnt to tackle some real-world problems. Remember... statistics is very much a 'real-life' subject — you can apply it in all sorts of areas.

Modelling real problems with a Poisson distribution

Make sure you understand what's going on in the next few examples.

Tip: In exam questions, you'll almost always be asked about the Poisson distribution in a real-life context — make sure you're completely comfortable with questions like the ones on the next few pages.

Example 1

A car randomly breaks down twice a week on average. The random variable X represents the number of times the car will break down next week.

a) What probability distribution could be used to model X? Explain your answer.

- The breakdowns occur randomly, singly and (on average) at a constant rate. Since X is the total number of breakdowns in one week, X follows a Poisson distribution with an expected value of 2: $X \sim \text{Po}(2)$

b) Find the probability that the car breaks down fewer than 3 times next week.

- Using tables with $\lambda = 2$: $P(X < 3) = P(X \leq 2) = 0.6767$

c) Find the probability that the car breaks down more than 4 times next week.

- Again, using tables with $\lambda = 2$: $P(X > 4) = 1 - P(X \leq 4)$
  $= 1 - 0.9473 = 0.0527$

d) Find the probability that the car breaks down exactly 6 times in the next fortnight.

- If the random variable Y represents the number of breakdowns in the next fortnight, then $Y \sim \text{Po}(2 \times 2) = \text{Po}(4)$.
- So using Poisson tables with $\lambda = 4$: $P(Y = 6) = P(Y \leq 6) - P(Y \leq 5)$
  $= 0.8893 - 0.7851$
  $= 0.1042$

Tip: See page 25 for more about the additive property of the Poisson distribution.

e) Find the probability that the car doesn't break down tomorrow.

- This time, let the random variable T represent the number of breakdowns tomorrow. This is a single day, so $T \sim \text{Po}(2 \div 7) = \text{Po}(\frac{2}{7})$.
- $\lambda = \frac{2}{7}$ isn't in your tables, so you'll have to work this out using the probability function.
- The probability that the car doesn't break down tomorrow is $P(T = 0)$.

$$P(T = 0) = \frac{e^{-\frac{2}{7}} \times \left(\frac{2}{7}\right)^0}{0!} = 0.751477... = 0.751 \text{ (to 3 sig. fig.)}$$

Example 2

A restaurant owner needs to buy a large number of apples, so she visits a farm that sells apples by the crate. Bad apples are randomly distributed between the crates, where the number of bad apples in each crate can be modelled by the random variable $X \sim \text{Po}(2.25)$.

The restaurant owner opens a random crate and inspects each apple.

- **If there are no bad apples in this crate, then the restaurant owner will buy the apples she needs from this farm.**
- **If more than 2 apples in this first crate are bad, then the restaurant owner will not buy from this farm.**
- **If only 1 or 2 apples in the first crate are bad, then a second crate is opened. The restaurant owner will then only buy from this farm if the second crate contains at most 1 bad apple.**

a) Find the probability that none of the apples in the first crate are bad.

- $P(X = 0) = \frac{e^{-2.25} \times 2.25^0}{0!} = e^{-2.25} = 0.10539... = 0.1054$ (to 4 d.p.)

b) Find the probability that more than 2 apples in the first crate are bad.

- You need to find $P(X > 2) = 1 - P(X \leq 2)$.
- $P(X = 1) = \frac{e^{-2.25} \times 2.25^1}{1!} = e^{-2.25} \times 2.25 = 0.23714...$
- $P(X = 2) = \frac{e^{-2.25} \times 2.25^2}{2!} = \frac{e^{-2.25} \times 2.25^2}{2} = 0.26679...$
- So $P(X > 2) = 1 - P(X = 0) - P(X = 1) - P(X = 2)$
  $= 1 - 0.10539... - 0.23714... - 0.26679... = 0.3907$ (to 4 d.p.)

c) Find the probability that a second crate is opened.

- A second crate is opened if $X = 1$ or $X = 2$.
- $P(X = 1 \text{ or } X = 2) = 0.23714... + 0.26679...$
  $= 0.50394... = 0.5039$ (to 4 d.p.)

d) What is the probability of the restaurant owner buying the apples she needs from this farm?

- There are two ways the owner will buy apples from this farm:
  - **Either:** the first crate will contain no bad apples (probability = 0.10539...)
  - **Or:** the first crate will contain 1 or 2 bad apples **and** the second crate will contain 0 or 1 bad apples.
- Thinking about that second possibility...
  P(1st crate has 1 or 2 bad **and** 2nd crate has 0 or 1 bad)
  = P(1st crate has 1 or 2 bad) × P(2nd crate has 0 or 1 bad)
  = 0.50394... × (0.10539... + 0.23714...)
  = 0.17262...
- So putting all that together...
  P(restaurant owner buys from this farm) = 0.10539... + 0.17262...
  = 0.2780 (to 4 d.p.)

Tip: Since the bad apples are randomly distributed, the number of bad apples in the first crate does not affect the number in the second crate — so you can multiply the probabilities in the second step of d).

Example 3

Carol runs an online shop selling honeymoon getaways.
She makes an average of 2 sales per day.

a) Assuming sales occur at random, find the probability that she sells at least 3 honeymoon getaways on any particular day.

- Sales of honeymoon getaways should occur singly. So if the random variable X is the number of honeymoon getaways sold in a day, you have all the conditions for a Poisson distribution.
- In fact, since the average number of sales per day is 2, $X \sim \text{Po}(2)$.
- $P(X \geq 3) = 1 - P(X < 3) = 1 - P(X \leq 2)$.
- From tables, $P(X \leq 2) = 0.6767$.
  So $P(X \geq 3) = 1 - 0.6767 =$ **0.3233**

b) Find the probability that she sells at least 3 honeymoon getaways on at least 2 of the 7 days next week.

- This time, you have a fixed number (7) of trials, so this will **not** follow a Poisson distribution.
- In fact, all the conditions for a **binomial** distribution are satisfied. There is a **fixed number** of **independent** trials where there are only **two possible outcomes** ('sell at least 3 honeymoon getaways' or 'don't sell at least 3 honeymoon getaways'), and a **constant probability** of success (0.3233).
- So if the random variable Y represents the total number of 'successes' next week, then $Y \sim B(7, 0.3233)$.
- Now then... $P(Y \geq 2) = 1 - P(Y < 2) = 1 - P(Y = 0) - P(Y = 1)$.
- $P(Y = 0) = \binom{7}{0} \times 0.3233^0 \times (1 - 0.3233)^7$
  $= 0.6767^7 = 0.064979...$
- $P(Y = 1) = \binom{7}{1} \times 0.3233^1 \times (1 - 0.3233)^6$
  $= 7 \times 0.3233 \times 0.6767^6$
  $= 0.217310...$
- So $P(Y \geq 2) = 1 - 0.064979... - 0.217310... =$ **0.718 (to 3 sig. fig.)**

Tip: With a Poisson distribution, you're not counting the number of successes in a **fixed number of trials**, but the number of successes in a **fixed period**.

Tip: Here, a 'success' means a day on which Carol sells at least 3 honeymoon getaways.

Tip: Remember... the binomial probability function is:

$P(X = x)$
$= \binom{n}{x} \times p^x \times (1 - p)^{n-x}$

Review Exercise — Chapter 2

Q1 If $X \sim \text{Po}(3.1)$, find (correct to 4 decimal places):

a) $P(X = 2)$ b) $P(X = 1)$ c) $P(X = 0)$ d) $P(X < 3)$ e) $P(X \geq 3)$

Q2 If $X \sim \text{Po}(8.7)$, find (correct to 4 decimal places):

a) $P(X = 2)$ b) $P(X = 1)$ c) $P(X = 0)$ d) $P(X < 3)$ e) $P(X \geq 3)$

Q3 For the following distributions, find: (i) $E(X)$, (ii) $\text{Var}(X)$, and (iii) the standard deviation of X.

a) Po(8) b) Po(12.11) c) Po(84.2227)

Q4 For the following distributions, find: (i) $P(X \leq \mu)$ (ii) $P(X \leq \mu - \sigma)$

a) Po(9) b) Po(4)

Q5 Which of the following would follow a Poisson distribution? Explain your answers.

a) The number of defective products coming off a factory's production line in one day if defective products occur at random at an average of 25 per week.

b) The number of heads thrown using a coin in 25 tosses if the probability of getting a head is always 0.5.

c) The number of people joining a post-office queue each minute during lunchtime if people arrive at an average rate of 3 every five minutes.

d) The total number of spelling mistakes in a document if mistakes are randomly made at an average rate of 3 per page.

Q6 In a radioactive sample, atoms decay at an average rate of 2000 per hour.
State how the following quantities are distributed, giving as much detail as possible.

a) The number of atoms decaying per minute.

b) The number of atoms decaying per day.

Q7 Atoms in one radioactive sample decay at an average rate of 60 per minute, while in another they decay at an average rate of 90 per minute.
The atoms in each sample decay independently of each other.

a) How would the total number of atoms decaying each minute be distributed?

b) How would the total number of atoms decaying each hour be distributed?

Q8 If $X \sim \text{Po}(8)$, use Poisson tables to find:

a) $P(X \leq 2)$ b) $P(X \leq 7)$ c) $P(X \leq 5)$ d) $P(X < 9)$ e) $P(X \geq 8)$

f) $P(X > 1)$ g) $P(X > 7)$ h) $P(X = 6)$ i) $P(X = 4)$ j) $P(X = 3)$

Q9 A gaggle of 100 geese is randomly scattered throughout a field measuring 10 m × 10 m.
What is the probability that in a randomly selected square metre of field, I find:

a) no geese? b) 1 goose? c) 2 geese? d) more than 2 geese?

Exam-Style Questions — Chapter 2

1 a) State two conditions needed for a Poisson distribution to be a suitable model for a quantity.

(2 marks)

b) A birdwatcher knows that the number of chaffinches visiting a particular observation spot per hour follows a Poisson distribution with mean 7.

Find the probability that in a randomly chosen hour during the day:

(i) fewer than 4 chaffinches visit the observation spot,

(2 marks)

(ii) at least 7 chaffinches visit the observation spot,

(2 marks)

(iii) exactly 9 chaffinches visit the observation spot.

(2 marks)

c) The number of birds other than chaffinches visiting the same observation spot per hour can be modelled by the Poisson distribution Po(22).

Find the probability that exactly 3 birds (of any species) visit the observation spot in a random 15-minute period.

(4 marks)

2 The number of calls received at a call centre each hour can be modelled by a Poisson distribution with mean 20.

a) Find the probability that in a random 30-minute period:

(i) exactly 8 calls are received,

(3 marks)

(ii) more than 8 calls are received.

(2 marks)

b) For a Poisson distribution to be a suitable model, events have to occur independently. What is meant by "independently" in this context?

(1 mark)

3 A researcher has determined that ancient works of literature copied out in monasteries contain wrong letters scattered randomly throughout the text at a rate of 1 error in every 5 lines of text.

a) In a document with 20 lines of text, find the probability that:

(i) no errors were made,

(2 marks)

(ii) more than 10 errors were made.

(2 marks)

b) The number of errors in a document of 180 lines is represented by the random variable Y.

(i) State the distribution of Y.

(1 mark)

(ii) State the standard deviation of Y.

(1 mark)

4 An outdoor-equipment store sells a certain type of rucksack at an average rate of 6 a month. The number of these rucksacks they sell each month, X, is assumed to follow a Poisson distribution.

a) Calculate $P(4 < X \leq 7)$ *(2 marks)*

b) Calculate the probability that the store sells more than 14 of these rucksacks in a random two-month period. *(3 marks)*

c) Find the probability that the store sells exactly 6 of these rucksacks each month for three consecutive months. Give your answer to one significant figure. *(3 marks)*

d) The number of these rucksacks they sell in each of a random sample of 8 months is shown below.

1, 12, 8, 3, 6, 6, 2, 10

Calculate the mean and variance of this data.
Use your answers to comment on the validity of the assumption that X follows a Poisson distribution. *(4 marks)*

5 The number of people per hour mistyping their passwords while trying to log in to a particular website is thought to follow a Poisson distribution. On average, it is assumed that 30 people per hour mistype their password while trying to log in.

a) Find the probability that in a randomly chosen 10-minute period:

(i) more than 10 people mistype their password, *(2 marks)*

(ii) at least 10 but no more than 15 people mistype their password. *(2 marks)*

The number of people per hour (x) mistyping their passwords was counted during 24 consecutive hours. The results are summarised below.

$$\sum x = 752 \qquad \sum x^2 = 24\,338$$

b) (i) Calculate the mean and the variance of the x-values. *(3 marks)*

(ii) Explain why these results support the use of a Poisson distribution. *(1 mark)*

(iii) Using the mean you obtained in part b) (i) above, find the probability that exactly 30 people mistype their password in a randomly chosen hour. *(3 marks)*

Chapter 3 Continuous Random Variables

1. Probability Density Functions

Learning Objectives:

- Understand what is meant by a continuous random variable and how it is different from a discrete random variable.
- Know the properties of probability density functions.
- Be able to find probabilities using probability density functions.

You learnt all about probability functions for discrete random variables in Chapter 1. Probability density functions are the same sort of thing, but for continuous random variables — they give you the probability of a continuous random variable taking a value in a certain range.

Probability density functions

Discrete random variables

Remember that with **discrete** random variables (like the ones you've seen with a binomial distribution back in S1 and the ones you've seen in Chapters 1 and 2) there are **gaps** between the possible **values** that the random variable can take:

For example, if $X \sim$ **B(3, 0.4)**, then you know that X can only take the values **0**, **1**, **2** or **3**, and you could work out the probability of each value using the **probability function**. You could even draw a graph of what this probability function looks like.

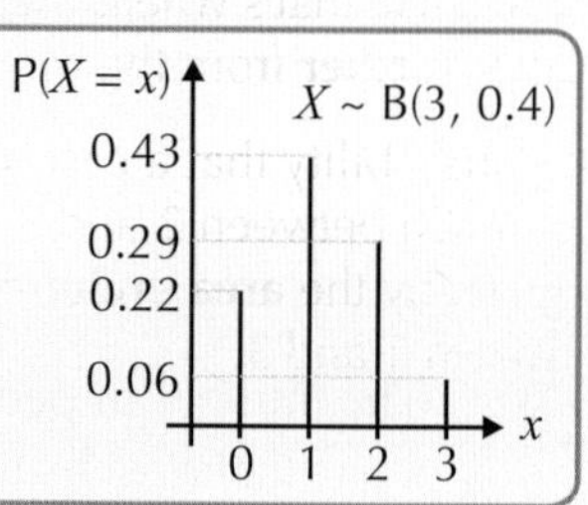

Tip: $X \sim B(n, p)$ means X follows a binomial distribution with n trials and a probability p of success.

Continuous random variables

- Continuous random variables are similar to discrete random variables — but there is one important **difference**:

A **continuous random variable** is a random variable which can take **any value** in a certain range.

- They represent things like length, height, weight, rainfall etc. — things that are measured on a **continuous** scale.

Tip: Remember... a continuous scale doesn't have 'gaps' between its possible values.

Tip: You've already seen examples of continuous random variables in S1 — ones that follow a normal distribution.

You can still draw a **graph** showing how likely a continuous random variable is to take values within its possible range. But instead of a series of bars, it will be a **continuous line**.

- These graphs are called **probability density functions** (or **p.d.f.s**). Here, **f(x)** is a p.d.f.
- The **area under** a p.d.f. between two points shows the **probability** that the random variable will take a value in that **range**. For example, the **shaded area** shows the probability that this continuous random variable will take a value between **1** and **2**.

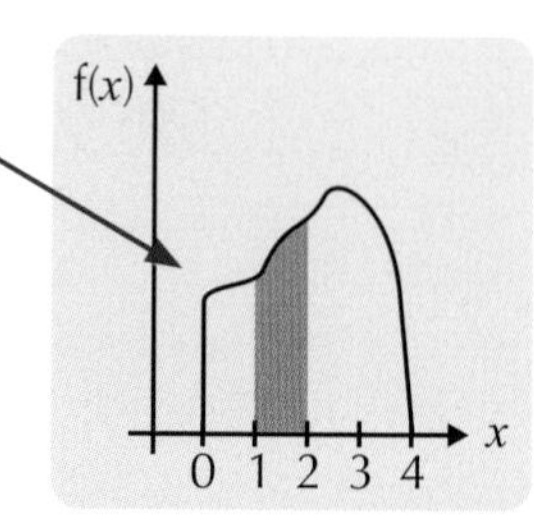

Tip: Remember... the area under the graph of a function is found by integrating the function.

You saw the graphs of some p.d.f.s back in S1 when you looked at **normal distributions**. The formula for the p.d.f. of the normal distribution **N(μ, σ^2)** is given in your exam formula book. In theory, you could integrate it to work out the **probability** of a **normally distributed** random variable taking a value in a certain range (but see the tip in the margin).

Tip: The p.d.f. for the normal distribution $X \sim N(\mu, \sigma^2)$ is:
$$f(x) = \frac{1}{\sigma\sqrt{2\pi}}e^{-\frac{1}{2}\left(\frac{x-\mu}{\sigma}\right)^2}$$
Unfortunately, it's really awkward to integrate, which is why you used tables in S1 to find probabilities for the normal distribution.

For example, the numbers of octaves that cast members in a musical can reach with their voices are **normally distributed** with a mean of 2.2 octaves and a standard deviation of 0.3 octaves.

This normal distribution has a probability density function f(x) which looks like this:

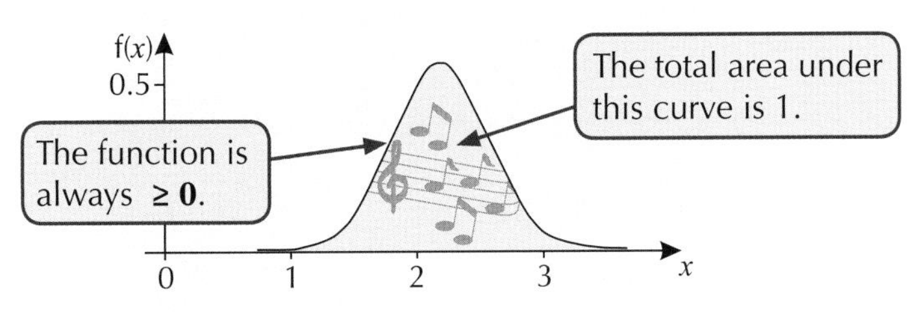

Tip: See below for more about the properties of a p.d.f.

The **most likely** number of octaves is around the **mean** at 2.2 — because that's where the **p.d.f.** is **greatest**.
Values **further** from the mean are **less likely** since the p.d.f. drops away.

The probability that a cast member can reach between 2 and 3 octaves is given by the **area under** the p.d.f. **between** 2 and 3.

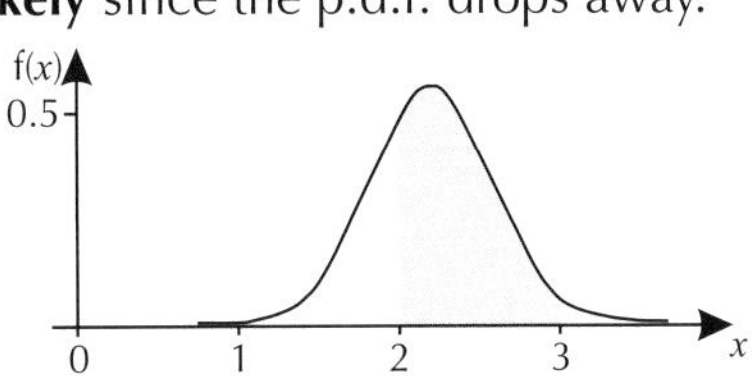

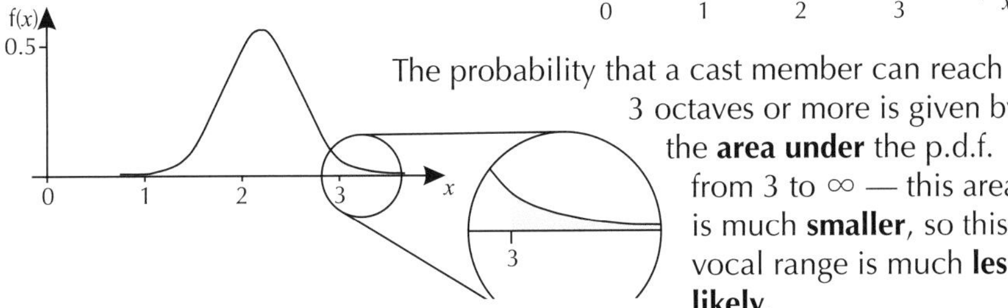

The probability that a cast member can reach 3 octaves or more is given by the **area under** the p.d.f. from 3 to ∞ — this area is much **smaller**, so this vocal range is much **less likely**.

Properties of a p.d.f.

Because (i) **probabilities** can **never** take **negative** values,
and (ii) the **total probability** of a random variable taking a value is **1**,
a p.d.f. **always** has the following **properties**:

For a **continuous random variable** X, with **probability density function f(x)**:

- **f(x) ≥ 0 for all $x \in \mathbb{R}$**
  — probabilities can never be negative.
- $\int_{-\infty}^{\infty} f(x)\,dx = 1$
  — the total probability (the area under the whole curve) must be 1.

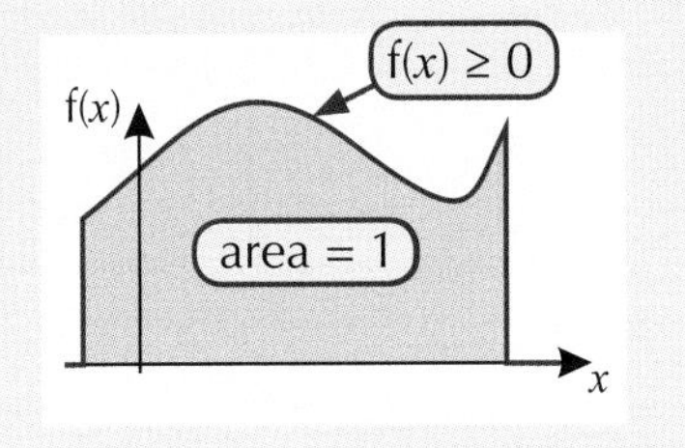

Tip: Where a formula relating to a discrete random variable involves a summation (Σ), the equivalent formula relating to a continuous random variable involves an integral.

For example, $\int_{-\infty}^{\infty} f(x)\,dx = 1$ is the 'continuous equivalent' of $\sum p_i = 1$.

You need to be able to decide whether a function is a p.d.f. or not by using the **properties** of p.d.f.s on p39.

Tip: P.d.f.s are often defined 'piecewise' (bit by bit). You've seen probability functions like this for discrete random variables (p2) — it just means you have to use a different formula for different values of x.

Tip: If you're struggling to work out whether the curve stays positive, try sketching it in the given range — you'll often be asked to sketch a p.d.f. in the exam, so it's good practice.

Tip: When the p.d.f. is equal to zero, the area under the p.d.f. will also be zero — so you only need to integrate the non-zero bits of the function.

Examples

Decide whether the following are p.d.f.s:

a) $f(x) = \begin{cases} x^4 & -1 \le x \le 1 \\ 0 & \text{otherwise} \end{cases}$

- First check that $f(x) \ge 0$ for all $x \in \mathbb{R}$ — a sketch of the p.d.f. will help:

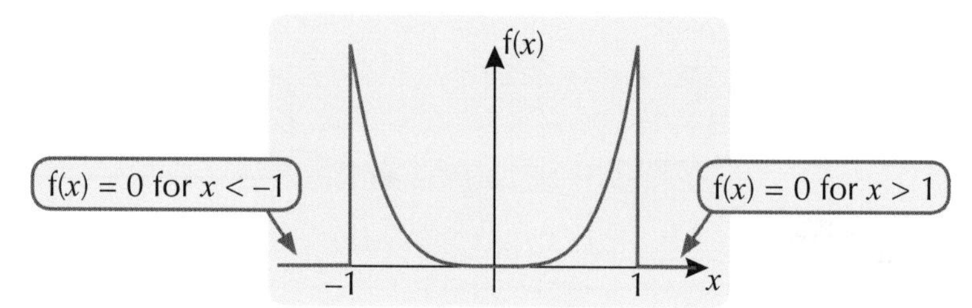

So you can see from the sketch that this function is **non-negative** for all x.

- Now you only need to check that the total probability is 1:

Split up the integral into the different ranges given by the piecewise function.

$$\int_{-\infty}^{\infty} f(x)\,dx = \int_{-\infty}^{-1} f(x)\,dx + \int_{-1}^{1} f(x)\,dx + \int_{1}^{\infty} f(x)\,dx$$

$$= \int_{-\infty}^{-1} 0\,dx + \int_{-1}^{1} x^4\,dx + \int_{1}^{\infty} 0\,dx = \int_{-1}^{1} x^4\,dx$$

$$= \left[\frac{x^5}{5}\right]_{-1}^{1} = \left(\frac{1^5}{5}\right) - \left(\frac{(-1)^5}{5}\right) = \frac{1}{5} + \frac{1}{5} = \frac{2}{5}$$

The integrals where the p.d.f. is zero will 'disappear'.

The total probability is **not 1**, so this function is **not a p.d.f.**

b) $f(x) = \begin{cases} \frac{1}{12}(3 - x) & -2 \le x \le 2 \\ 0 & \text{otherwise} \end{cases}$

- First check that $f(x) \ge 0$ for all $x \in \mathbb{R}$:

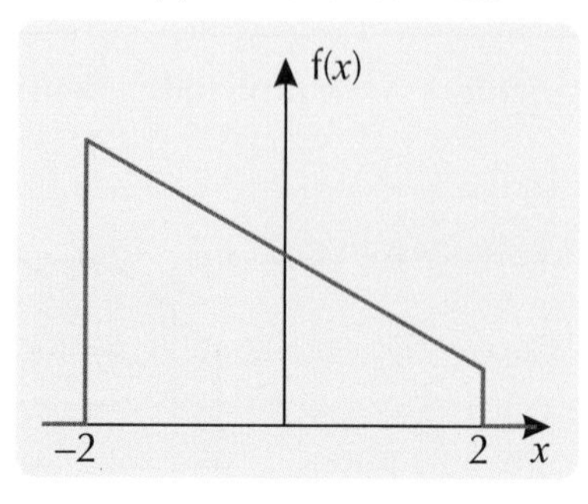

So this function is **non-negative** for all x.

- Now you only need to check that the total probability is 1:

$$\int_{-\infty}^{\infty} f(x)\,dx = \int_{-\infty}^{-2} f(x)\,dx + \int_{-2}^{2} f(x)\,dx + \int_{2}^{\infty} f(x)\,dx$$
$$= \int_{-2}^{2} \frac{1}{12}(3 - x)\,dx$$
$$= \frac{1}{12}\left[3x - \frac{x^2}{2}\right]_{-2}^{2}$$
$$= \frac{1}{12}[(6 - 2) - (-6 - 2)] = \frac{1}{12}[12] = 1$$

Again, you can ignore the integrals where the p.d.f. is zero.

The p.d.f. is non-negative for all x and the total probability **is 1**, so this function **is a p.d.f.**

Tip: If the function is made up of straight lines, it is sometimes easier to work out the total area under the graph by splitting it into shapes you can easily find the area of, instead of integrating. For example, this one is a trapezium so the area would be $\frac{\frac{5}{12} + \frac{1}{12}}{2} \times 4 = 1$.

Examples

Decide whether the following are p.d.f.s:

a) $f(x) = \begin{cases} \frac{1}{24}(x - 2) & 1 \le x \le 9 \\ 0 & \text{otherwise} \end{cases}$

- First check that $f(x) \ge 0$ for all $x \in \mathbb{R}$ — again, draw a sketch:

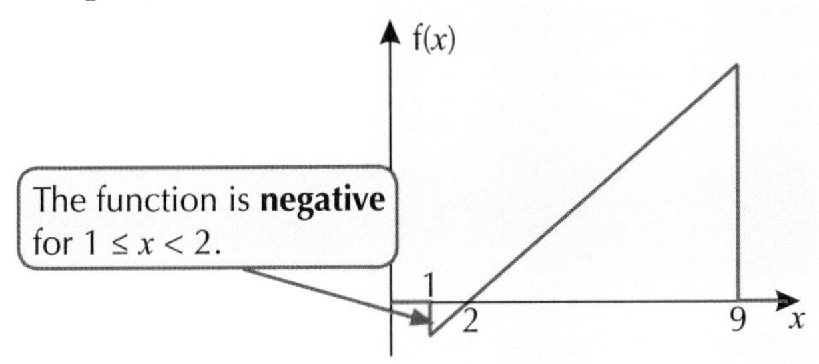

So $f(x)$ is **not a p.d.f.**, as it is **negative** for some values of x.

b) $f(x) = \begin{cases} kx & \text{for } -2 \le x \le 2 \\ 0 & \text{otherwise} \end{cases}$

- If k is positive, then $f(x)$ is negative for $-2 \le x < 0$, so k cannot be positive.
- If k is negative, then $f(x)$ is negative for $0 < x \le 2$, so k cannot be negative.
- If $k = 0$, then $\int_{-\infty}^{\infty} f(x)dx = \int_{-\infty}^{\infty} 0dx = 0$.
  This integral must equal 1 for $f(x)$ to be a p.d.f., so k cannot be 0.

There are no possible values of k for which $f(x)$ is a p.d.f.

So $f(x)$ is not a p.d.f.

You can use the property $\int_{-\infty}^{\infty} f(x)\,dx = 1$ to find **unknown values** in a p.d.f.

Examples

a) The continuous random variable X has the probability density function:

$$f(x) = \begin{cases} kx & 0 < x < 4 \\ 0 & \text{otherwise} \end{cases}$$

Find the value of k.

> **Tip:** You've been told that this function **is** a p.d.f. so you don't need to check that $f(x) \geq 0$.

- The total **area under** the p.d.f. must equal **1**. So just integrate the function to find the area in terms of k.

$$\int_0^4 kx\,dx = \left[\frac{kx^2}{2}\right]_0^4 = \left(\frac{k \times 4^2}{2}\right) - \left(\frac{k \times 0^2}{2}\right) = 8k$$

- You could also just use a sketch of $f(x)$ and work out the **area of the triangle**, but integrating will be easier when the functions get more complicated.

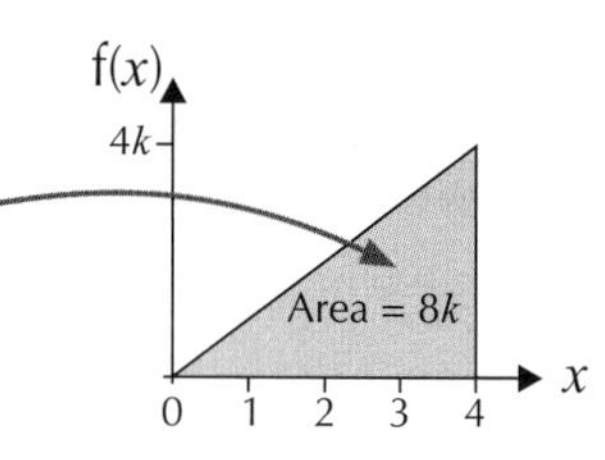

- Use the fact that the area **equals 1** to find k.

  So $8k = 1$, which gives $k = \frac{1}{8} = 0.125$

b) The continuous random variable X has the probability density function:

$$f(x) = \begin{cases} 2k & 0 < x < 4 \\ k(4x - 6) & 4 \leq x < 6 \\ 0 & \text{otherwise} \end{cases}$$

Find the value of k.

> **Tip:** This continuous random variable is defined by more than one 'non-zero piece'. It just means there are different formulas for different ranges. You'll need to integrate each piece separately.

- The total **area under** the p.d.f. must equal **1**. So just integrate the function to find the area.

$$\text{Total area} = \int_{-\infty}^{\infty} f(x)\,dx$$

$$= \int_0^4 2k\,dx + \int_4^6 k(4x - 6)\,dx$$

> You need to integrate **both** non-zero bits of the 'piecewise' p.d.f. separately between their limits and **add them together**.

$$= [2kx]_0^4 + [k(2x^2 - 6x)]_4^6$$

$$= [(2k \times 4) - (2k \times 0)]$$

$$+ [k(2 \times 6^2 - 6 \times 6) - k(2 \times 4^2 - 6 \times 4)]$$

$$= 8k + 36k - 8k = 36k$$

- Let this expression for the area **equal 1** to find k.

  So $36k = 1$, which means $k = \frac{1}{36}$

Exercise 1.1

Q1 (i) For each function f(x) below decide whether or not it is a valid p.d.f. Explain your answer.

(ii) If it is a valid p.d.f. then sketch its graph.

> **Q1 Hint:** When the p.d.f. has several 'pieces', you just need to sketch each separate piece for the relevant range and then join the pieces up.

a) $f(x) = \begin{cases} \frac{1}{2}x^2 & 0 < x < 2 \\ 0 & \text{otherwise} \end{cases}$

b) $f(x) = \begin{cases} \frac{3}{4}x^2 & 1 < x < 2 \\ 0 & \text{otherwise} \end{cases}$

c) $f(x) = \begin{cases} 1 - \frac{1}{2}x & 0 < x < 2 \\ 0 & \text{otherwise} \end{cases}$

d) $f(x) = \begin{cases} \frac{1}{4}x^3 & 0 < x < 2 \\ 1 & \text{otherwise} \end{cases}$

e) $f(x) = \begin{cases} x^2 + 5 & 1 < x < 2 \\ 0 & \text{otherwise} \end{cases}$

f) $f(x) = \begin{cases} \frac{2}{9}(3x - x^2) & 0 < x < 3 \\ 0 & \text{otherwise} \end{cases}$

g) $f(x) = \begin{cases} \frac{1}{3} & 0 < x < 1 \\ x^2 - \frac{5}{3} & 1 \leq x < 2 \\ 0 & \text{otherwise} \end{cases}$

h) $f(x) = \begin{cases} 0.2 & 0 < x < 1 \\ 0.5x^2 & 1 \leq x < 3 \\ 0 & \text{otherwise} \end{cases}$

Q2 The continuous random variable X has the probability density function f(x). Find the value of k for each definition of f(x) below.

a) $f(x) = \begin{cases} kx^2 & 1 < x < 2 \\ 0 & \text{otherwise} \end{cases}$

b) $f(x) = \begin{cases} kx^3 & 0 < x < 2 \\ 0 & \text{otherwise} \end{cases}$

c) $f(x) = \begin{cases} k & 0 < x < 1 \\ kx & 1 \leq x < 2 \\ 0 & \text{otherwise} \end{cases}$

d) $f(x) = \begin{cases} \frac{1}{3} & 0 < x < 1 \\ k(1 - x^2) & 1 \leq x < 2 \\ 0 & \text{otherwise} \end{cases}$

Finding probabilities from probability density functions

Remember from p38 that probabilities are represented by **areas under** p.d.f.s.
Now then... areas under curves can be found by **integrating**, so if X has p.d.f. f(x):

$$\mathbf{P(a < X < b) = \int_a^b f(x)\,dx}$$

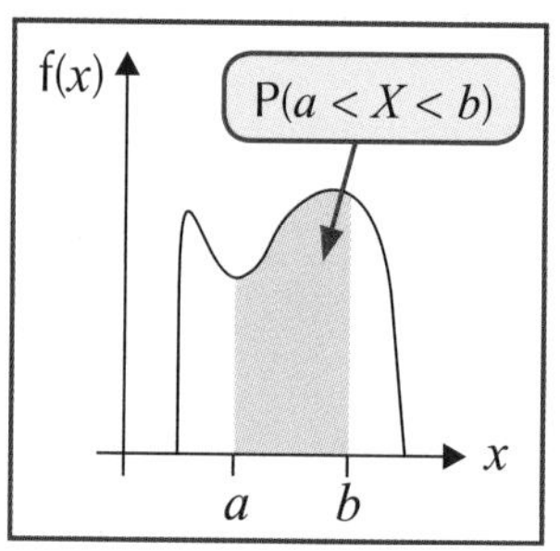

Notice a couple of things...

- The **probability** of a continuous random variable, X, equalling any **single value**, $P(X = x)$, is always **zero** because the area under a graph at a single point always equals zero.
  So it only makes sense to find the probability of X taking a value **within a particular range**.
- This also means that for any continuous random variable, X, and any k:

$$\mathbf{P(X < k) = P(X \leq k)}$$

Tip: Remember that
$$\int_a^a f(x)\,dx = 0$$
for any value of a.

Tip: Remember that:
$P(X \leq k)$
$= P(X < k) + P(X = k)$
(since the events $X < k$ and $X = k$ are mutually exclusive).
So, since $P(X = k) = 0$:
$P(X \leq k) = P(X < k) + 0$
$= P(X < k)$

Example 1

The continuous random variable X has the probability density function:

$$f(x) = \begin{cases} \frac{3-x}{4} & 0 < x < 2 \\ 0 & \text{otherwise} \end{cases}$$

a) Sketch f(x).

The function $\frac{3-x}{4}$ can be written as $\frac{3}{4} - \frac{1}{4}x$ — so the graph looks like this:

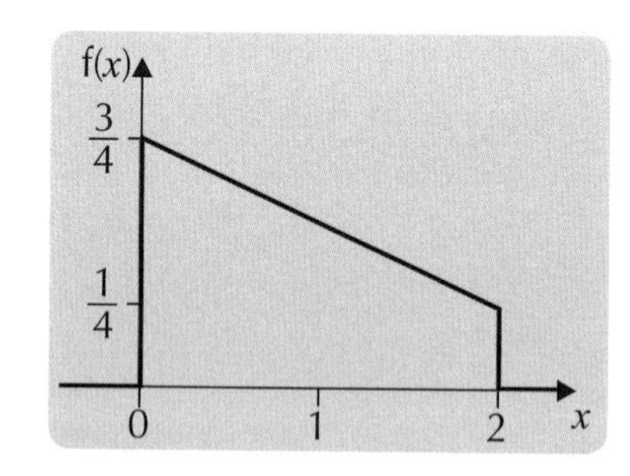

b) Find $P(0 < x < 1)$.

You just need to find the area under the p.d.f. between 0 and 1.

Integrate:

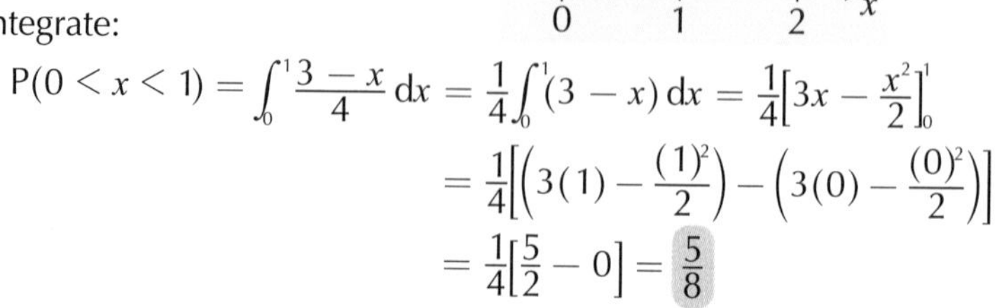

$$P(0 < x < 1) = \int_0^1 \frac{3-x}{4}\,dx = \frac{1}{4}\int_0^1 (3-x)\,dx = \frac{1}{4}\left[3x - \frac{x^2}{2}\right]_0^1$$
$$= \frac{1}{4}\left[\left(3(1) - \frac{(1)^2}{2}\right) - \left(3(0) - \frac{(0)^2}{2}\right)\right]$$
$$= \frac{1}{4}\left[\frac{5}{2} - 0\right] = \frac{5}{8}$$

Tip: You could also work out the area using the formula for the area of a trapezium.

Example 2

The continuous random variable X has the probability density function:

$$f(x) = \begin{cases} x^2 + a & 0 \le x \le 1 \\ 0 & \text{otherwise} \end{cases}$$

a) Sketch f(x), and find the value of a.

- The non-zero bit of the p.d.f. is a quadratic function, and so f(x) looks like this:

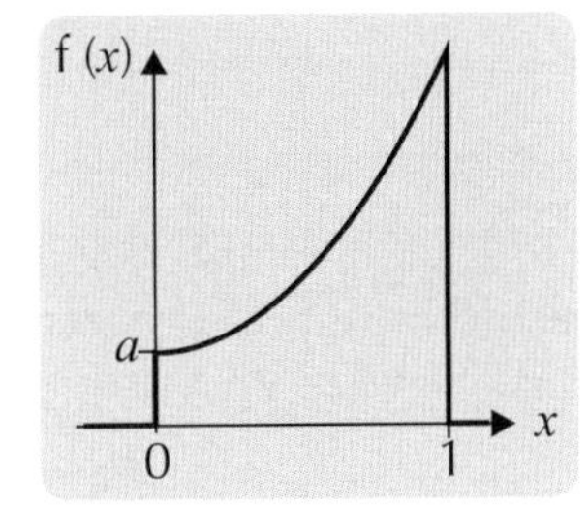

- The area under the graph must equal **1**, so integrate:

$$\int_{-\infty}^{\infty} f(x)dx = \int_{-\infty}^{0} f(x)dx + \int_{0}^{1} f(x)dx + \int_{1}^{\infty} f(x)dx$$
$$= \int_{0}^{1} (x^2 + a)dx$$
$$= \left[\frac{x^3}{3} + ax\right]_0^1 = \left(\frac{1}{3} + a\right)$$

So $\frac{1}{3} + a = 1 \Rightarrow a = \frac{2}{3}$

b) Find $P(X > \frac{1}{2})$.

Integrate again — this time between $x = \frac{1}{2}$ and $x = 1$.

$$P\left(X > \frac{1}{2}\right) = \int_{\frac{1}{2}}^{1} \left(x^2 + \frac{2}{3}\right) dx$$
$$= \left[\frac{x^3}{3} + \frac{2}{3}x\right]_{\frac{1}{2}}^{1}$$
$$= \left(\frac{1}{3} + \frac{2}{3}\right) - \left(\frac{1}{24} + \frac{1}{3}\right)$$
$$= \frac{15}{24} = \frac{5}{8}$$

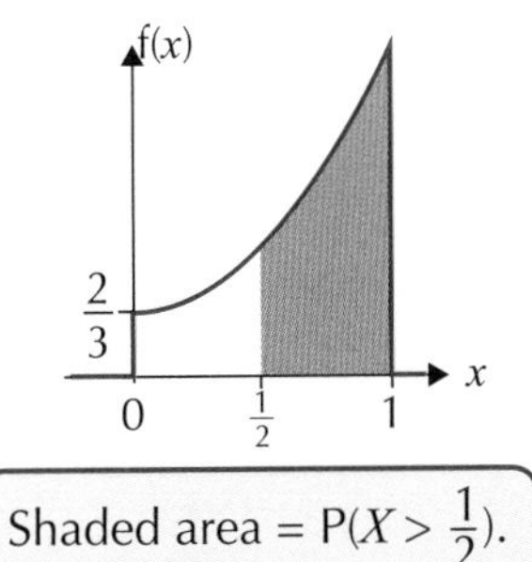

Shaded area = $P(X > \frac{1}{2})$.

Tip: You don't need to bother with the integral $\int_{1}^{\infty} f(x)\,dx$ because you can see from the definition and from the graph that the p.d.f. is zero, so the integral will also be zero.

Example 3

The continuous random variable X has the probability density function:

$$f(x) = \begin{cases} 3x^2 + 1 & 0 < x \le \frac{1}{2} \\ \frac{3}{4} & \frac{1}{2} < x < 1 \\ 0 & \text{otherwise} \end{cases}$$

a) Sketch f(x).

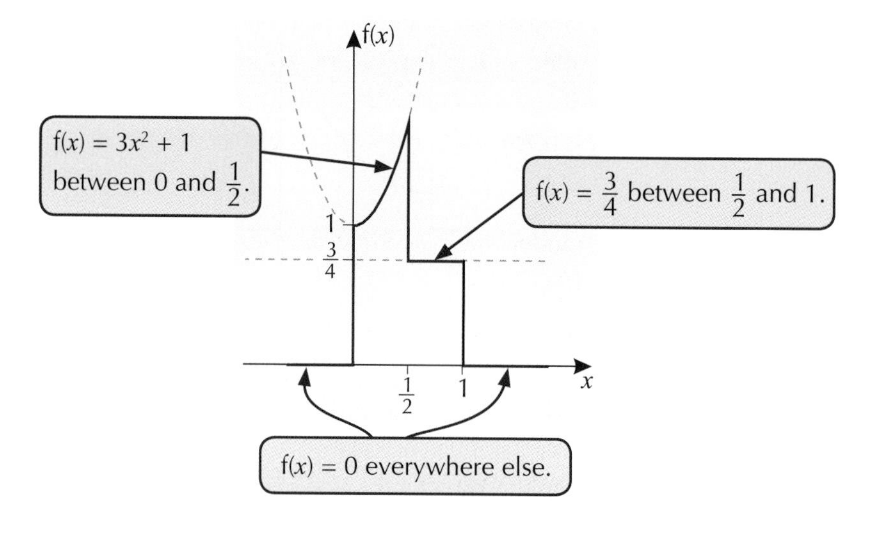

b) Find P$\left(\frac{1}{4} < x < \frac{3}{4}\right)$.

- You need to find the area under the p.d.f. between $\frac{1}{4}$ and $\frac{3}{4}$ — but the formula used to define the p.d.f. changes between these two values, so you'll need to **split** the area up into two bits, find the area of these bits separately, and **add** the results together.

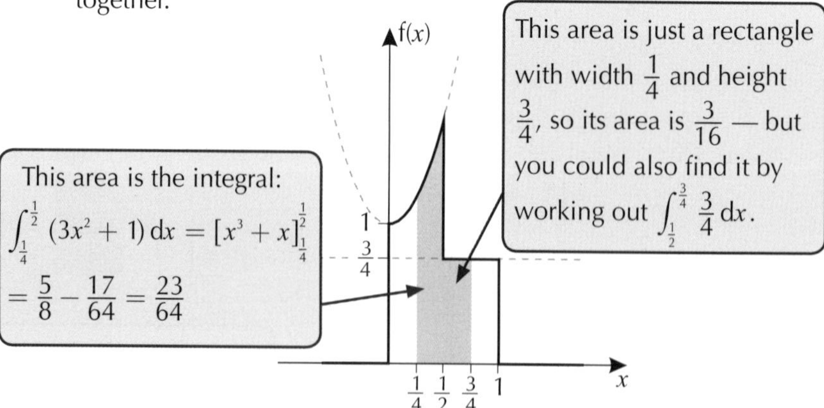

- **Add** the areas together to get the total probability:

$$P\left(\frac{1}{4} < x < \frac{3}{4}\right) = \frac{23}{64} + \frac{3}{16} = \frac{35}{64}$$

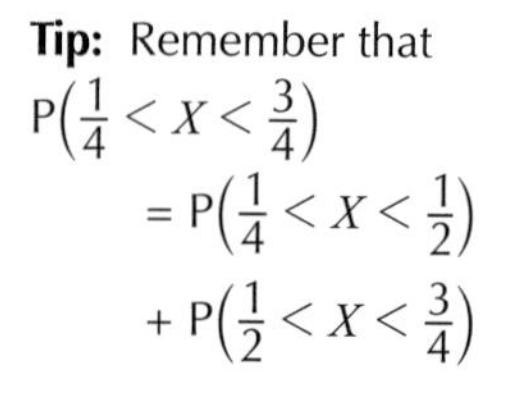

Tip: Remember that $P\left(\frac{1}{4} < X < \frac{3}{4}\right) = P\left(\frac{1}{4} < X < \frac{1}{2}\right) + P\left(\frac{1}{2} < X < \frac{3}{4}\right)$

Exercise 1.2

Q1 The continuous random variable X has the probability density function:

$$f(x) = \begin{cases} 1 - \frac{1}{2}x & 0 < x < 2 \\ 0 & \text{otherwise} \end{cases}$$

a) Find $P(0 < X < 1)$.

b) Find $P(\frac{1}{2} < X < 1)$.

Q2 The continuous random variable X has the probability density function:

$$f(x) = \begin{cases} 2(1 - x) & 0 < x < 1 \\ 0 & \text{otherwise} \end{cases}$$

Find $P(0.25 < X < 0.75)$.

Q3 The continuous random variable X has the probability density function:

$$f(x) = \begin{cases} \frac{1}{4}x^3 & 0 < x < 2 \\ 0 & \text{otherwise} \end{cases}$$

a) Find $P(X < 1)$.

b) Find $P(1 < X < 2)$.

Q4 The continuous random variable X has the probability density function:

$$f(x) = \begin{cases} \frac{2}{9}(3x - x^2) & 0 < x < 3 \\ 0 & \text{otherwise} \end{cases}$$

Find $P(1 < X < 2)$.

Q5 The continuous random variable X has the probability density function:

$$f(x) = \begin{cases} \frac{2}{5} & 0 < x < 1 \\ \frac{2}{5}x & 1 \leq x < 2 \\ 0 & \text{otherwise} \end{cases}$$

a) Find $P(X < 1)$.

b) Find $P\left(\frac{1}{2} < X < \frac{3}{2}\right)$.

Q6 The continuous random variable X has the probability density function:

$$f(x) = \begin{cases} \frac{1}{3} & 0 < x < 1 \\ \frac{1}{3}(2x - 1) & 1 \leq x < 2 \\ 0 & \text{otherwise} \end{cases}$$

a) Find $P(0 < X < 1.5)$.

b) Find $P(X = 1)$.

2. Cumulative Distribution Functions

The cumulative distribution function of a continuous random variable gives the area under the probability distribution function up to a certain point. You saw one in S1 when using statistical tables for the normal distribution.

Learning Objectives:

- Be able to use the p.d.f. of a continuous random variable to find its c.d.f., and vice versa.
- Be able to find probabilities using a c.d.f.

Cumulative distribution functions

A **cumulative distribution function** (c.d.f.) for a **continuous** random variable X gives the **area under the curve** of its p.d.f. up to a certain point. You find a c.d.f. by **integrating** the corresponding p.d.f.

> If X is a continuous random variable with **p.d.f.** $f(x)$, then its **cumulative distribution function, F(x)**, is given by:
> $$F(x) = \int_{-\infty}^{x} f(t)dt$$

Tip: In the definition of a c.d.f., the integral is with respect to t. But when you put in the limits, t disappears — leaving a function of just x.

C.d.f.s are usually labelled with capital letters, e.g. **F(x)** — unlike p.d.f.s, which are usually labelled with lower case letters, e.g. **f(x)**.

For any value of x, the c.d.f. shows the **probability** that X is between $-\infty$ and x.

Since the area under a p.d.f. gives probability, this means: $F(x) = P(X \leq x)$

Tip: $P(X \leq x) = P(X < x)$ for a continuous random variable X (see p44).

Tip: Remember that a discrete random variable, X, has a c.d.f. $F(x)$ where $F(x) = P(X \leq x)$ — it's just the same thing really.

There are **2 properties** of c.d.f.s which will help you to recognise them:

- **$0 \leq F(x) \leq 1$**
  — all probabilities are ≥ 0 and the total probability is 1.
- $F(x)$ is **non-decreasing** and **continuous**
  — all probabilities are ≥ 0 so $F(x)$ cannot decrease as x increases.

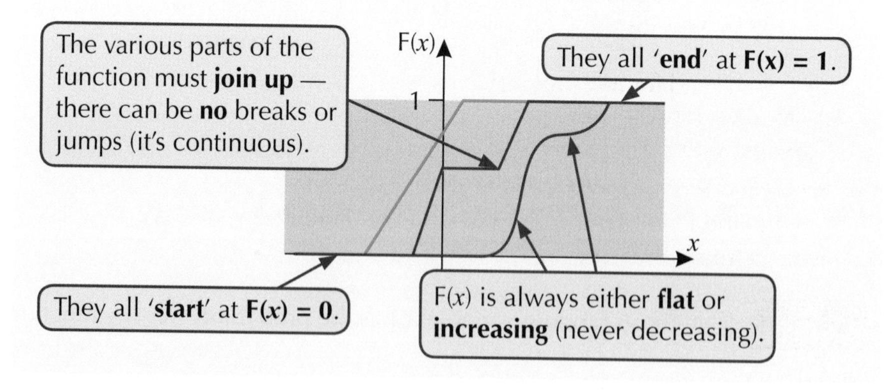

Tip: You can think about the properties of a c.d.f. another way...

$F(x)$ shows the area under a p.d.f. to the left of x.

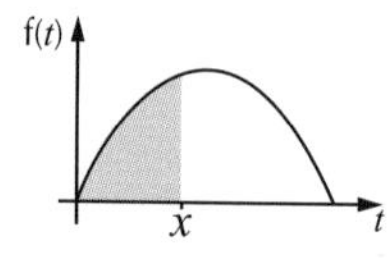

- This area will always be between 0 and 1.
- As x increases, the area under the p.d.f. to the left of x cannot decrease.
- So $F(x)$ is a non-decreasing function between 0 and 1.

To find a cumulative distribution function you need to integrate the probability density function. You'll need to make sure that:

- You define $F(x)$ for **all** values of x — even when $f(x)$ is 0.
- There are no **'jumps'** (i.e. $F(x)$ is continuous) — if you've got a p.d.f. that's defined piecewise then the value of $F(x)$ at the **end** of one interval should be the same as its value at the **start** of the next.

When the p.d.f. is only defined by one 'piece' (and 0 otherwise) it's easy:

Example 1

A continuous random variable X has probability density function f(x), where:

$$f(x) = \begin{cases} 2x - 2 & \text{for } 1 \le x \le 2 \\ 0 & \text{otherwise} \end{cases}$$

Find the cumulative distribution function of X.

- All c.d.f.s must 'start' at F(x) = 0 and 'end' at F(x) = 1 (see p48).

  Here, f(x) = 0 for all $x < 1$, and so F(x) = 0 for all $x < 1$.
  Similarly, f(x) = 0 for all $x > 2$, and so F(x) = 1 for all $x > 2$.

  So the c.d.f. looks like this either side of $1 \le x \le 2$ and you just need to find out what happens in the **middle** (remember it can do anything **except** decrease and jump or break.)

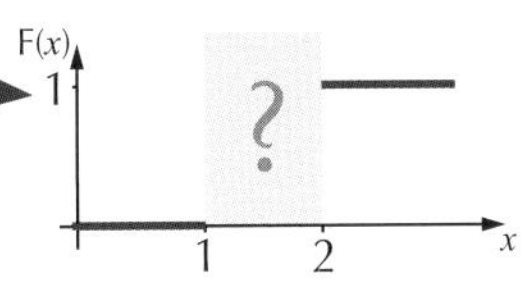

- To find F(x) in the range $1 \le x \le 2$, you need to integrate between $-\infty$ and x.

  Split up the integral because f(t) is different for different values of t.

  For $1 \le x \le 2$:

$$F(x) = \int_{-\infty}^{x} f(t)\,dt = \int_{-\infty}^{1} f(t)\,dt + \int_{1}^{x} f(t)\,dt = \int_{-\infty}^{1} 0\,dt + \int_{1}^{x} (2t - 2)\,dt$$
$$= 0 + [t^2 - 2t]_1^x = x^2 - 2x - (1 - 2) = x^2 - 2x + 1$$

- So putting all this together:

$$F(x) = \begin{cases} 0 & \text{for } x < 1 \\ x^2 - 2x + 1 & \text{for } 1 \le x \le 2 \\ 1 & \text{for } x > 2 \end{cases}$$

  F(x) is defined for all values of x and the 'pieces' join together with 'no jumps' — i.e. F(1) = 0 using both the first and second 'pieces', and F(2) = 1 using both the second and third.

Tip: It sometimes helps to draw the p.d.f. Here, it looks like this:

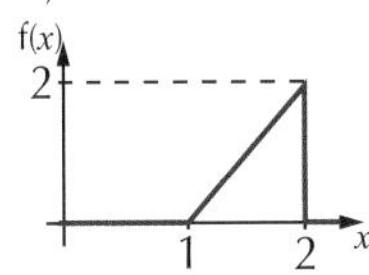

Tip: If f(x) = 0 for all $x < a$ (for some a) then $F(x) = \int_{-\infty}^{x} f(t)\,dt = \int_{-\infty}^{x} 0\,dt = 0$ for all $x < a$.

Tip: Remember to write the function inside the integral as a function of t. The variable t will disappear when you put the limits in.

Tip: Notice that all the 'pieces' of the c.d.f. join up. This is one of the properties of a c.d.f. and it'll always happen as long as you remember to integrate from $-\infty$.

But you **don't** always need to **write down** the terms like $\int_{-\infty}^{1} 0\,dt$ (because you know they're going to disappear).

Once you've found F(x) you can use it to find $P(X \le x_0)$ for a given value x_0.

Example 1 continued

For the continuous random variable X defined in the example above, find P($X \le 1.5$).

- P($X \le 1.5$) is just F(1.5) (see p48).
- So you find F(1.5) by substituting 1.5 into the expression for F(x).
- Since 1.5 lies in the interval $1 \le x \le 2$, use the formula $F(x) = x^2 - 2x + 1$.

  $P(X \le 1.5) = F(1.5) = 1.5^2 - (2 \times 1.5) + 1 = 2.25 - 3 + 1 = 0.25$

If the p.d.f. is defined by **more than one** 'piece', you need to be careful with the c.d.f. where the 'pieces' **join**. There are two methods for working out the c.d.f. correctly.

Example 2

Find the cumulative distribution function of X, whose probability density function is

$$f(x) = \begin{cases} 0.5 & \text{for } 3 \le x < 4 \\ 1.5 - 0.25x & \text{for } 4 \le x \le 6 \\ 0 & \text{otherwise} \end{cases}$$

Tip: Don't forget about 'piece 1' of the p.d.f., where $F(x) = 0$ for all values of x less than 3.

The graph of this **p.d.f.** is on the right. There'll be **4 pieces** to your c.d.f.

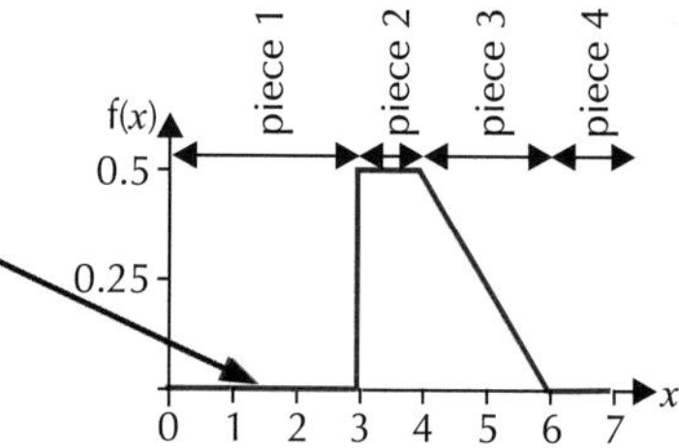

- For $x < 3$, $\int_{-\infty}^{x} f(t)\,dt = 0$ — i.e. $F(x) = 0$.
- To join on from this smoothly, $F(3)$ must be equal to 0.
- Then there are **two ways** to make sure the middle pieces join on smoothly:

1 Always start your integral at $-\infty$:

For **piece 2**, when $3 \le x < 4$:

$$F(x) = \int_{-\infty}^{x} f(t)dt = \int_{-\infty}^{3} f(t)dt + \int_{3}^{x} f(t)dt$$

(= F(3))

$$= F(3) + \int_{3}^{x} 0.5dt$$
$$= 0 + [0.5t]_3^x$$
$$= \mathbf{0.5x - 1.5}$$

So for the next piece to join on smoothly, you must have $F(4) = 0.5 \times 4 - 1.5 = 2 - 1.5 = 0.5$.

For **piece 3**, when $4 \le x \le 6$:

(= F(4))

$$F(x) = \int_{-\infty}^{4} f(t)dt + \int_{4}^{x} f(t)dt = F(4) + \int_{4}^{x} f(t)dt$$
$$= 0.5 + \int_{4}^{x} (1.5 - 0.25t)dt$$

(Because F(4) = 0.5)

$$= 0.5 + [1.5t - 0.125t^2]_4^x$$
$$= 0.5 + (1.5x - 0.125x^2) - (6 - 2)$$
$$= \mathbf{1.5x - 0.125x^2 - 3.5}$$

2 **Use an indefinite integral** and choose the **constant of integration** so that the join is 'smooth'.

For **piece 2**, when $3 \leq x < 4$:

$$F(x) = \int f(x)dx = \int 0.5dx = 0.5x + k_1$$

But $F(3) = 1.5 + k_1 = 0$ (to join the first piece of c.d.f. smoothly).
So $k_1 = -1.5$, which gives $\mathbf{F(x) = 0.5x - 1.5}$.

For **piece 3**, when $4 \leq x \leq 6$:

$$F(x) = \int f(x)dx = \int (1.5 - 0.25x)dx$$
$$= 1.5x - 0.125x^2 + k_2$$

Now find k_2 so that these two pieces join **smoothly** at $x = 4$.
$F(4) = 0.5 \times 4 - 1.5 = 0.5$ (using 'piece 2').
And $F(4) = 1.5 \times 4 - 0.125 \times 4^2 + k_2 = 4 + k_2$ (using 'piece 3').
This means $0.5 = 4 + k_2$, or $k_2 = -3.5$.
So $\mathbf{F(x) = 1.5x - 0.125x^2 - 3.5}$.

Tip: Use x rather than t in this integral. There are no limits so the t won't disappear.

Notice that both of these methods give you the same answer.

Now, all that's left is '**piece 4**' where $x > 6$:
A c.d.f. always ends up at 1, so for $x > 6$, $F(x) = F(6) = 1$ — but check that this makes a smooth join with the previous part of the c.d.f.
Using $F(x) = 1.5x - 0.125x^2 - 3.5$ gives $F(6) = 9 - 4.5 - 3.5 = \mathbf{1}$, so it's fine.

Put the bits together to get:

$$F(x) = \begin{cases} 0 & \text{for } x < 3 \\ 0.5x - 1.5 & \text{for } 3 \leq x < 4 \\ 1.5x - 0.125x^2 - 3.5 & \text{for } 4 \leq x \leq 6 \\ 1 & \text{for } x > 6 \end{cases}$$

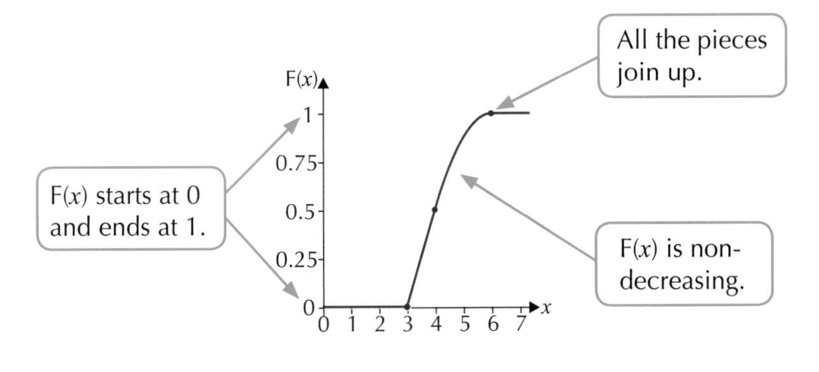

Exercise 2.1

Q1 Decide whether each of the following functions is a valid c.d.f., giving a reason for your answer.

a) $F(x) = \begin{cases} 0 & x < 0 \\ \frac{1}{2}(2 - x^2) & 0 \leq x \leq 2 \\ 1 & x > 2 \end{cases}$

b) $F(x) = \begin{cases} 0 & x < -\frac{1}{3} \\ 1 + 3x & -\frac{1}{3} \leq x \leq 0 \\ 1 & x > 0 \end{cases}$

c) $F(x) = \begin{cases} 0 & x < 0 \\ 2x - 2x^2 & 0 \leq x \leq 1 \\ 1 & x > 1 \end{cases}$

Q2 For the following p.d.f.s, f(x), find the corresponding c.d.f., F(x):

a) $f(x) = \begin{cases} 1 - \frac{1}{2}x & 0 \leq x \leq 2 \\ 0 & \text{otherwise} \end{cases}$

b) $f(x) = \begin{cases} 2(1 - x) & 0 \leq x \leq 1 \\ 0 & \text{otherwise} \end{cases}$

c) $f(x) = \begin{cases} \frac{3}{7}x^2 & 1 \leq x \leq 2 \\ 0 & \text{otherwise} \end{cases}$

d) $f(x) = \begin{cases} \frac{1}{4}(6x^2 - 3x^3) & 0 \leq x \leq 2 \\ 0 & \text{otherwise} \end{cases}$

e) $f(x) = \begin{cases} \frac{2}{9}(3x - x^2) & 0 \leq x \leq 3 \\ 0 & \text{otherwise} \end{cases}$

Q3 For the following p.d.f.s, f(x), find the corresponding c.d.f., F(x):

a) $f(x) = \begin{cases} \frac{2}{5} & 0 \leq x < 1 \\ \frac{2}{5}x & 1 \leq x \leq 2 \\ 0 & \text{otherwise} \end{cases}$

b) $f(x) = \begin{cases} \frac{1}{3} & 0 < x < 1 \\ \frac{1}{3}(2x - 1) & 1 \leq x < 2 \\ 0 & \text{otherwise} \end{cases}$

Q4 a) Find the c.d.f. for the continuous random variable X with p.d.f.

$$f(x) = \begin{cases} \frac{1}{3} & 0 \leq x < 1 \\ -\frac{1}{2}(1 - x^2) & 1 \leq x \leq 2 \\ 0 & \text{otherwise} \end{cases}$$

b) Hence find $P(X \leq \frac{3}{4})$.

Finding probability density functions by differentiating

To find a c.d.f. from a p.d.f., you **integrate**, so it makes sense that if you already know the c.d.f., you can **differentiate** to find the p.d.f.

$$f(x) = \frac{d}{dx}(F(x))$$

Examples

Find the p.d.f. of the continuous random variable X with c.d.f. F(x), where

$$F(x) = \begin{cases} 0 & \text{for } x < 0 \\ \frac{1}{2}(3x - x^3) & \text{for } 0 \le x \le 1 \\ 1 & \text{for } x > 1 \end{cases}$$

Differentiate each 'piece' of the c.d.f. separately to find the p.d.f.:

$$\frac{d}{dx}\left(\frac{1}{2}(3x - x^3)\right) = \frac{d}{dx}\left(\frac{3}{2}x - \frac{x^3}{2}\right) = \frac{3}{2} - \frac{3}{2}x^2$$

$$f(x) = \frac{dF(x)}{dx} = \begin{cases} 0 & x < 0 \\ \frac{3}{2} - \frac{3}{2}x^2 & 0 \le x \le 1 \\ 0 & x > 1 \end{cases} = \begin{cases} \frac{3}{2} - \frac{3}{2}x^2 & \text{for } 0 \le x \le 1 \\ 0 & \text{otherwise} \end{cases}$$

$$\frac{d}{dx}(0) = \frac{d}{dx}(1) = 0$$

Exercise 2.2

Q1 For each c.d.f. F(x) below, find the p.d.f. f(x).

a) $F(x) = \begin{cases} 0 & x < 0 \\ 3x^2 - 2x^3 & 0 \le x \le 1 \\ 1 & x > 1 \end{cases}$

b) $F(x) = \begin{cases} 0 & x < 0 \\ \frac{1}{4}(x^3 + 3x^2) & 0 \le x \le 1 \\ 1 & x > 1 \end{cases}$

c) $F(x) = \begin{cases} 0 & x < 0 \\ \frac{1}{4}x & 0 \le x < 1 \\ \frac{1}{20}x^4 + \frac{1}{5} & 1 \le x \le 2 \\ 1 & x > 2 \end{cases}$

Q2 For each c.d.f. F(x) below, find the p.d.f. f(x) and sketch its graph.

a) $F(x) = \begin{cases} 0 & x < 1 \\ \frac{1}{3}x^2 - \frac{1}{3} & 1 \le x \le 2 \\ 1 & x > 2 \end{cases}$

b) $F(x) = \begin{cases} 0 & x < 0 \\ \frac{1}{3}x & 0 \le x < 2 \\ \frac{2x}{3} - \frac{x^2}{12} - \frac{1}{3} & 2 \le x \le 4 \\ 1 & x > 4 \end{cases}$

Tip: The ideas covered in this topic are the same ones you've already used when finding probabilities for binomial, Poisson and normal distributions.

Finding probabilities using a cumulative distribution function

It's really easy to work out a probability of the form $\mathbf{P(X \leq x)}$ with a c.d.f. — you just put the value of x into $F(x)$. But you can easily work out the **probability** of a continuous random variable falling within other **ranges** too.

Example 1

The cumulative distribution function F(x) of the continuous random variable X is given below.

$$F(x) = \begin{cases} 0 & x < 0 \\ 0.5(3x - x^3) & 0 \leq x \leq 1 \\ 1 & x > 1 \end{cases}$$

Find:

a) $P(X \leq 0.5)$

Tip: $P(X \leq 0.5)$ is just F(0.5).

This one's easy — just put 0.5 into $F(x)$.
0.5 is between 0 and 1 so use the middle 'piece' of the c.d.f.

$P(X \leq 0.5) = F(0.5) = 0.5 \times (3 \times 0.5 - 0.5^3) =$ **0.6875**

b) $P(X > 0.25)$

The c.d.f. only tells you the probability of X being less than or equal to a value, but you can use the fact that the total probability is 1:

$P(X > 0.25) = 1 - P(X \leq 0.25)$ ← $P(X > x) = 1 - P(X \leq x)$
$= 1 - F(0.25)$
$= 1 - 0.5 \times (3 \times 0.25 - 0.25^3)$ ← Use the formula for $F(x)$
$= 1 - 0.3671... =$ **0.633 (to 3 d.p.)**

c) $P(0.1 \leq X \leq 0.2)$

Tip: It's easy to see why $P(0.1 \leq X \leq 0.2) = P(X \leq 0.2) - P(X \leq 0.1)$ on this graph.
The green area (= $P(0.1 \leq X \leq 0.2)$) is equal to:
the area under the graph to the left of $x = 0.2$ (= $P(X \leq 0.2)$)
...minus...
the area under the graph to the left of $x = 0.1$ (= $P(X \leq 0.1)$).

This is the probability that X is less than or equal to 0.2 but **not** less than 0.1.

It's given by the probability that X is less than 0.2 **minus** the probability that X is less than 0.1.

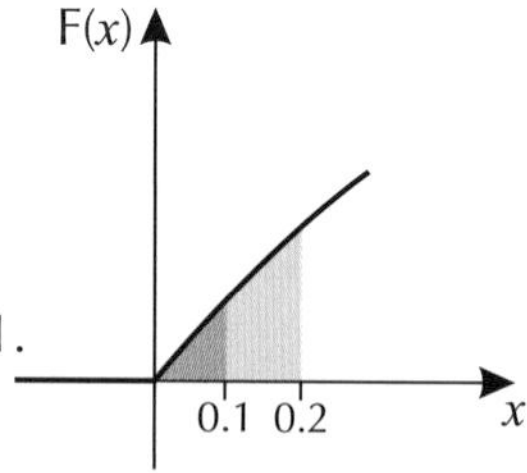

$P(0.1 \leq X \leq 0.2) = P(X \leq 0.2) - P(X < 0.1)$
$= P(X \leq 0.2) - P(X \leq 0.1)$
$= F(0.2) - F(0.1)$
$= 0.296 - 0.1495 =$ **0.1465**

For a continuous random variable, $P(X \leq k) = P(X < k)$ since $P(X = k) = 0$ (see p44).

d) $P(X < 0.5)$

This one's easy too because $P(X \leq k) = P(X < k)$ since $P(X = k) = 0$.

So $P(X < 0.5) = P(X \leq 0.5) =$ **0.6875** from part a).

If you have a p.d.f. and you need to find **a few** different probabilities, then it can be easier to:

(i) use the p.d.f. to work out the c.d.f. first,
(ii) then use the c.d.f. to find the probabilities.

This way you only need to do a single integration.

Example 2

The continuous random variable X has p.d.f. f(x), where

$$f(x) = \begin{cases} \frac{x^3}{4} & 0 \le x \le 2 \\ 0 & \text{otherwise} \end{cases}$$

a) Find F(x)

- For $x < 0$, $P(X \le x) = 0$ so $F(x) = 0$.
  To join on from this smoothly, F(0) must be equal to 0.

- For $0 \le x \le 2$:

$$F(x) = \int_{-\infty}^{x} f(t)\,dt = \int_{-\infty}^{0} f(t)\,dt + \int_{0}^{x} f(t)\,dt$$
$$= F(0) + \int_{0}^{x} \left(\frac{t^3}{4}\right) dt$$
$$= 0 + \left[\frac{t^4}{4 \times 4}\right]_0^x = \left[\frac{t^4}{16}\right]_0^x = \frac{x^4}{16}$$

- For $x > 2$, $F(x) = 1$.
  You can check the previous piece joins up with this by putting $x = 2$ into the above expression for F(x):

$$F(2) = \frac{2^4}{16} = \frac{16}{16} = 1$$

- So putting all this together:

$$F(x) = \begin{cases} 0 & x < 0 \\ \frac{x^4}{16} & 0 \le x \le 2 \\ 1 & x > 2 \end{cases}$$

b) Find $P(X \le 1.5)$

$P(X \le 1.5) = F(1.5) = \frac{(1.5)^4}{16} = 0.31640... =$ 0.316 (3 d.p.)

c) Find $P(X > 0.5)$

$P(X > 0.5) = 1 - P(X \le 0.5) = 1 - F(0.5)$

$= 1 - \frac{(0.5)^4}{16} = 1 - 0.00390... =$ 0.996 (3 d.p.)

d) Find $P(0.5 \le X \le 1.5)$

$P(0.5 \le X \le 1.5) = P(X \le 1.5) - P(X \le 0.5) = F(1.5) - F(0.5)$

$= 0.31640... - 0.00390... =$ 0.313 (3 d.p.)

Exercise 2.3

Q1 $$\mathrm{F}(x) = \begin{cases} 0 & x < 0 \\ \frac{1}{4}(x^3 + 3x^2) & 0 \le x \le 1 \\ 1 & x > 1 \end{cases}$$

Use the c.d.f. F(x) above to find:

a) $P(X \le 0.2)$ b) $P(X < 0.5)$ c) $P(0.3 \le X \le 0.8)$

Q2 $$\mathrm{F}(x) = \begin{cases} 0 & x < 0 \\ \frac{1}{3}x & 0 \le x < 2 \\ \frac{2}{3}x - \frac{1}{12}x^2 - \frac{1}{3} & 2 \le x \le 4 \\ 1 & x > 4 \end{cases}$$

Use the c.d.f. F(x) above to find:

a) $P(X \le 1)$ b) $P(X > 3)$ c) $P(1 \le X \le 2)$

Q3 $$\mathrm{f}(x) = \begin{cases} \frac{1}{8}x & 0 \le x \le 4 \\ 0 & \text{otherwise} \end{cases}$$

a) For the p.d.f. f(x) above, find the c.d.f. F(x).

b) Use the c.d.f. F(x) to find:

(i) $P(X < 1)$ (ii) $P(2 < X < 3)$

Q4 The function f(x) below is the p.d.f. for the continuous random variable X.

$$\mathrm{f}(x) = \begin{cases} \frac{1}{12} & 0 \le x \le 1 \\ -\frac{1}{3}(1 - x^3) & 1 < x \le 2 \\ 0 & \text{otherwise} \end{cases}$$

a) Find the indefinite integral $\int \frac{1}{12}\mathrm{d}x$.

b) The c.d.f. of X, F(x), equals 0 at $x = 0$.
Use this fact to find the constant of integration in part a).

c) Find the indefinite integral $\int -\frac{1}{3}(1 - x^3)\mathrm{d}x$.

d) Use the fact that F(2) = 1 to find the constant of integration in c).

e) Hence state the cumulative distribution function of X for all values of x.

f) Use F(x) to find:

(i) $P(X < 0.5)$ (ii) $P(X > 1.5)$

Q5 $$\mathrm{f}(x) = \begin{cases} \frac{1}{4} & 0 \le x < 3 \\ \frac{1}{8}(5 - x) & 3 \le x \le 5 \\ 0 & \text{otherwise} \end{cases}$$

a) For the p.d.f. f(x) above, find the c.d.f. F(x).

b) Use the c.d.f. F(x) to find:

(i) $P(X < 2)$ (ii) $P(X > 4)$ (iii) $P(1 \le X \le 3)$ (iv) $P(X = 4.5)$

3. Mean and Variance

In Chapter 1 you learnt how to find the mean (expected value) and variance of a discrete random variable. And surprise, surprise... you can find them for continuous random variables too by using the probability density function.

Learning Objectives:

- Be able to calculate the mean (expected value), variance and standard deviation of a continuous random variable.
- Be able to calculate the mean of a function of a continuous random variable.
- Be able to calculate the mean and variance of transformations of continuous random variables of the form $aX + b$.

Mean of a continuous random variable

The expected value (mean) of X: E(X) or μ

For every continuous random variable you can work out the **mean** (or **expected value**) from the probability density function.

To find E(X) for a **continuous** random variable, you use **integration**.

> If X is a continuous random variable with p.d.f. f(x), then its mean (μ) or expected value (E(X)) is given by:
>
> $$\mu = \mathrm{E}(X) = \int_{-\infty}^{\infty} x\mathrm{f}(x)\,\mathrm{d}x$$

You'll have to **split** the integral up into the different **ranges** that f(x) is **defined** for and work out each integral separately.

Tip: Remember that E(X) for a discrete random variable is given by the summation:

$$\mathrm{E}(X) = \sum x_i p_i$$

In the formula for the expected value of a continuous random variable you need to replace p_i with f(x) dx and integrate.

Example 1

Find the expected value of the continuous random variable X with p.d.f. f (x) given below:

$$\mathrm{f}(x) = \begin{cases} \frac{3}{32}(4 - x^2) & \text{for } -2 \le x \le 2 \\ 0 & \text{otherwise} \end{cases}$$

Split the integral up into the **three** different ranges: $-\infty < x < -2$, $-2 \le x \le 2$, $2 < x < \infty$

$$\mathrm{E}(X) = \int_{-\infty}^{\infty} x\mathrm{f}(x)\mathrm{d}x = \int_{-\infty}^{-2} x\mathrm{f}(x)\mathrm{d}x + \int_{-2}^{2} x\mathrm{f}(x)\mathrm{d}x + \int_{2}^{\infty} x\mathrm{f}(x)\mathrm{d}x$$

Two of the integrals are 0.

$$= \int_{-\infty}^{-2} 0\,\mathrm{d}x + \int_{-2}^{2} x \times \frac{3}{32}(4 - x^2)\mathrm{d}x + \int_{2}^{\infty} 0\,\mathrm{d}x$$

$$= \int_{-2}^{2}\left(\frac{3}{8}x - \frac{3x^3}{32}\right)\mathrm{d}x = \left[\frac{3x^2}{16} - \frac{3x^4}{128}\right]_{-2}^{2}$$

$$= \left(\frac{3 \times 2^2}{16} - \frac{3 \times 2^4}{128}\right) - \left(\frac{3 \times (-2)^2}{16} - \frac{3 \times (-2)^4}{128}\right)$$

$$= 0$$

You'd expect a mean of **0** here, since f(x) is **symmetrical** about the ***y*-axis**.

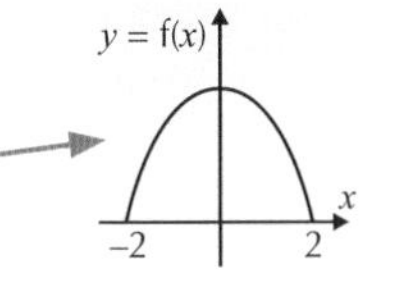

Tip: From now on you can ignore the bits of the p.d.f. defined as 0 and just integrate the non-zero bits.

Example 2

Find the expected value of the continuous random variable X with p.d.f. f (x) given below:

$$f(x) = \begin{cases} \frac{1}{3} & 0 < x < 1 \\ \frac{1}{3}(2x - 1) & 1 \le x < 2 \\ 0 & \text{otherwise} \end{cases}$$

Split the integral up into the two different ranges where f(x) is non-zero: $0 < x < 1$, $1 \le x < 2$

$$E(X) = \int_{-\infty}^{\infty} xf(x)dx = \int_0^1 xf(x)dx + \int_1^2 xf(x)dx$$

$$= \int_0^1 x \times \frac{1}{3}dx + \int_1^2 x \times \left(\frac{1}{3}(2x-1)\right)dx$$

$$= \int_0^1 \frac{x}{3}dx + \int_1^2 \left(\frac{2}{3}x^2 - \frac{1}{3}x\right)dx$$

$$= \left[\frac{x^2}{6}\right]_0^1 + \left[\frac{2x^3}{9} - \frac{x^2}{6}\right]_1^2$$

$$= \frac{1}{6} + \left[\left(\frac{2(2)^3}{9} - \frac{(2)^2}{6}\right) - \left(\frac{2(1)^3}{9} - \frac{(1)^2}{6}\right)\right]$$

$$= \frac{11}{9}$$

Expected value of a function of X

Just like with discrete random variables, you can find the expected value of a **function** of a continuous random variable X:

$$E(g(X)) = \int_{-\infty}^{\infty} g(x)f(x)\,dx$$

Tip: $aX + b$ is called a linear transformation of X.

If your function is of the form $g(X) = aX + b$, it's easier still:

$$E(aX + b) = aE(X) + b$$

Tip: This second formula comes from putting $g(X) = aX + b$ into the first formula. It is exactly the same as the one for discrete random variables (p13).

Examples

The continuous random variable X has p.d.f. f (x), where

$$f(x) = \begin{cases} \frac{3}{37}x^2 & \text{for } 3 \le x \le 4 \\ 0 & \text{otherwise} \end{cases}$$

a) Find the expected value, μ.

Use the formula from p57.

$$\mu = E(X) = \int_{-\infty}^{\infty} xf(x)dx = \int_3^4 x \times \frac{3}{37}x^2dx$$

$$= \int_3^4 \frac{3}{37}x^3dx = \frac{3}{37}\left[\frac{x^4}{4}\right]_3^4 = \frac{3}{37 \times 4}(4^4 - 3^4) = \frac{3 \times (256 - 81)}{148} = \frac{525}{148}$$

Tip: Always check your mean looks sensible. Here, you'd expect the mean to be somewhere between 3 and 4 (so $525 \div 148 = 3.547...$ seems 'about right').

b) Find $E(X^2)$.

$g(X) = X^2$, so $g(x) = x^2$.

$$E(X^2) = \int_{-\infty}^{\infty} x^2 f(x)dx = \int_3^4 x^2 \times \frac{3}{37}x^2 dx = \int_3^4 \frac{3}{37}x^4 dx$$

$$= \frac{3}{37}\left[\frac{x^5}{5}\right]_3^4 = \frac{3}{37 \times 5}(4^5 - 3^5) = \frac{2343}{185}$$

c) Find $E(3X + 2)$.

$E(aX + b) = aE(X) + b$

$$E(3X + 2) = 3E(X) + 2 = 3 \times \frac{525}{148} + 2 = \frac{1575 + 296}{148} = \frac{1871}{148}$$

You already know $E(X)$ from part a)

Exercise 3.1

Q1 Find $E(X)$ for the continuous random variable X with p.d.f. $f(x)$:

a) $f(x) = \begin{cases} 1 - \frac{1}{2}x & 0 \leq x \leq 2 \\ 0 & \text{otherwise} \end{cases}$

b) $f(x) = \begin{cases} \frac{1}{4}x^3 & 0 \leq x \leq 2 \\ 0 & \text{otherwise} \end{cases}$

c) $f(x) = \begin{cases} \frac{2}{9}(3x - x^2) & 0 \leq x \leq 3 \\ 0 & \text{otherwise} \end{cases}$

Q2 A continuous random variable X has p.d.f. $f(x)$, where:

$$f(x) = \begin{cases} \frac{3}{7}x^2 & 1 \leq x \leq 2 \\ 0 & \text{otherwise} \end{cases}$$

Find: a) μ b) $E\left(\frac{1}{3X}\right)$ c) $E(2X - 1)$ d) $P(X < \mu)$

Q3 A continuous random variable X has p.d.f. $f(x)$, where:

$$f(x) = \begin{cases} \frac{2}{5} & 0 \leq x < 1 \\ \frac{2}{5}x & 1 \leq x \leq 2 \\ 0 & \text{otherwise} \end{cases}$$

Find: a) μ b) $E(5X^2)$ c) $E(4X + 2)$

Q4 A continuous random variable X has p.d.f. $f(x)$, where:

$$f(x) = \begin{cases} \frac{1}{3} & 0 \leq x \leq 1 \\ -\frac{1}{2}(1 - x^2) & 1 < x \leq 2 \\ 0 & \text{otherwise} \end{cases}$$

Find: a) μ b) $E(X^2 + 1)$ c) $E(3X - 2)$

Q5 a) Find $\int_0^4 \frac{1}{4}x^2\, dx$.

b) Hence find $E(X)$ for the continuous random variable X with p.d.f.:

$$f(x) = \begin{cases} \frac{1}{8}x & 0 \leq x \leq 4 \\ 0 & \text{otherwise} \end{cases}$$

Variance of a continuous random variable

Tip: You should have learnt about dispersion in S1.

The variance of X: Var(X) or σ^2

The **variance** of a continuous random variable, X, is a measure of **dispersion** — basically how **spread out** the probability density function is from the **mean**.

For example, consider two continuous random variables which can be modelled by **normal distributions** with mean **0** but different **variances**.

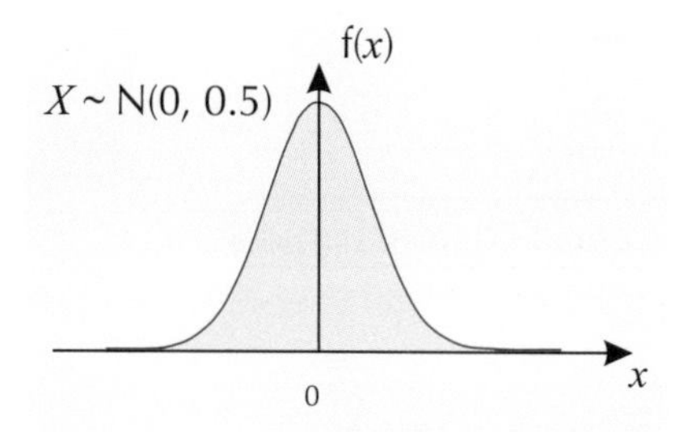

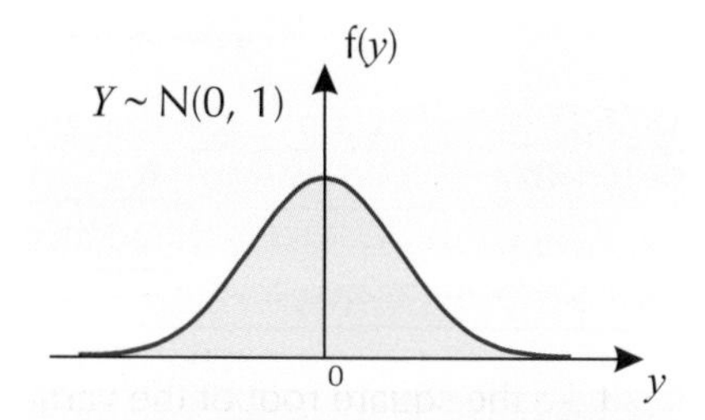

Y has a greater **variance** than X, and you can see by the graph that the p.d.f. of Y is more **spread out** about the mean than that of X.

You can find the variance of a continuous random variable using the same formula that you learnt for discrete random variables in Chapter 1. But to work it out, you need to **integrate** rather than use a summation.

If X is a continuous random variable with **p.d.f.** f(x), then its variance, Var(X), is:

$$\text{Var}(X) = \text{E}(X^2) - [\text{E}(X)]^2$$

This is the same formula as on p10.

$$= \text{E}(X^2) - \mu^2$$

$\text{E}(X) = \mu$

$$= \int_{-\infty}^{\infty} x^2 \text{f}(x)\text{d}x - \mu^2$$

See the tip in the margin for more about E(X^2).

Tip: Remember... if X is a continuous random variable then: $\text{E}(X^2) = \int x^2\text{f}(x)\,\text{d}x$. See p58 for more information.

Example

The continuous random variable X has p.d.f. f(x) given below, and a mean of 0. Find the variance of X.

$$\text{f}(x) = \begin{cases} \frac{3}{32}(4 - x^2) & \text{for } -2 \le x \le 2 \\ 0 & \text{otherwise} \end{cases}$$

You saw on page 57 that the mean of this p.d.f. is 0.

Just use the **formula** and **integrate**:

$$\text{Var}(X) = \text{E}(X^2) - \mu^2 = \int_{-\infty}^{\infty} x^2\text{f}(x)\text{d}x - \mu^2 = \int_{-2}^{2} x^2 \times \frac{3}{32}(4 - x^2)\text{d}x - 0^2$$

$$= \int_{-2}^{2}\left(\frac{3x^2}{8} - \frac{3x^4}{32}\right)\text{d}x = \left[\frac{x^3}{8} - \frac{3x^5}{160}\right]_{-2}^{2}$$

$$= \left(\frac{2^3}{8} - \frac{3 \times 2^5}{160}\right) - \left(\frac{(-2)^3}{8} - \frac{3 \times (-2)^5}{160}\right) = 0.8$$

The standard derivation of X: σ

The **standard deviation** is just another measure of a random variable's **dispersion** — sometimes used **instead** of the variance.

It's found by taking the **square root** of the **variance**, and it's written $\boldsymbol{\sigma}$.

If X is a continuous random variable with **p.d.f.** $f(x)$, then:

$$\text{Standard deviation} = \sigma = \sqrt{\text{Var}(X)}$$

Example

Find the standard deviation of X, where X is the continuous random variable in the Example at the bottom of the previous page.

Just take the square root of the variance:

$$\sigma = \sqrt{\text{Var}(X)} = \sqrt{0.8} = 0.894 \text{ (3 d.p.)}$$

Var($aX + b$)

You can easily find the variance of $\boldsymbol{aX + b}$, where a and b are constants. You've seen this formula before in Chapter 1:

For a **continuous random variable** X with p.d.f. $f(x)$:

$$\text{Var}(aX + b) = a^2\text{Var}(X)$$

Just square the a and get rid of the b altogether.

Tip: You can find the variance of any function of X. But when the function is a linear transformation (i.e. of the form $aX + b$), the formula is nice and easy.

Example

The continuous random variable X has p.d.f. $f(x)$, where

$$f(x) = \begin{cases} \frac{3}{37}x^2 & \text{for } 3 \le x \le 4 \\ 0 & \text{otherwise} \end{cases}$$

If $E(X) = \frac{525}{148}$, find:

a) Var(X)

$$\text{Var}(X) = E(X^2) - \mu^2 = \int_{-\infty}^{\infty} x^2 f(x)dx - \left(\frac{525}{148}\right)^2 = \int_3^4 x^2 \times \frac{3}{37}x^2 dx - \left(\frac{525}{148}\right)^2$$

$$= \frac{3}{37}\left[\frac{x^5}{5}\right]_3^4 - \left(\frac{525}{148}\right)^2 = \frac{3}{185}(4^5 - 3^5) - \left(\frac{525}{148}\right)^2 = 0.0815467...$$

$$= 0.0815 \text{ (to 4 d.p.)}$$

b) Var($3X + 2$)

$\text{Var}(3X + 2) = 3^2 \times \text{Var}(X) = 9 \times 0.0815467... = 0.734$ (to 3 d.p.).

$\text{Var}(aX + b) = a^2\text{Var}(X)$

Tip: See page 58 for the calculation of the mean of this p.d.f.

Exercise 3.2

Q1-4 Hint: You worked out the values of E(X) for these p.d.f.s in Exercise 3.1, Questions 1-4 — see page 59.

Q1 Find the variance of each of the following p.d.f.s, f(x):

a) $f(x) = \begin{cases} 1 - \frac{1}{2}x & 0 \leq x \leq 2 \\ 0 & \text{otherwise} \end{cases}$

b) $f(x) = \begin{cases} \frac{1}{4}x^3 & 0 \leq x \leq 2 \\ 0 & \text{otherwise} \end{cases}$

c) $f(x) = \begin{cases} \frac{2}{9}(3x - x^2) & 0 \leq x \leq 3 \\ 0 & \text{otherwise} \end{cases}$

Q2 A random variable X has p.d.f. $f(x) = \begin{cases} \frac{3}{7}x^2 & 1 \leq x \leq 2 \\ 0 & \text{otherwise} \end{cases}$

Find:

a) the variance, σ^2.

b) Var($2X$).

c) Var($2X + 1$).

d) the standard deviation, σ.

Q3 A random variable X has p.d.f. $f(x) = \begin{cases} \frac{2}{5} & 0 \leq x \leq 1 \\ \frac{2}{5}x & 1 < x \leq 2 \\ 0 & \text{otherwise} \end{cases}$

Find:

a) the variance of X.

b) the variance of $4X + 2$.

Q4 A random variable X has p.d.f. $f(x) = \begin{cases} \frac{1}{3} & 0 \leq x \leq 1 \\ -\frac{1}{2}(1 - x^2) & 1 < x \leq 2 \\ 0 & \text{otherwise} \end{cases}$

Find:

a) Var(X).

b) Var($-X$).

c) Var($3X + 2$).

d) the standard deviation.

Q5 Hint: Remember...
Var(X) = E(X^2) – [E(X)]^2
So Var(X^3)
= E((X^3)^2) – [E(X^3)]^2

Q5 A continuous random variable X has a probability density function given by $f(x) = \begin{cases} \frac{4 - x}{8} & 0 \leq x \leq 4 \\ 0 & \text{otherwise} \end{cases}$

a) Find E(X^3).

b) Find E(X^6)

c) Use your answers to find Var(X^3).

4. Quartiles and Percentiles

There are a few more measures that you need to know how to calculate for continuous random variables. You should have come across most of the basic ideas in S1 when you were looking at data sets, though.

Learning Objective:

- Be able to calculate the median, upper and lower quartiles, and percentiles of a continuous random variable.

Finding the quartiles and percentiles

The **quartiles** and **percentiles** are values of x for which a certain percentage of the **area** under the p.d.f. is **to the left** of x.
The **quartiles** split the area under the p.d.f. into quarters.

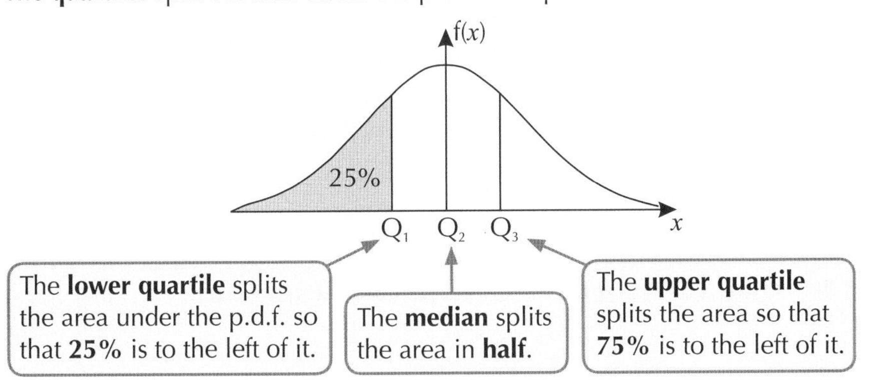

Tip: You should have learnt about the median and quartiles for data sets in S1 — it's the same concept here really.

In other words...

If X is a **continuous random variable** with probability density function f(x):

- The **lower quartile** (Q_1) of X is given by $\int_{-\infty}^{Q_1} f(x)dx = 0.25$.
- The **median** (Q_2) of X is given by $\int_{-\infty}^{Q_2} f(x)dx = 0.5$.
- The **upper quartile** (Q_3) of X is given by $\int_{-\infty}^{Q_3} f(x)dx = 0.75$.

Tip: You can use these definitions to find quartiles and percentiles. However, it's usually easier to find quartiles and percentiles using a c.d.f. (see p64).

Percentiles

- Percentiles are similar to quartiles... but they divide the distribution into **100 parts**.
- n% of the total probability is less than the nth percentile, P_n.
- In other words: $\int_{-\infty}^{P_n} f(x)\,dx = \frac{n}{100}$

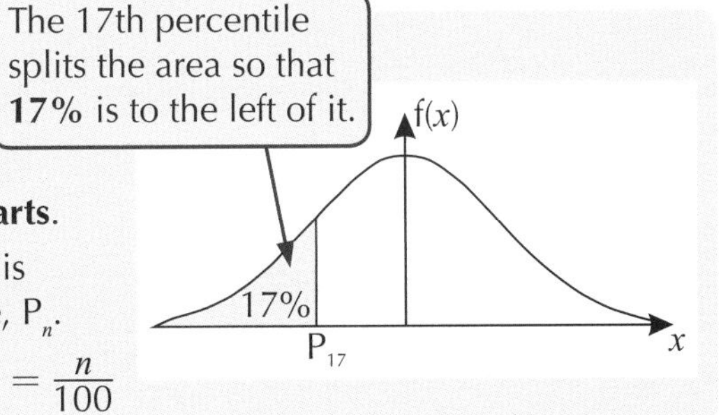

You can use the above definitions to find quartiles and percentiles...

Example

The continuous random variable X has the p.d.f. $f(x) = \begin{cases} \frac{x}{6} & \text{for } 2 \le x \le 4 \\ 0 & \text{otherwise} \end{cases}$
Find the value of the median of X, Q_2.

$$\int_{-\infty}^{Q_2} f(x)dx = 0.5 \Rightarrow \int_2^{Q_2} \frac{x}{6}dx = 0.5 \Rightarrow \frac{1}{6}\int_2^{Q_2} x dx = 0.5 \Rightarrow \frac{1}{6}\left[\frac{x^2}{2}\right]_2^{Q_2} = 0.5$$

$$\Rightarrow \frac{1}{6}\left[\frac{(Q_2)^2}{2} - \frac{4}{2}\right] = 0.5 \Rightarrow \frac{(Q_2)^2 - 4}{12} = 0.5 \Rightarrow (Q_2)^2 - 4 = 6 \Rightarrow Q_2 = \sqrt{10}$$

Tip: Always check that your answer seems sensible. Here, it has to be between 2 and 4, so $\sqrt{10}$ = 3.16... looks fine.

Using the c.d.f. to find quartiles and percentiles

Since the c.d.f. $F(x)$ gives $\mathbf{P(X \leq x)}$ for a given value of x, you can easily use it to find the median, quartiles and percentiles

Tip: The formulas on the right are basically the same as the ones on p63.

To see this, remember from p48 the definition of a c.d.f.:
$F(x) = \int_{-\infty}^{x} f(t)\,dt$

This means, for example, the median (Q_2) is given by:

$$F(Q_2) = \int_{-\infty}^{Q_2} f(t)\,dt = \int_{-\infty}^{Q_2} f(x)\,dx = 0.5$$

(It doesn't matter whether you use t or x in the integrals above — this variable disappears when you put the limits in.)

If X is a **continuous random variable** with **cumulative distribution function** $F(x)$ then:

- The **lower quartile** (Q_1) of X is given by $\mathbf{F(Q_1) = 0.25}$.
- The **median** (Q_2) of X is given by $\mathbf{F(Q_2) = 0.5}$.
- The **upper quartile** (Q_3) of X is given by $\mathbf{F(Q_3) = 0.75}$.
- The ***n*th percentile** (P_n) of X is given by $\mathbf{F(P_n) = \frac{n}{100}}$.

Example 1

The continuous random variable X has c.d.f. $F(x)$, where

$$F(x) = \begin{cases} 0 & x < 0 \\ \frac{1}{4}x^2 & 0 \leq x \leq 2 \\ 1 & x > 2 \end{cases}$$

Find the lower quartile (Q_1), the upper quartile (Q_3) and the 47th percentile (P_{47}).

- $F(0) = 0$ and $F(2) = 1$, so both Q_1 and Q_3 must lie in the range $0 \leq x \leq 2$. This means you'll need to use $F(x) = \frac{1}{4}x^2$.

- To find the **lower quartile**, let $F(Q_1) = \mathbf{0.25}$

$$\Rightarrow \frac{1}{4}Q_1^2 = 0.25$$
$$\Rightarrow Q_1^2 = 4 \times 0.25 = 1$$
$$\Rightarrow Q_1 = 1$$

- To find the **upper quartile**, let $F(Q_3) = \mathbf{0.75}$

$$\Rightarrow \frac{1}{4}Q_3^2 = 0.75$$
$$\Rightarrow Q_3^2 = 4 \times 0.75 = 3$$
$$\Rightarrow Q_3 = \sqrt{3} = 1.732 \text{ (3 d.p.)}$$

- To find the **47th percentile**, let $F(P_{47}) = \mathbf{0.47}$

$$\Rightarrow \frac{1}{4}P_{47}^2 = 0.47$$
$$\Rightarrow P_{47}^2 = 4 \times 0.47 = 1.88$$
$$\Rightarrow P_{47} = \sqrt{1.88} = 1.371 \text{ (3 d.p.)}$$

Watch out for when F(x) is defined **piecewise** — you'll have to work out F(x) at the point where the pieces join to see which 'piece' Q_1, Q_2 and Q_3 lie in.

Example 2

The continuous random variable X has p.d.f. f(x), where

$$f(x) = \begin{cases} 0.4 & \text{for } 1 \le x < 2 \\ 0.4(x-1) & \text{for } 2 \le x \le 3 \\ 0 & \text{otherwise} \end{cases}$$

a) Find the c.d.f., F(x).

- Integrate to find the c.d.f., making sure the 'joins are smooth'.
  - For $x < 1$, F(x) = 0
  - For $1 \le x < 2$:

$$F(x) = \int_{-\infty}^{x} f(t)\,dt = \int_{-\infty}^{1} f(t)\,dt + \int_{1}^{x} f(t)\,dt$$
$$= F(1) + \int_{1}^{x} 0.4\,dt = 0 + [0.4t]_1^x = 0.4x - 0.4$$

  - For $2 \le x \le 3$:

$$F(x) = \int_{-\infty}^{x} f(t)\,dt = \int_{-\infty}^{2} f(t)\,dt + \int_{2}^{x} f(t)\,dt$$
$$= F(2) + \int_{2}^{x} 0.4(t-1)\,dt = 0.4 + \left[0.4\left(\frac{t^2}{2} - t\right)\right]_2^x$$
$$= 0.4 + [0.2t^2 - 0.4t]_2^x$$
$$= 0.4 + [(0.2x^2 - 0.4x) - (0.2 \times 2^2 - 0.4 \times 2)]$$
$$= 0.2x^2 - 0.4x + 0.4$$

$$\text{So } F(x) = \begin{cases} 0 & \text{for } x < 1 \\ 0.4x - 0.4 & \text{for } 1 \le x < 2 \\ 0.2x^2 - 0.4x + 0.4 & \text{for } 2 \le x \le 3 \\ 1 & \text{for } x > 3 \end{cases}$$

Tip: This means F(1) = 0.

Tip: This means F(2) = 0.4 × 2 – 0.4 = 0.4

Tip: This means F(3) = 0.2(3)² – 0.4(3) + 0.4 = 1

So the pieces join together smoothly.

b) Find the quartiles Q_1 and Q_3.

- Find the values of F(x) where the pieces join to work out which piece contains each quartile.

F(1) = 0, F(2) = 0.4, F(3) = 1

$F(Q_1) = 0.25$ so $1 < Q_1 < 2$

$F(Q_3) = 0.75$ so $2 < Q_3 < 3$

Tip: Once you've found the c.d.f., it's easy to find out which pieces the quartiles lie in.

- Solve $F(Q_1) = 0.25$ to find the lower quartile.

You know $1 < Q_1 < 2$, so solve: $0.4Q_1 - 0.4 = 0.25$

$$\Rightarrow 0.4Q_1 = 0.65$$
$$\Rightarrow Q_1 = \frac{0.65}{0.4} = 1.625$$

- Solve $F(Q_3) = 0.75$ to find the upper quartile.

You know $2 < Q_3 < 3$, so solve: $0.2Q_3^2 - 0.4Q_3 + 0.4 = 0.75$

$$\Rightarrow 0.2Q_3^2 - 0.4Q_3 - 0.35 = 0$$
$$\Rightarrow Q_3 = \frac{0.4 + \sqrt{0.44}}{0.4} = 1 + \frac{\sqrt{0.44}}{0.4} = 2.658 \text{ (3 d.p.)}$$

Tip: The other solution to the quadratic is not in the correct range.

Example 3

The continuous random variable X has p.d.f. f(x), where

$$f(x) = \begin{cases} \frac{1}{3} & 0 < x < 2 \\ (x-2)^2 & 2 \le x < 3 \\ 0 & \text{otherwise} \end{cases}$$

a) Find the lower quartile.

- Start by working out the c.d.f.

For $x \le 0$, $F(x) = 0$

For $0 < x < 2$, $F(x) = \int_{-\infty}^{x} f(t)\,dt = F(0) + \int_0^x \frac{1}{3}\,dt = \left[\frac{1}{3}t\right]_0^x = \frac{1}{3}x$

For $2 \le x < 3$, $F(x) = \int_{-\infty}^{x} f(t)\,dt = F(2) + \int_2^x (t-2)^2\,dt$

$$= \frac{2}{3} + \int_2^x (t^2 - 4t + 4)\,dt = \frac{2}{3} + \left[\frac{t^3}{3} - 2t^2 + 4t\right]_2^x$$

$$= \frac{2}{3} + \left[\left(\frac{x^3}{3} - 2x^2 + 4x\right) - \left(\frac{8}{3} - 8 + 8\right)\right]$$

$$= \frac{x^3}{3} - 2x^2 + 4x - 2$$

Tip: So $F(0) = 0$.

Tip: So $F(2) = \frac{2}{3}$.

Tip: So $F(3) = 9 - 18 + 12 - 2 = 1$

$$\text{So } F(x) = \begin{cases} 0 & x \le 0 \\ \frac{1}{3}x & 0 < x < 2 \\ \frac{x^3}{3} - 2x^2 + 4x - 2 & 2 \le x < 3 \\ 1 & x \ge 3 \end{cases}$$

- $F(2) = \frac{2}{3}$ and so since $F(Q_1) = 0.25$, Q_1 must be less than 2:

So $F(Q_1) = 0.25$

$\Rightarrow \frac{1}{3}Q_1 = 0.25$

$\Rightarrow Q_1 = 0.25 \times 3 = 0.75$

b) Find the median.

Again, since $F(2) = \frac{2}{3}$, Q_2 must be less than 2.

So $F(Q_2) = 0.5$

$\Rightarrow \frac{1}{3}Q_2 = 0.5 \Rightarrow Q_2 = 0.5 \times 3 = 1.5$

c) Show that the upper quartile lies between 2.6 and 2.7.

- The upper quartile is Q_3 where $F(Q_3) = 0.75$.
F(x) is a c.d.f., which means it is an increasing function and so if Q_3 lies between 2.6 and 2.7, then $F(2.6) \le F(Q_3) \le F(2.7)$.

So you only need to show:

$$F(2.6) = \frac{(2.6)^3}{3} - 2(2.6)^2 + 4(2.6) - 2 = 0.739 \text{ (3 d.p.)}$$

$$F(2.7) = \frac{(2.7)^3}{3} - 2(2.7)^2 + 4(2.7) - 2 = 0.781$$

These are either side of 0.75, so Q_3 lies between 2.6 and 2.7.

Tip: The formula for F(x) is quite complicated for $2 \le x < 3$ (where Q_3 lies), so it would be difficult to find Q_3. But showing it lies between two values is easy.

Exercise 4.1

Q1 A random variable X has p.d.f. $f(x) = \begin{cases} 2x & 0 \leq x \leq 1 \\ 0 & \text{otherwise} \end{cases}$

By evaluating the integral $\int_{-\infty}^{Q_2} f(x)\,dx$, find the median, Q_2.

Q2 A random variable has the c.d.f. $F(x) = \begin{cases} 0 & x < -\frac{1}{3} \\ 1 + 3x & -\frac{1}{3} \leq x \leq 0 \\ 1 & x > 0 \end{cases}$

Find:

a) the median b) the lower quartile c) the upper quartile

Q3 A random variable has the c.d.f. $F(x) = \begin{cases} 0 & x < 0 \\ \frac{2}{5}x & 0 \leq x < 1 \\ \frac{1}{5}(x^2 + 1) & 1 \leq x \leq 2 \\ 1 & x > 2 \end{cases}$

Find:

a) the median b) the upper quartile c) the 14th percentile

Q4 Show that the median of X lies between 1.56 and 1.57,
where X has the c.d.f. F(x) given by:

$$F(x) = \begin{cases} 0 & x < 0 \\ \frac{1}{4}x & 0 \leq x < 1 \\ \frac{1}{20}x^4 + \frac{1}{5} & 1 \leq x \leq 2 \\ 1 & x > 2 \end{cases}$$

Q5 A random variable X has p.d.f. $f(x) = \begin{cases} \frac{3}{34}(x^3 - x^2) & 1 \leq x \leq 3 \\ 0 & \text{otherwise} \end{cases}$

a) Find the c.d.f. F(x).
b) Show that the median lies between 2.6 and 2.7.
c) By evaluating F(x) for one more value of x, give the median to one decimal place.

Q6 A random variable X has the p.d.f. $f(x) = \begin{cases} \frac{1}{2}(3 - x) & 1 \leq x \leq 3 \\ 0 & \text{otherwise} \end{cases}$

Find:

a) the c.d.f. F(x) b) the median
c) the lower quartile d) the 40th percentile
e) the mean and variance f) the mean and variance of $3X - 2$

5. The Rectangular Distribution

Learning Objectives:

- Be able to recognise when the rectangular distribution is a suitable model for a distribution.
- Be able to use the rectangular distribution to find probabilities.
- Be able to derive and use formulas for the mean and variance of a rectangular distribution.

This chapter has been all about continuous random variables, in general. Here you're introduced to the rectangular distribution, which is a particular type of distribution that a continuous random variable can follow.

Rectangular distributions

A random variable with a **rectangular distribution** can take any value in a particular range, and its value is **equally likely** to be **anywhere** in the range.

This means that its **probability density function** (p.d.f.) is **constant** — i.e. it takes the **same value** over the whole range of the distribution.

For example, suppose that the continuous random variable X has a **rectangular distribution** and can take any value from 1 to 5. And we want to sketch the graph of the probability density function of X, f(x).

- We know that the **range** of possible values is **1 to 5**.
- And we know that **f(x) is constant** over this range — i.e. it's shown by a **horizontal line**.
- So using the fact that the **total area** under the p.d.f. must equal **1**, the graph will be a rectangle with **width** (5 – 1) = **4**, and **height** (1 ÷ 4) = **0.25**.

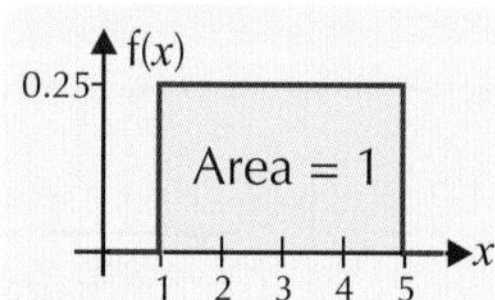

Using the graph, we can define the **probability density function f(x)** as:

$$f(x) = \begin{cases} 0.25 & \text{for } 1 \leq x \leq 5 \\ 0 & \text{otherwise} \end{cases}$$

Tip: See p38-39 for more about the area under a p.d.f.

Tip: The p.d.f. of a rectangular distribution is (unsurprisingly) always rectangular. These distributions can also be called continuous **uniform** distributions.

You can go through the above process for **any** rectangular distribution, but there's a **general formula** that makes things much easier.

If X is a random variable with a **rectangular distribution** over the interval $[a, b]$ then the **probability density function** of X is:

$$f(x) = \begin{cases} \dfrac{1}{b-a} & \text{for } a \leq x \leq b \\ 0 & \text{otherwise} \end{cases}$$

where a and b are constants

Tip: The interval $[a, b]$ means that a is the lower limit for X and b is the upper limit for X. In other words, $a \leq X \leq b$.

Example 1

The continuous random variable X has a rectangular distribution and can take any value between –5 and 5.

a) Write down the probability density function of X, $f(x)$.

- First, work out $\frac{1}{b-a}$ for your values of a and b:

  a is the lower limit for X — so $a = -5$.
  b is the upper limit for X — so $b = 5$.

  So $\frac{1}{b-a} = \frac{1}{5-(-5)} = \frac{1}{10} = \mathbf{0.1}$

- Now you can define **f(x)**: $f(x) = \begin{cases} 0.1 & \text{for } -5 \le x \le 5 \\ 0 & \text{otherwise} \end{cases}$

b) Sketch the graph of f(x).

The graph will be a rectangle with **width** = 5 – (–5) = **10** and **height** = f(x) = **0.1**.

Continue the line a short distance along the x-axis to show that f(x) = 0 for x outside the range [–5, 5].

Tip: Always make sure you define f(x) for all x-values — i.e. **outside** the range $[a, b]$ as well.

One of the **key things** to remember about a **probability density function** is that the **area underneath** it = **1**. You can use this fact to find missing values.

Example 2

The continuous random variable X has the probability density function:

$$f(x) = \begin{cases} 0.5 & \text{for } 0 \le x \le k \\ 0 & \text{otherwise} \end{cases}$$

Find the value of k.

- The easiest way to see what's going on here is to **sketch** f(x).
- You know that the area under f(x) = 1, so:

  Area of rectangle = (k – 0) × 0.5 = 1

  $\Rightarrow 0.5k = 1$

  $\Rightarrow k = 2$

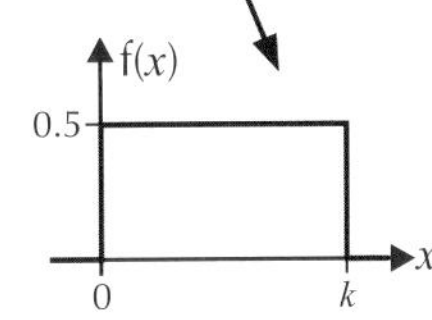

Tip: If you're happy doing this without a sketch, you can just use the definition of f(x) to find k:

You know that: $\frac{1}{b-a} = 0.5$,

$\Rightarrow \frac{1}{k-0} = 0.5$

$\Rightarrow k - 0 = 2$

$\Rightarrow k = 2$

Rectangular distributions describe things that are **equally likely** to take **any** value within an interval. This means that they're good for modelling quantities that take different values within an interval **completely at random**.

You need to be able to **recognise** when a rectangular distribution is a **suitable model** for a distribution.

Example

A runner's time over 100 m is measured as 12.3 seconds, to the nearest 0.1 second. Let the random variable X represent the error (in seconds) in the recorded time.

a) Suggest a suitable model for the distribution of X and explain why your suggestion is suitable.

- The time is measured to the nearest 0.1 second, so the **actual time** could be anywhere between 12.25 and 12.35 seconds.
- This means that the **error, X,** could be anything up to 0.05 seconds above or below the recorded time. This error is **random** within the interval –0.05 to 0.05 seconds — there's no reason for it to be high, low or in the middle. So a suitable model for X is the **rectangular distribution over the interval [–0.05, 0.05]**.

b) Write down the probability density function of X.

$a = -0.05$ and $b = 0.05$, so $\mathrm{f}(x) = \begin{cases} 10 & \text{for } -0.05 \le x \le 0.05 \\ 0 & \text{otherwise} \end{cases}$

Tip: Here:

$\frac{1}{b-a} = \frac{1}{0.1} = 10$

Exercise 5.1

Q1 For each part, write down the probability density function of X, where X is a random variable with a rectangular distribution which can take any value between a and b. Then sketch the graph of this p.d.f.

a) $a = 2, b = 7$ b) $a = -0.5, b = 1.5$ c) $a = \frac{1}{3}, b = 1$

Q2 In each part, the continuous random variable X has a rectangular distribution with probability density function f(x). Find k in each case.

a) $\mathrm{f}(x) = \begin{cases} 0.25 & \text{for } -3 \le x \le k \\ 0 & \text{otherwise} \end{cases}$ b) $\mathrm{f}(x) = \begin{cases} \frac{5}{8} & \text{for } k \le x \le 7 \\ 0 & \text{otherwise} \end{cases}$

Q3 Each of the graphs below shows the probability density function of a continuous random variable X that follows a rectangular distribution. In each case, find k and write down the p.d.f. of X.

a) 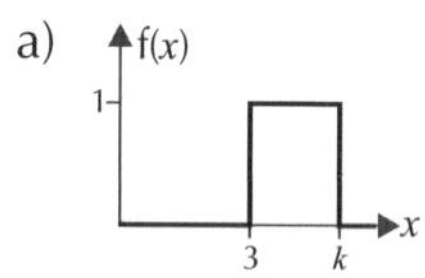

b) 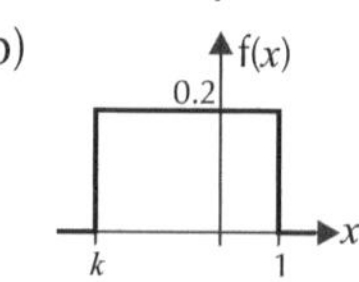

Q4 A loaf of bread weighs 800 g. The loaf is sliced into two at a random point. The random variable Y represents the weight (in grams) of the heavier piece. Describe the probability distribution of Y.

Q4 Hint: Notice that Y represents the weight of the **heavier** piece.

Q5 Fred gets the train to work each day. There's a train he can catch every 15 minutes. If Fred leaves his house at a random time and T is the time (in minutes) that he waits for a train, describe the distribution of T.

Q6 A machine makes circular biscuits with diameters, D cm, which are randomly distributed between 5.9 cm and 6.3 cm.

a) Describe the distribution of D.

b) Define the probability density function of D and sketch its graph.

Finding probabilities

Remember that for a continuous random variable, **probability** is shown by the **area under** the **probability density function**. So to find the probability that a random variable takes a value in a certain range, you need to calculate the area under the p.d.f. for the given range.

Luckily, for **rectangular distributions** this is nice and easy because the area is always a **rectangle**.

Tip: Often you have to integrate to find probabilities (see p44). But here it's just a matter of finding areas of rectangles.

Example

The continuous random variable X follows a rectangular distribution over the interval [8, 18]. Find:

a) **$P(10 < X < 14.1)$**

- It's best to start by drawing a sketch of the p.d.f.
- You know that it's a **rectangle** with an **area** of **1** and a **width** of $18 - 8 = $ **10**, so the **height** must be $1 \div 10 = $ **0.1**.
- $P(10 < X < 14.1)$ = the area under the p.d.f. between $x = 10$ and $x = 14.1$. Again, it's a good idea to draw yourself a quick sketch, marking on the area you want to find.

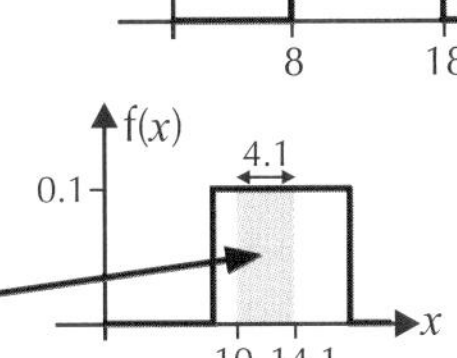

- This area $= (14.1 - 10) \times 0.1 = 4.1 \times 0.1 = 0.41$.

  So $P(10 < X < 14.1) = 0.41$

b) **$P(X \leq 14)$**

- $P(X \leq 14)$ = the area under the p.d.f. for $x \leq 14$.
- This area $= (14 - 8) \times 0.1 = 6 \times 0.1 = 0.6$.

  So $P(X \leq 14) = 0.6$

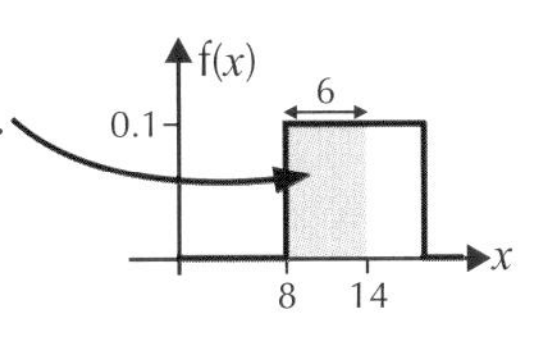

c) **$P(X < 14)$**

- For a continuous distribution, $P(X < x) = P(X \leq x)$.
- So $P(X < 14) = P(X \leq 14) = 0.6$

Tip: Remember, for continuous distributions $P(X = x) = 0$, so the signs $<$ and $\leq$ mean the same thing, as do the signs $>$ and $\geq$.

d) **$P(X \geq 10.5)$**

- $P(X \geq 10.5)$ = the area under the p.d.f. for $x \geq 10.5$.
- This area $= (18 - 10.5) \times 0.1 = 7.5 \times 0.1 = 0.75$.

  So $P(X \geq 10.5) = 0.75$

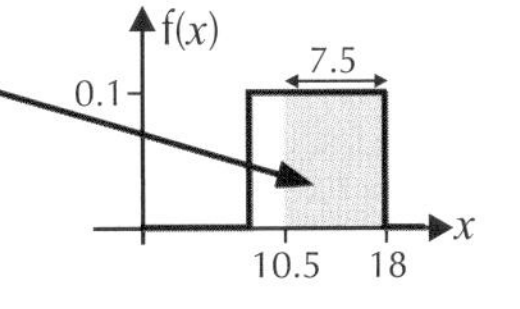

Now, suppose that the continuous random variable X has a rectangular distribution over the range $[a, b]$ and let Y be a **linear function** of **X**. Then **Y** will also follow a **rectangular distribution** and you can find the **limits for Y** simply by **substituting the limits for X** into the expression for Y.

In other words...

If X follows a rectangular distribution over the interval $[a, b]$ and $Y = cX + d$, then Y follows a rectangular distribution over the interval $[(c \times a + d), (c \times b + d)]$

Tip: A linear function is a function of the form $Y = cX + d$.

Example

If X has a rectangular distribution over the interval [4, 7] and $Y = 8X - 3$, describe the distribution of Y. Then find $P(Y > 50)$.

- **Substituting** the limits **4** and **7** into $Y = 8X - 3$, gives:
  $a = 8 \times 4 - 3 = 29$ and $b = 8 \times 7 - 3 = 53$

  So Y has a rectangular distribution over the interval [29, 53].

- Now you can sketch the p.d.f. of Y.
  The **width** of the rectangle is $(53 - 29) = \mathbf{24}$,
  so the **height** must be $\frac{1}{24}$.
- The area under the p.d.f. for $y > 50 = 3 \times \frac{1}{24} = \frac{1}{8}$.

  So $P(Y > 50) = \frac{1}{8}$

Tip: You need to be able to apply the usual probability rules to random variable problems.

Here's one more example. This time we have **two random variables**, and we need to find the probability that they **both** take values in a certain range.

Example

X and Y are independent random variables with p.d.f.s given below.

$$f(x) = \begin{cases} \frac{1}{2} & 1 \le x \le 3 \\ 0 & \text{otherwise} \end{cases} \qquad f(y) = \begin{cases} \frac{1}{5} & 0 \le y \le 5 \\ 0 & \text{otherwise} \end{cases}$$

Find the probability that both X and Y take values greater than 1.2.

- Since X and Y are **independent**:
  $P(X > 1.2 \text{ and } Y > 1.2) = P(X > 1.2) \times P(Y > 1.2)$
- As usual, draw a sketch to help you find the areas.
- **$P(X > 1.2)$** is the area under the p.d.f. for X between 1.2 and 3.
  That's $0.5 \times 1.8 = \mathbf{0.9}$.
- **$P(Y > 1.2)$** is the area under the p.d.f. for Y between 1.2 and 5.
  That's $0.2 \times 3.8 = \mathbf{0.76}$.

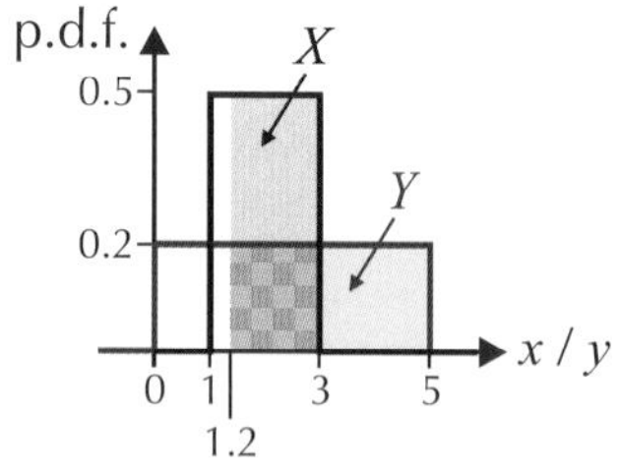

- So $P(X > 1.2 \text{ and } Y > 1.2)$
  $= P(X > 1.2) \times P(Y > 1.2) = 0.9 \times 0.76 = 0.684$

Tip: Remember, in S1 you learnt that for independent events A and B:
P(A and B) = P(A) × P(B).

Exercise 5.2

Q1 The continuous random variable X has a rectangular distribution with probability density function:

$$f(x) = \begin{cases} 0.125 & 1 \le x \le 9 \\ 0 & \text{otherwise} \end{cases}$$

Find:

a) $P(X > 5)$ b) $P(2 < X < 7)$ c) $P(X \le 2.4)$

Q2 The continuous random variable X has a rectangular distribution with probability density function:

$$f(x) = \begin{cases} 0.2 & -5 \leq x \leq 0 \\ 0 & \text{otherwise} \end{cases}$$

Find:

a) $P(X \geq -3)$
b) $P(-2.4 \leq X \leq -1.2)$
c) $P(X > -6)$

Q3 The continuous random variable X has a rectangular distribution with probability density function:

$$f(x) = \begin{cases} 0.1 \text{ for } 3 \leq x \leq 13 \\ 0 \text{ otherwise} \end{cases}$$

Find:

a) $P(X > 7)$
b) $P(4 < X < 11)$
c) $P(X \geq 10.1)$

Q4 The random variable X has a rectangular distribution with probability density function:

$$f(x) = \begin{cases} \frac{1}{k-2} & \text{for } 2 \leq x \leq k \\ 0 & \text{otherwise} \end{cases}$$

If $P(X \geq 3) = 0.5$, find k.

Q5 a) The random variable Y has a rectangular distribution with probability density function:

$$f(y) = \begin{cases} \frac{1}{7-k} & \text{for } k \leq y \leq 7 \\ 0 & \text{otherwise} \end{cases}$$

If $k < 2.5$ and $P(2.5 < Y < 4) = 0.25$, find k.

b) If $Z = 2Y + 1$, find $P(Z < 6)$.

Q6 X and Y are independent random variables with p.d.f.s given below:

$$f(x) = \begin{cases} \frac{1}{5} \text{ for } 2 \leq x \leq 7 \\ 0 \text{ otherwise} \end{cases} \qquad g(y) = \begin{cases} 1 \text{ for } 4 \leq y \leq 5 \\ 0 \text{ otherwise} \end{cases}$$

Find the probability that both X and Y are greater than 4.5.

Q7 A school nurse measures the heights of children correct to the nearest centimetre. Let the random variable X represent the error (in cm) in one of the nurse's measurements.

a) Write down the distribution of X.

b) Find the probability that a height recorded by the nurse is more than one millimetre higher than the child's exact height.

Q8 The weights of chocolate bars are measured correct to the nearest quarter of a gram. The random variable X represents the error (in grams) in the measurement of the weight of a chocolate bar.

a) Write down the distribution of X.

b) Find the probability that the recorded weight of a randomly selected chocolate bar will be inaccurate by at least 0.1 g.

c) Stating any assumptions you make, find the probability that two randomly selected chocolate bars will both have recorded weights that are inaccurate by at least 0.1 g.

Q8 a) Hint: Write the distribution using decimals.

Q8 b) Hint: You need to consider both ends of the distribution.

The mean and variance

Suppose you have a random variable X following a rectangular distribution over the interval $[a, b]$.

You can work out the **expected value** (or **mean**) and the **variance** of X using the formulas below.

Tip: Remember...
standard deviation
$= \sqrt{\text{variance}}$
$= \sqrt{\text{Var}(X)}$

$$E(X) = \frac{a+b}{2} \qquad \text{Var}(X) = \frac{(b-a)^2}{12}$$

Example 1

Find the expected value and the variance of the random variable X, which follows a rectangular distribution over the interval [4, 10].

- Use the formulas.

$$E(X) = \frac{a+b}{2} = \frac{4+10}{2} = 7$$

$$\text{Var}(X) = \frac{(b-a)^2}{12} = \frac{(10-4)^2}{12} = 3$$

Example 2

Find the expected value and the variance of the random variable Y, which follows a rectangular distribution over the interval [–6, 15].

- Again, just use the formulas.

$$E(Y) = \frac{a+b}{2} = \frac{-6+15}{2} = 4.5$$

$$\text{Var}(X) = \frac{(b-a)^2}{12} = \frac{(15-(-6))^2}{12} = \frac{21^2}{12} = \frac{147}{4} = 36.75$$

Example 3

If X follows a rectangular distribution over the interval $[a, b]$, and $E(X) = \text{Var}(X) = 1$, find a and b.

- First, use the formula for $E(X)$.

  $E(X) = \frac{a+b}{2} = 1.$

  So $a + b = 2$, or $a = 2 - b$.

- Next, use the formula for $\text{Var}(X)$.

  $\text{Var}(X) = \frac{(b-a)^2}{12} = 1.$

  So $(b - a)^2 = 12$

  Taking the square root gives $b - a = \pm\sqrt{12} = \pm 2\sqrt{3}$

- Substitute in your expression for a (= $2 - b$).

  $b - a = b - (2 - b) = \pm 2\sqrt{3}$

  i.e. $2b - 2 = \pm 2\sqrt{3}$

  or $b - 1 = \pm\sqrt{3}$

  or $b = 1 \pm \sqrt{3}$

- Pick the correct solution for b.

  It looks like there are two possible values here for b, but remember that $a = 2 - b$.

  So if $b = 1 - \sqrt{3}$, then $a = 2 - (1 - \sqrt{3}) = 1 + \sqrt{3}$.
  But this would mean that $a > b$ — and you know that $b > a$.

  So this means $b = 1 + \sqrt{3}$, giving $a = 2 - (1 + \sqrt{3})$, i.e. $a = 1 - \sqrt{3}$

Tip: You know that $b > a$, because X follows a rectangular distribution over the interval $[a, b]$.

Using the formulas to find the mean or variance is pretty easy.

But in the exam, you could be asked to **derive** the formulas from first principles — this means working the formulas out for yourself from scratch. The working is shown on the next couple of pages — make sure you can follow every line.

Deriving the formula for the expected value of a rectangular distribution over the interval [a, b]

You saw on p57 that if X is a continuous random variable with p.d.f. f(x), then its mean (μ) or expected value (E(X)) is given by:

$$E(X) = \mu = \int_{-\infty}^{\infty} x f(x)\,dx$$

So take this formula as your starting point, substitute in the expression for the p.d.f. of X, and then integrate very carefully.

$$\mathbf{E}(X) = \int_{-\infty}^{\infty} x f(x)\,dx = \int_a^b x\left(\frac{1}{b-a}\right)dx$$

Since $f(x) = \begin{cases} \frac{1}{b-a} & \text{for } a \le x \le b \\ 0 & \text{otherwise} \end{cases}$

$$= \frac{1}{b-a}\int_a^b x\,dx$$

Since $\frac{1}{b-a}$ is just a number

$$= \frac{1}{b-a}\left[\frac{x^2}{2}\right]_a^b$$

Integrating 'x'

$$= \frac{1}{b-a}\left[\frac{b^2}{2} - \frac{a^2}{2}\right]$$

$$= \frac{b^2 - a^2}{2(b-a)}$$

$$= \frac{(b-a)(b+a)}{2(b-a)}$$

Since $b^2 - a^2 = (b - a)(b + a)$

$$= \frac{b+a}{2} = \mathbf{\frac{a+b}{2}}$$

You can also see from the **symmetry** of the p.d.f. that the expected value of X must be **halfway between** a and b.

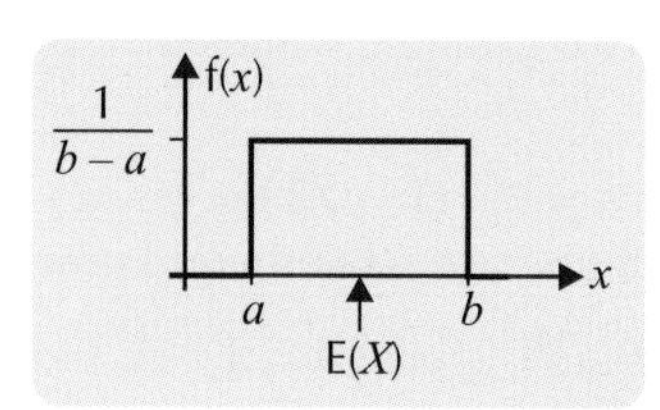

- The p.d.f. of the rectangular distribution is symmetrical about the midpoint of a and b, which is at $x = \frac{a+b}{2}$.
- X is equally likely to fall **anywhere** in this range. So every value that X takes **above** the midpoint is likely to be balanced by a value that falls just as far **below** the midpoint.
- Eventually, all these values will 'cancel each other out', meaning the expected value must be at $x = \frac{a+b}{2}$.

Deriving the formula for the variance of a rectangular distribution over the interval [a, b]

Deriving the formula for the **variance** is slightly trickier...

Tip: Remember...
$\text{Var}(X) = \text{E}(X^2) - [\text{E}(X)]^2$
$= \text{E}(X^2) - \mu^2$

You saw on p60 that if X is a continuous random variable with p.d.f. f(x), then its variance ($\text{Var}(X) = \sigma^2$) is given by:

$$\sigma^2 = \int_{-\infty}^{\infty} x^2 \text{f}(x)\text{d}x - \mu^2$$

Tip: Remember...
$$\frac{b^3 - a^3}{3(b-a)} = \frac{(b-a)(b^2+ab+a^2)}{3(b-a)} = \frac{b^2+ab+a^2}{3}$$

$$\textbf{Var}(X) = \int_{-\infty}^{\infty} x^2 \text{f}(x)\text{d}x - \mu^2$$

$$= \int_a^b x^2\left(\frac{1}{b-a}\right)\text{d}x - \mu^2$$ ← Since $\text{f}(x) = \begin{cases} \frac{1}{b-a} & \text{for } a \le x \le b \\ 0 & \text{otherwise} \end{cases}$

$$= \frac{1}{b-a}\int_a^b x^2\text{d}x - \mu^2$$ ← Since $\frac{1}{b-a}$ is just a number

$$= \frac{1}{b-a}\left[\frac{x^3}{3}\right]_a^b - \mu^2$$ ← Integrating 'x^2'

$$= \frac{1}{b-a}\left[\frac{b^3}{3} - \frac{a^3}{3}\right] - \mu^2$$

$$= \frac{b^3 - a^3}{3(b-a)} - \left(\frac{a+b}{2}\right)^2$$ ← Since $\mu = \frac{a+b}{2}$

$$= \frac{b^2+ab+a^2}{3} - \frac{(a+b)(a+b)}{4}$$ ← Since $b^3 - a^3 = (b-a)(b^2+ab+a^2)$

$$= \frac{b^2+ab+a^2}{3} - \frac{a^2+2ab+b^2}{4}$$

$$= \frac{4b^2+4ab+4a^2-3a^2-6ab-3b^2}{12}$$

$$= \frac{b^2-2ab+a^2}{12}$$

$$= \mathbf{\frac{(b-a)^2}{12}}$$

Once you've derived the formula for variance, deriving the **standard deviation** of a rectangular distribution is easy.

Remember... if X is a random variable then its standard deviation is given by the square root of the variance. So...

$$\text{standard deviation} = \sqrt{\text{variance}} = \sqrt{\frac{(b-a)^2}{12}}$$
$$= \frac{b-a}{\sqrt{12}} = \frac{b-a}{\sqrt{4}\sqrt{3}} = \frac{b-a}{2\sqrt{3}}$$

Exercise 5.3

Q1 Find E(X), where X follows a rectangular distribution over each of the following intervals.

a) [1, 7]   b) $[0, \frac{1}{3}]$ c) [–24, –6]

Q2 Find Var(X), where X follows a rectangular distribution over each of the following intervals.

a) [2, 5]   b) [–0.25, 0.75]   c) [–30, –18]

Q3 The continuous random variable X has the following probability density function:

$$f(x) = \begin{cases} 0.4 & 3.9 \leq x \leq 6.4 \\ 0 & \text{otherwise} \end{cases}$$

Find E(X) and Var(X).

Q4 The continuous random variable X has a rectangular distribution with p.d.f. f(x) shown below.

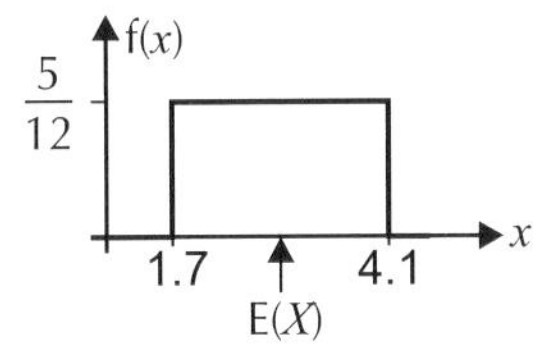

Find E(X) and Var(X).

Q5 The continuous random variable X follows a rectangular distribution over the interval [13, 17].

a) Find E(X) and Var(X).

b) The continuous random variable $Y = 2X - 9$. Find E(Y) and Var(Y).

Q6 The continuous random variable X follows a rectangular distribution over the interval [3, k]. If E(X) = 4.5, find k.

Q7 Babies' weights are measured to the nearest 10 g. If X represents the errors in the measurements (in grams):

a) State the distribution of X.

b) Find E(X) and Var(X).

Review Exercise — Chapter 3

Q1 Find the value of k for each of the probability density functions below.

a) $f(x) = \begin{cases} kx \text{ for } 1 \leq x \leq 10 \\ 0 \text{ otherwise} \end{cases}$

b) $g(x) = \begin{cases} 0.2x + k \text{ for } 0 \leq x \leq 1 \\ 0 \text{ otherwise} \end{cases}$

Q2 For each of the probability density functions below, find:

(i) $P(X < 1)$, (ii) $P(2 \leq X \leq 5)$, (iii) $P(X = 4)$.

a) $f(x) = \begin{cases} 0.08x \text{ for } 0 \leq x \leq 5 \\ 0 \text{ otherwise} \end{cases}$

b) $g(x) = \begin{cases} 0.02(10 - x) \text{ for } 0 \leq x \leq 10 \\ 0 \text{ otherwise} \end{cases}$

Q3 Find the exact value of k for each of the probability density functions below. Then for each p.d.f., find $P(X < 1)$.

a) $f(x) = \begin{cases} kx^2 \text{ for } 0 \leq x \leq 5 \\ 0 \text{ otherwise} \end{cases}$

b) $g(x) = \begin{cases} 0.1x^2 + kx \text{ for } 0 \leq x \leq 2 \\ 0 \text{ otherwise} \end{cases}$

Q4 Say whether the following are probability density functions. Explain your answers.

a) $f(x) = \begin{cases} 0.1x^2 + 0.2 \text{ for } 0 \leq x \leq 2 \\ 0 \text{ otherwise} \end{cases}$

b) $g(x) = \begin{cases} x \text{ for } -1 \leq x \leq 1 \\ 0 \text{ otherwise} \end{cases}$

Q5 Find the cumulative distribution function (c.d.f.) for each of the following p.d.f.s.

a) $f(x) = \begin{cases} 0.08x \text{ for } 0 \leq x \leq 5 \\ 0 \text{ otherwise} \end{cases}$

b) $g(x) = \begin{cases} 0.02(10 - x) \text{ for } 0 \leq x \leq 10 \\ 0 \text{ otherwise} \end{cases}$

c) $h(x) = \begin{cases} 2x \text{ for } 0 \leq x \leq 0.5 \\ 1 \text{ for } 0.5 \leq x \leq 1 \\ 3 - 2x \text{ for } 1 \leq x \leq 1.5 \\ 0 \text{ otherwise} \end{cases}$

d) $m(x) = \begin{cases} 0.5 - 0.1x \text{ for } 2 \leq x \leq 4 \\ 0.1 \text{ for } 4 \leq x \leq 10 \\ 0 \text{ otherwise} \end{cases}$

Q6 Find the probability density function (p.d.f.) for each of the following c.d.f.s.

a) $F(x) = \begin{cases} 0 \text{ for } x < 0 \\ x^4 \text{ for } 0 \leq x \leq 1 \\ 1 \text{ for } x > 1 \end{cases}$

b) $G(x) = \begin{cases} 0 \text{ for } x < 1 \\ \frac{1}{100}(x - 1)^2 \text{ for } 1 \leq x < 6 \\ \frac{3}{8}x - 2 \text{ for } 6 \leq x \leq 8 \\ 1 \text{ for } x > 8 \end{cases}$

Q7 The continuous random variable X has p.d.f. f(x) given below. Find E(X).

$$f(x) = \begin{cases} \frac{2}{3}(x-1) & 1 \leq x \leq 2 \\ \frac{2}{3} & 2 \leq x \leq 3 \\ 0 & \text{otherwise} \end{cases}$$

Q8 The random variables X and Y have p.d.f.s f(x) and g(y) respectively, where

$$f(x) = \begin{cases} 0.08x \text{ for } 0 \leq x \leq 5 \\ 0 \text{ otherwise} \end{cases} \quad \text{and} \quad g(y) = \begin{cases} 0.02(10-y) \text{ for } 0 \leq y \leq 10 \\ 0 \text{ otherwise} \end{cases}$$

a) Find the mean and variance of X and Y.

b) Find the mean and variance of X^2.

c) Find the mean and variance of $4X + 2$ and $3Y - 4$.

d) Find median of X.

e) Find the upper and lower quartiles of X.

Q9 The continuous random variable X has p.d.f. f(x), where

$$f(x) = \begin{cases} k(x^2 - 3x) & 1 \leq x \leq 2 \\ 0 & \text{otherwise} \end{cases}$$

a) Find the value of k such that f(x) is a valid p.d.f.

b) Find the c.d.f. F(x).

c) Show that the median equals 1.5.

d) Show that $1.2 \leq Q_1 \leq 1.3$ and $1.7 \leq Q_3 \leq 1.8$.

e) Find Q_1 and Q_3 to one decimal place.

Q10 The random variable X follows a rectangular distribution over the interval [0, 10].

a) Define and sketch the p.d.f., f(x).

b) Find: (i) $P(X < 4)$, (ii) $P(X \geq 8)$, (iii) $P(X = 5)$, (iv) $P(3 < X \leq 7)$.

Q11 If X follows a rectangular distribution over the interval [1, 4] and $Y = 5X + 2$, define and sketch the probability density function of Y.

Q12 The distance between two stars is measured to the nearest light year. If the random variable X represents the experimental error (in light years), write down the probability distribution of X.

Q13 X and Y are independent random variables following rectangular distributions over the intervals [4, 8] and [–8, 12] respectively. Find:

a) $P(X < 6 \text{ and } Y > 0)$, b) $P(X < 6 \text{ or } Y > 0)$.

Q14 I travel by train to work five days per week.
My morning train is randomly delayed every morning by anything up to 12 minutes.
If the delay is any greater than 8 minutes, I arrive late for work.

a) Find the probability that I am late for work on a randomly chosen workday.

b) Find the probability that I arrive on time every day during a particular working week.

Exam-Style Questions — Chapter 3

1 The continuous random variable X has probability density function $f(x)$, as defined below:

$$f(x) = \begin{cases} \frac{x}{2} & 0 \leq x < 1 \\ 3\left(1 - \frac{x}{2}\right) & 1 \leq x \leq 2 \\ 0 & \text{otherwise} \end{cases}$$

a) Sketch the graph of $f(x)$. *(1 mark)*

b) Find the cumulative distribution function of X, $F(x)$. *(6 marks)*

c) Show that the lower quartile (Q_1) equals 1, and find the median (Q_2) and upper quartile (Q_3) of X. *(7 marks)*

2 The continuous random variable X has cumulative distribution function:

$$F(x) = \begin{cases} 0 & x < 0 \\ 3x^2 - 2x^3 & 0 \leq x \leq 1 \\ 1 & x > 1 \end{cases}$$

a) Find $P(0.25 \leq X \leq 0.75)$. *(2 marks)*

b) Show that the upper quartile of X lies between 0.67 and 0.68. *(3 marks)*

c) Show that the median of X is 0.5. *(2 marks)*

d) (i) Specify the probability density function of X, $f(x)$. *(2 marks)*

(ii) Sketch the graph of $f(x)$. *(1 mark)*

e) Find the mean (μ) of X. *(3 marks)*

3 A 40 cm length of ribbon is cut in two at a random point.
The random variable X represents the length of the shorter piece of ribbon in cm.

a) Specify the probability distribution of X. *(2 marks)*

b) Sketch the probability density function of X. *(1 mark)*

c) Calculate $E(X)$ and $Var(X)$. *(3 marks)*

d) Find:

(i) $P(X > 5)$, *(1 mark)*

(ii) $P(X = 2)$. *(1 mark)*

4 The continuous random variable X has probability density function $f(x)$, as defined below.

$$f(x) = \begin{cases} \frac{1}{k}(x+4) & \text{for } 0 \leq x \leq 2 \\ 0 & \text{otherwise} \end{cases}$$

a) Find the value of k. *(3 marks)*

b) Find the cumulative distribution function of X, $F(x)$. *(5 marks)*

c) Calculate $E(X)$. *(3 marks)*

d) Calculate the variance of:

(i) X *(3 marks)*

(ii) $4X - 2$ *(2 marks)*

e) Find the median of X. *(4 marks)*

5 The continuous random variable X has cumulative distribution function $F(x)$, as defined below.

$$F(x) = \begin{cases} 0 & \text{for } x < 1 \\ k(x-1) & \text{for } 1 \leq x < 3 \\ 0.5(x-2) & \text{for } 3 \leq x \leq 4 \\ 1 & \text{for } x > 4 \end{cases}$$

a) Calculate the value of k. *(2 marks)*

b) (i) Specify the probability density function of X, $f(x)$. *(3 marks)*

(ii) Sketch the graph of $f(x)$. *(1 mark)*

c) Find the mean (μ) and variance (σ^2) of X. *(6 marks)*

6 A continuous random variable X has a rectangular distribution over the interval $[-2, 7]$. A continuous random variable Y is defined by $Y = 3X + 6$.

a) Specify fully the probability density function of X. *(2 marks)*

b) Sketch the probability density function of X. *(1 mark)*

c) Calculate the mean and variance of Y. *(4 marks)*

d) Find:

(i) $P(Y < 20)$, *(1 mark)*

(ii) $P(10 < Y < 20)$, *(1 mark)*

(iii) $P(10 < Y < 20 \mid Y < 20)$. *(3 marks)*

Chapter 4 Estimation and Hypothesis Testing

1. Confidence Intervals

Learning Objective:

- Be able to find a confidence interval for the mean of a normally distributed population if the population variance is unknown and the sample size is small.

You saw confidence intervals in S1. Remember... a confidence interval for a population mean is a range of values, worked out using sample data, which is very likely to contain that population's true mean.

Confidence intervals

In S1, you saw how to find confidence intervals as long as certain conditions were satisfied. Here's a quick recap...

A confidence interval for the mean of a normally distributed population modelled by a random variable X with variance σ^2 is:

$$\left(\overline{X} - \frac{\sigma}{\sqrt{n}}z, \overline{X} + \frac{\sigma}{\sqrt{n}}z\right)$$

Here...

- $\overline{X}$ is the mean of a **random sample** of n observations of X,
- 'z' is a value from the standard normal distribution ($Z \sim N(0, 1)$) which depends on the **level of confidence** required. For example, for a **95%** confidence interval, choose z so that $P(-z < Z < z) = \mathbf{0.95}$.

Now then... the above formula works as long as **two conditions** hold:

① The sampling distribution of $\overline{X}$ is **normal** with mean μ and variance $\frac{\sigma^2}{n}$. You saw two cases:

- You saw that if $X \sim N(\mu, \sigma^2)$ (i.e. if the population itself is normally distributed), then $\overline{X} \sim N(\mu, \frac{\sigma^2}{n})$.
- And you saw that **if the sample size was large** ($n \geq 30$), then the **Central Limit Theorem** tells you that for **any** population with mean μ and variance σ^2, $\overline{X} \sim N(\mu, \frac{\sigma^2}{n})$ (approximately).

② You know σ (or can estimate it pretty well).

- In S1, you were either told the population variance (σ^2)...
- ...or the sample size was large and you could estimate it well using the sample variance $S^2 = \frac{\sum(X_i - \overline{X})^2}{n-1} = \frac{n}{n-1}\left[\frac{\sum X_i^2}{n} - \left(\frac{\sum X_i}{n}\right)^2\right]$.

As long as these two conditions are satisfied, then the quantity Z follows the standard normal distribution N(0, 1), where:

- $Z = \frac{\overline{X} - \mu}{\sigma/\sqrt{n}}$ (or $Z = \frac{\overline{X} - \mu}{S/\sqrt{n}}$ if you estimate σ using a large sample)

This then leads directly to the confidence-interval formula above.

Tip: Remember... the **standard error** of the sample mean = $\frac{\sigma}{\sqrt{n}}$. So a confidence interval for the population mean extends a distance 'z × **standard error of the mean**' from your sample mean.

Tip: The **Central Limit Theorem** says: If you take a sample of n readings from **any** distribution with mean μ and variance σ^2 then for **large** n ($n \geq 30$), the distribution of the sample mean, $\overline{X}$, is approximately normal: i.e. $\overline{X} \sim N\left(\mu, \frac{\sigma^2}{n}\right)$

Tip: Remember... to **standardise** a normal random variable, subtract the mean and divide by the standard deviation. So if $\overline{X} \sim N(\mu, \frac{\sigma^2}{n})$, then $Z = \frac{\overline{X} - \mu}{\sigma/\sqrt{n}} \sim N(0, 1)$.

In S2, you're going to see how to find a confidence interval if $X \sim N(\mu, \sigma^2)$ but:

(i) you **don't know** the population variance (σ^2),

and (ii) n is **small**.

Basically, the problem you face here is that the quantity $\frac{\overline{X} - \mu}{S/\sqrt{n}}$ doesn't follow the standard normal distribution N(0, 1) closely enough. But this turns out not to be too bad a problem, because instead it follows a ***t*-distribution**.

The 'family' of *t*-distributions

- ***t*-distributions** are very similar to the standard normal distribution. Their graphs are **bell-shaped** and are **symmetrical** about a **mean** of **zero**.
- A *t*-distribution has one parameter, ν, called the **degrees of freedom**, and a *t*-distribution with ν degrees of freedom is written $t_{(\nu)}$.
- As ν becomes large, $t_{(\nu)}$ becomes very close to N(0, 1):

Tip: ν is the Greek letter 'nu'.

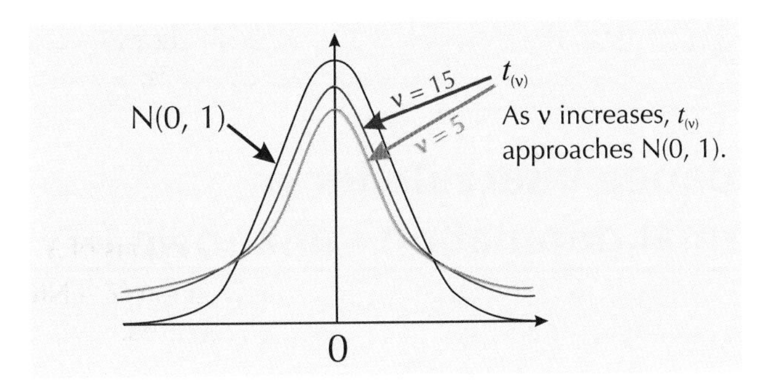

Tip: The *t*-distribution is also known as **'Student's *t*-distribution'**.

If you're curious... William Sealy Gosset, who first studied these distributions, worked for Guinness at the time and wasn't allowed to publish his research papers — so he used the pen-name 'Student' instead.

t-tables

In the exam, you'll be given ***t*-tables**, which are similar to the normal percentage-points table you used in S1. So if a random variable X follows a *t*-distribution with ν degrees of freedom and you're given a value of p, you can find a value of x for which $P(X \leq x) = p$.

Here's an extract from the *t*-tables.

Tip: Your *t*-tables only contain certain values of p — but they're the most useful ones.

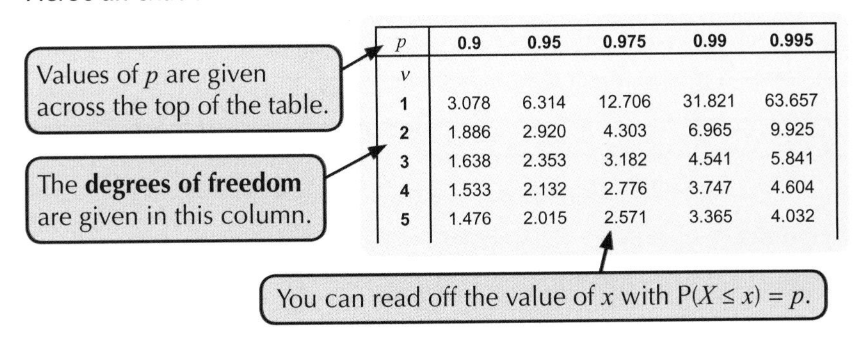

p / ν	0.9	0.95	0.975	0.99	0.995
1	3.078	6.314	12.706	31.821	63.657
2	1.886	2.920	4.303	6.965	9.925
3	1.638	2.353	3.182	4.541	5.841
4	1.533	2.132	2.776	3.747	4.604
5	1.476	2.015	2.571	3.365	4.032

Tip: This is an extract from the *t*-tables — see p129 for the full tables.

- For example, if X follows a *t*-distribution with $\nu = 5$ degrees of freedom, and you need to find x with $P(X \leq x) = 0.975$, then you can quickly see that $x = 2.571$.
- And just like with the normal percentage-points table, you can then use the **symmetry** of the *t*-distribution to say that $P(-2.571 \leq X \leq 2.571) = 0.95$.

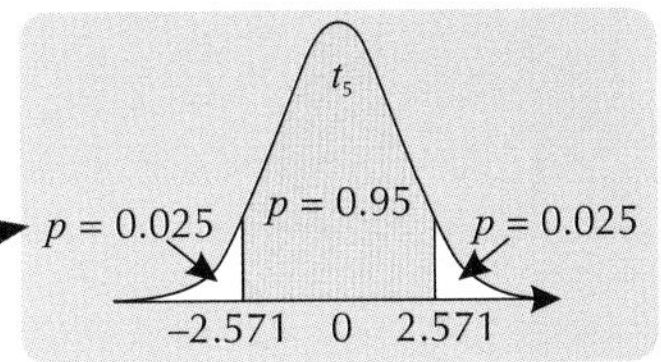

Tip: Always draw a sketch of a *t*-distribution if it helps you to see how you can use its symmetry.

Exercise 1.1

Q1 Use the t-tables to find the values of x satisfying the following:

a) $P(X < x) = 0.90$ for $\nu = 8$

b) $P(X > x) = 0.05$ for $\nu = 10$

c) $P(X \geq x) = 0.975$ for $\nu = 15$

d) $P(X \leq x) = 0.95$ for $\nu = 20$

Q1 and 2 Hint: t-distributions are continuous, so $P(X < x) = P(X \leq x)$ and $P(X > x) = P(X \geq x)$.

Q2 Find the value of p, given each of the following probabilities.

a) $P(X < 1.943) = p$ for $\nu = 6$

b) $P(X > -1.86) = p$ for $\nu = 8$

c) $P(X \geq 2.228) = p$ for $\nu = 10$

d) $P(X \leq -1.341) = p$ for $\nu = 15$

Tip: Remember... if your sample data is labelled X_i, then the sample variance (S^2) is:

$$S^2 = \frac{\sum(X_i - \overline{X})^2}{n-1} = \frac{n}{n-1}\left[\frac{\sum X_i^2}{n} - \left(\frac{\sum X_i}{n}\right)^2\right]$$

This then means that the **standard error of the mean** ($\frac{\sigma}{\sqrt{n}}$) can be estimated by $\frac{S}{\sqrt{n}}$.

And remember... S^2 is an **unbiased estimator** of σ^2 (which means that $E(S^2) = \sigma^2$).

Confidence intervals for μ — normal population / unknown σ^2 / small n

You can use t-distributions to find confidence intervals in some situations that you couldn't have dealt with in S1. Here's how...

- If $X \sim N(\mu, \sigma^2)$ but the sample size n is small, the quantity $T = \frac{\overline{X} - \mu}{S/\sqrt{n}}$ follows a t-distribution with $\nu = (n - 1)$ degrees of freedom.
- In other words:

$$T = \frac{\overline{X} - \mu}{S/\sqrt{n}} \sim t_{(n-1)}$$

This means that if $X \sim N(\mu, \sigma^2)$ but σ^2 is unknown and the sample size (n) is small, you have to use a different formula from the one on p82 to find a confidence interval.

Tip: You'll only need to use the Student's t-distribution for $n < 30$, and you'll look up $n - 1$ in the tables. This means you won't need to use t-tables for $\nu > 28$.

Let X be a **normally distributed** random variable with unknown variance, and $\overline{X}$ be the **sample mean** where the sample size n is small.

A **confidence interval** for the **population mean** is:

$$\left(\overline{X} - \frac{S}{\sqrt{n}}t_{(n-1)}, \ \overline{X} + \frac{S}{\sqrt{n}}t_{(n-1)}\right)$$

where the value of $t_{(n-1)}$ depends on the 'level of confidence' you need.

For example, for a **95%** confidence interval, choose $t_{(n-1)}$ so that $P(-t_{(n-1)} < T < t_{(n-1)}) = \mathbf{0.95}$.

Tip: This formula just says a confidence interval for the population mean extends a distance '**$t_{(n-1)}$ × estimated standard error of the mean**' from your sample mean (in both directions).

Here are some examples...

Example 1

A shop manager wants to check that the mean weight of the jars of pickled onions she sells is at least 300 g. The weights (x grams) of a random sample of 8 jars from the shop are given below.

289, 301, 302, 304, 298, 310, 302, 298

a) The manager wishes to construct a confidence interval for the mean weight of the jars of pickled onions she sells. What assumption does she need to make before she can do this?

- Because the population variance is unknown and this sample size is small, the manager needs to work out the confidence interval using a t-distribution, so she needs to make the assumption that **the jar weights follow a normal distribution.**

Tip: Remember... you still need the **population** to follow a normal distribution.

b) Find a 99% confidence interval for the mean weight of the jars.

- Start by finding the **sample mean**: $\bar{x} = \frac{\sum x}{n} = \frac{2404}{8} = 300.5\text{ g}$
- Next, estimate the **population variance**:

$$s^2 = \frac{n}{n-1}\left[\frac{\sum x^2}{n} - \left(\frac{\sum x}{n}\right)^2\right] = \frac{8}{7}\left[\frac{722\,654}{8} - 300.5^2\right] = \frac{8}{7} \times 31.5 = 36$$

- $n = 8$, so you need to look up $t_{(7)}$ in the t-distribution tables (p129). For a 99% confidence interval, you need to find t with $P(T \leq t) = 0.995$, so read across to $p = 0.995$ to get $t_{(7)} = 3.499$.
- So, your confidence interval is:

$s = \sqrt{36} = 6$ $n = 8$

$$\left(\bar{x} - \frac{s}{\sqrt{n}}t_{(n-1)}, \bar{x} + \frac{s}{\sqrt{n}}t_{(n-1)}\right) = \left(300.5 - \frac{6}{\sqrt{8}} \times 3.499, 300.5 + \frac{6}{\sqrt{8}} \times 3.499\right)$$

$$= (293, 308) \text{ (3 sig. fig.)}$$

$\bar{x} = 300.5$

Tip: Remember... if $P(T \leq t) = 0.995$, then $P(-t \leq T \leq t) = 0.99$.

Example 2

A random sample of 10 potato plants is selected from a field of potato plants, and the heights, x cm, recorded. The heights are assumed to be normally distributed, and for the 10 plants: $\sum x = 350$ and $\sum x^2 = 12\,528$.

a) Calculate a 95% confidence interval for the mean height of all the potato plants in the field.

- The heights of the potato plants are **normally distributed** with **unknown variance**, and the sample size is small (< 30). So work out the confidence interval using a t-distribution.
- Start by finding the **sample mean**, $\bar{x}$...

$$\bar{x} = \frac{350}{10} = 35\text{ cm}$$

...and an estimate of the **population variance**, s^2.

$$s^2 = \frac{10}{9}\left[\frac{12\,528}{10} - 35^2\right] = \frac{278}{9}$$

> **Tip:** Remember... if $P(T \le t) = 0.975$, then $P(-t \le T \le t) = 0.95$.

- $n = 10$, so you need to look up $t_{(9)}$ in the t-distribution tables (p129). It's a 95% confidence interval, so look up $p = 0.975$ — this gives $t_{(9)} = 2.262$.
- So your confidence interval is:

$$\left(\overline{x} - \frac{s}{\sqrt{n}}t_{(n-1)},\ \overline{x} + \frac{s}{\sqrt{n}}t_{(n-1)}\right) = \left(35 - \frac{\sqrt{278/9}}{\sqrt{10}} \times 2.262, 35 + \frac{\sqrt{278/9}}{\sqrt{10}} \times 2.262\right)$$

$$= (31.0, 39.0) \text{ (3 sig. fig.)}$$

b) Comment on the claim that the mean height of all the potato plants is 42 cm.

The claimed mean height lies outside the confidence interval, so there is evidence to doubt this claim.

You could be asked to find the sample mean or standard error, given a confidence interval. You need to remember that the confidence interval $\left(\overline{X} - \frac{S}{\sqrt{n}}t_{(n-1)}, \overline{X} + \frac{S}{\sqrt{n}}t_{(n-1)}\right)$ is **symmetrical** about the **sample mean**.

Example 3

A random sample of 12 observations is taken from a normal distribution with mean μ and variance σ^2. This data is used to calculate a 95% confidence interval for μ of (8.6, 23.8).

a) Find the sample mean $\overline{x}$.

The confidence interval is **symmetrical** about the sample mean, which means $\overline{x}$ will be right in the middle of the interval.

$$\overline{x} = \frac{8.6 + 23.8}{2} = 16.2$$

b) Calculate an estimate of the standard error of the sample mean.

> **Tip:** There are 12 observations, so you need to look up x in the table for $t_{(11)}$, where $P(X \le x) = 0.975$.

- Remember, the standard error of the sample mean is $\frac{\sigma}{\sqrt{n}}$, and this is estimated by $\frac{s}{\sqrt{n}}$. You can find the value of this estimate by substituting what you know into the formula for a confidence interval.
- You know the **upper limit** of the confidence interval is given by $\overline{x} + \frac{s}{\sqrt{n}}t_{(n-1)} = 23.8$.
- From part a) you know $\overline{x} = 16.2$
- It's a **95%** confidence interval so $t_{(11)} = 2.201$.
- So **substituting in** these values...

$$16.2 + \frac{s}{\sqrt{n}} \times 2.201 = 23.8$$

$$\Rightarrow \frac{s}{\sqrt{n}} = \frac{23.8 - 16.2}{2.201} = 3.45 \text{ (3 sig. fig.)}$$

> **Tip:** You could use the lower limit of the confidence interval instead — you'll get the same answer:
> $$\frac{s}{\sqrt{n}} = \frac{16.2 - 8.6}{2.201} = 3.45 \text{ (3 sig. fig.)}$$

> **Tip:** You don't need to substitute in a value for n because it is part of the standard error.

Or you could be asked to find the **confidence level** for a confidence interval of a **particular width**. You'll need to use symmetry again.

You might also need to use the fact that a confidence interval $\left(\overline{X} - \frac{S}{\sqrt{n}}t_{(n-1)}, \overline{X} + \frac{S}{\sqrt{n}}t_{(n-1)}\right)$ has a width of $\frac{2S}{\sqrt{n}}t_{(n-1)}$.

Example 4

Lesedi supplies bags of pumpkin seeds to a shop selling organic foods. She knows that the weights, w grams, of the bags can be modelled by a normal distribution with unknown mean μ and standard deviation σ.

For a sample of 10 bags, Lesedi finds that $\sum w = 2277$ and $\sum w^2 = 518767$.

a) Calculate a confidence interval for μ which has a width of 5 grams.

- Start by finding the **sample mean**: $\overline{w} = \frac{2277}{10} = 227.7$ g
- The confidence interval you need is **symmetrical** about the mean with a width of 5 g. So it will be ($\overline{w}$ – 2.5 g, $\overline{w}$ + 2.5 g) = (225.2 g, 230.2 g).

b) Find the confidence level for the above confidence interval.

- Estimate the **population variance**:

$$s^2 = \frac{10}{9}\left[\frac{518767}{10} - 227.7^2\right] = 32.677...$$

- The confidence interval has a width of 5 g, and its width is: $\frac{2s}{\sqrt{n}}t_{(n-1)}$
So **substitute** in the information you know:

$$\frac{2 \times \sqrt{32.677...}}{\sqrt{10}}t_{(9)} = 5$$

$$\Rightarrow t_{(9)} = \frac{5\sqrt{10}}{2 \times \sqrt{32.677...}} = 1.383 \text{ (to 3 d.p.)}$$

- Using tables with $\nu = 9$, you can find that $P(T \le 1.383) = 0.90$.
Now it's best to draw a graph to show what you've found.

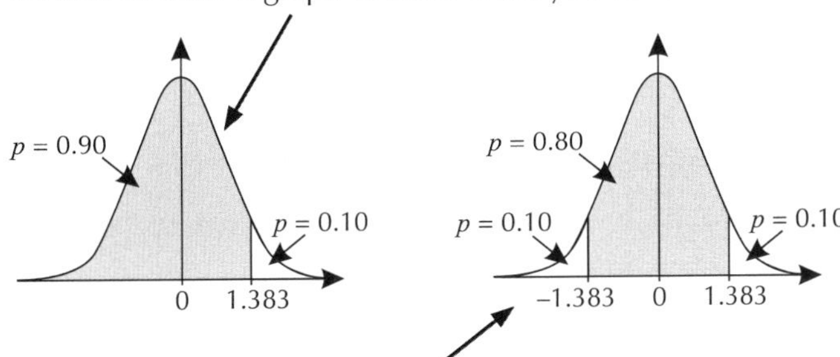

- Using the symmetry of the t-distribution, this means $P(-1.383 \le T \le 1.383) = 0.80$
- This means this is an 80% confidence interval.

Tip: Here you're using the t-tables 'backwards' — you have a value of x and you're finding a value of p.

Exercise 1.2

Q1 A sample of 8 observations of a normally distributed random variable, X, gives these values:

37, 45, 39, 42, 41, 48, 39, 40.

a) Find the sample mean, $\bar{x}$, and estimate the population standard deviation using s.

b) Determine a 95% confidence interval for the unknown population mean μ.

Q2 The weights, w grams, of a random sample of 9 pears from an orchard are measured. The results can be summarised as:

$$\sum w = 1162 \text{ and } \sum w^2 = 151200.$$

a) Calculate a 98% confidence interval for the mean weight of the pears in the orchard, stating any assumptions you need to make.

b) Comment on the claim that the mean weight is 140 g.

Q3 A random sample of 15 observations is taken from a normal distribution with unknown mean μ and variance σ^2.
A 99% confidence for the mean is (12.7, 19.5).

a) Find the sample mean, $\bar{x}$.

b) Calculate an estimate of the standard error of the sample mean.

Q4 The time, t minutes, taken by a machine to make a component is measured for 12 randomly chosen components.
The results are summarised as:

$$\sum t = 156 \text{ and } \sum (t - \bar{t})^2 = 33 \text{ (where } \bar{t} \text{ is the sample mean).}$$

a) Construct a 99% confidence interval for the mean time, μ, stating any assumptions that you make.

b) Comment on the claim that the time taken has a mean greater than 15 minutes.

Q5 A market gardener sells sacks of potatoes to a supermarket. The weights, x kg, of the sacks can be modelled as a normal distribution with unknown mean, μ kg, and unknown standard deviation, σ kg.

The supermarket manager selects a random sample of 12 sacks and uses a t-distribution to calculate a 95% confidence interval for μ of (19.14 kg, 21.46 kg).

a) Show that the sample mean is 20.3 kg.

b) Calculate an estimate of the standard error of the mean.

c) Calculate an unbiased estimate of σ^2.

d) Construct a 99% confidence interval for μ, based on the sample of 12 sacks.

e) Determine the percentage confidence level for the confidence interval (19.5817 kg, 21.0183 kg).

2. Hypothesis Testing

Hypothesis testing means checking if your theories about a population are consistent with the observations from a sample. In other words, you'll be using data from a sample to test whether a statement about a whole population is believable... or really unlikely.

Learning Objectives:

- Be able to formulate null and alternative hypotheses.
- Be able to decide when to use a one- or two-tailed test.
- Understand what is meant by significance levels.
- Understand what is meant by a test statistic, and be able to find a test statistic's sampling distribution.
- Know how to test an observed value of a test statistic for significance.
- Understand what is meant by type I and type II errors.

Null and alternative hypotheses

A **hypothesis** (plural: **hypotheses**) is a claim or a statement that **might** be true, but which might **not** be.

- A **hypothesis test** is a method of testing a hypothesis about a **population** using **observed data** from a **sample**.
- You'll need **two** hypotheses for every hypothesis test — a **null** hypothesis and an **alternative** hypothesis.

Null hypothesis

- The **null hypothesis** is a statement about the **value** of a population parameter (e.g. a mean μ).
  The null hypothesis is always referred to as $\mathbf{H_0}$.
- H_0 needs to assume a **specific value** for the parameter, since all the calculations in your hypothesis test will be based on this value.

The example below (which I'll keep coming back to throughout the section) shows how you could use a hypothesis test to check whether a claim about the mean of a population is likely to be true.

Tip: Remember...
A **parameter** describes a characteristic of a whole **population**.
A **statistic** is calculated using only observations from a **sample**.

> The lengths of the carrots sold by a particular farm are normally distributed with a variance, σ^2, of 2.5 cm². The farm manager claims that the mean length, μ, of all the carrots sold is 9 cm.
> Milly wants to test this claim, and decides to carry out a hypothesis test.
>
> - This is a test about μ, the mean length in cm of the population of carrots sold by this farm.
> - Milly's null hypothesis needs to assume a **specific** value for μ.
>   So Milly's null hypothesis is:
>
> $$H_0: \mu = 9$$

- Now then... the fact that Milly is carrying out this test at all probably means that she has some doubts about whether the mean carrot length is 9 cm.
- But that's okay... you **don't** have to **believe** your null hypothesis — it's just an assumption you make for the purposes of carrying out the test.
- In fact, as you'll soon see, it's pretty common to choose a null hypothesis that you think is **false**.

Tip: Hypothesis testing is sometimes called **significance testing**.

There are **two** possible results of a hypothesis test.
Depending on your data, you can:

a) **'Fail to reject $\mathbf{H_0}$'** — this means that your data provides **no evidence** to think that your null hypothesis is **untrue**.

b) **'Reject $\mathbf{H_0}$'** — this means that your data provides evidence to think that your null hypothesis is **unlikely to be true**.

In case you need to reject H_0, you need an alternative hypothesis 'standing by'.

Tip: There's more about the possible outcomes of a hypothesis test on p91.

Two kinds of alternative hypothesis

Tip: You **must** decide what your alternative hypothesis is **before** you collect any data.

Before you collect any data, you need to think ahead and decide what you're going to conclude if you end up rejecting H_0 — i.e. what you're rejecting H_0 in favour of.

This is your **alternative hypothesis**.
The alternative hypothesis is always referred to as $\mathbf{H_1}$.

There are **two kinds** of alternative hypothesis:

- A **one-tailed** alternative hypothesis.

  A one-tailed alternative hypothesis specifies whether the parameter you're investigating is **greater than** or **less than** the value you used in H_0. Using a one-tailed alternative hypothesis means you're carrying out a **one-tailed hypothesis test.**

Tip: You'll see more about one-tailed tests and two-tailed tests later.

- A **two-tailed** alternative hypothesis.

  A two-tailed alternative hypothesis **doesn't specify** whether the parameter you're investigating is greater than or less than the value you used in H_0 — all it says is that it's **not equal** to the value in H_0.
  Using a two-tailed alternative hypothesis means you're carrying out a **two-tailed hypothesis test.**

Back to the example on carrot lengths...

Milly has a choice of alternative hypotheses for this test, and she'll need to choose which to use **before** she starts collecting data.

- She could use a **one-tailed** alternative hypothesis — there are two possibilities:

  $H_1: \mu > 9$ — this would say the mean length is **greater than** 9 cm

  or $H_1: \mu < 9$ — this would say the mean length is **less than** 9 cm

- She could use a **two-tailed** alternative hypothesis:

  $H_1: \mu \neq 9$ — this would say the mean is different from 9 cm, but **not** whether it's greater than or less than 9 cm

Tip: Notice that H_1 does not give a specific value to the population parameter — it gives a range of values.

To decide which alternative hypothesis to use, you have to consider:

- **What you want to find out** about the parameter.

  For example, if you were investigating the mean time (μ) taken by a factory to make a product, then you might only want to test whether μ has **increased** (you might not be so concerned about testing whether it's decreased).

- Any **suspicions** you might already have about the parameter's value.

  For example, if Milly in the example above thought that the mean, μ, was actually lower than 9 cm, then she'd use $H_1: \mu < 9$.
  So if her data means she can reject H_0, then she'll have gathered evidence to back up the suspicion she already has.

Possible conclusions after a hypothesis test

Okay... I'm going to assume now that you've written your null and alternative hypotheses, and then **collected some data**. You need to know the **possible conclusions** that you can come to after performing a hypothesis test.

There are **two** possibilities:

- Your **observed data** is **really unlikely** under the null hypothesis, H_0.
  - If your observed data is **really unlikely** when you assume that H_0 is true, then you might start to think 'Well, maybe H_0 isn't true after all.'
  - It could be that your observed data is actually **much** more likely to happen under your **alternative hypothesis**. Then you'd perhaps think H_1 is more likely to be true than H_0.
  - In this case, you would **reject H_0** in favour of H_1.
  - This **doesn't** mean that H_0 is **definitely false**. After all, as long as your observed data isn't impossible under H_0, then H_0 could still be true. All it means is that 'on the balance of probabilities', H_1 seems to be **more likely** to be true than H_0.

- The **observed data isn't especially unlikely** under the null hypothesis, H_0.
  - If your observed data could easily have come about under H_0, then you **can't reject H_0**.
  - In this case, you would '**fail to reject H_0**'.
  - However, this is **not** the same as saying that you have evidence that H_0 is **true** — all it means is that H_0 appears to be **believable**, and that you have **no evidence** that it's false.
  - But it's not really any better than having collected no data at all — you didn't have evidence to disbelieve the null hypothesis before you did your experiment... and you still don't. That's all this conclusion means.

Because the conclusion of 'not rejecting H_0' is so 'weak' (i.e. you might as well not have bothered to collect any data), it's actually more interesting and 'meaningful' when you can 'reject H_0' in favour of H_1.

- This is why the alternative hypothesis H_1 is usually 'more interesting' than the null hypothesis H_0. In the example with Milly, for instance, it's the **alternative** hypothesis that states that the farm manager's claim is false.
- It's also why H_0 often says something that you think is **false**. Your aim is to gather evidence to reject H_0 in favour of H_1 (and this is why H_1 might be what you actually **believe**).

Back to Milly's hypothesis test...

- If Milly **rejects H_0**:
  - She has **evidence** that H_0 is false.
  - Although she **can't** be certain, H_1 appears **more likely** to be true.
- If Milly **fails to reject H_0**:
  - H_0 **could** be true, but she has no evidence to say so.
  - H_0 **could** also be false, but she has no evidence for that either.

Tip: The details of how you draw these conclusions are explained later — for now, just try to understand the logic of what's going on.

Tip: 'Under the null hypothesis' / 'under H_0' just means 'assuming that the null hypothesis is true'.

Tip: How unlikely your results need to be before you reject H_0 is called the **significance level** — it's explained on p94.

Tip: Remember... the choice is between '**rejecting H_0**' and '**not rejecting H_0**'. You **never** 'accept H_0'.

Tip: A hypothesis test **can** provide evidence that H_1 is likely to be true, but it **can't** provide evidence that H_0 is likely to be true.

Example 1

Jemma thinks that the average length of the worms in her worm farm is greater than 8 cm. She measures the lengths of a random sample of the 50 worms and calculates the sample mean.

a) Write down a suitable null hypothesis to test Jemma's theory.

The parameter Jemma's interested in is the **mean length** (in cm) of the population of worms in her worm farm, μ.

The null hypothesis must give a **specific value** to μ, and it's the statement that Jemma is trying to get evidence to **reject**.

Jemma thinks that μ is greater than 8. So her null hypothesis should be that the mean length is equal to 8. So:

$$H_0: \mu = 8$$

b) Write down a suitable alternative hypothesis.

Jemma thinks that the mean length is greater than 8, so her alternative hypothesis should be:

$$H_1: \mu > 8$$

(This is the hypothesis that Jemma actually believes.)

Tip: The question will usually give you a hint about what H_1 should be. Here it says Jemma thinks that the mean is greater than 8.

c) State whether this test is one- or two-tailed.

The alternative hypothesis specifies that μ is greater than 8, so the test is one-tailed.

Your population parameter could be the mean of any continuous random variable, such as height, weight, time etc...

Example 2

In a particular post office, each customer usually queues for an average of 2 minutes. The manager of the post office wants to test whether the time that customers spend queuing is different between the hours of 1 pm and 2 pm.

a) Write down a suitable null hypothesis.

The manager is interested in the mean queue time, μ minutes, between 1 pm and 2 pm.

The null hypothesis must give a **specific value** to μ.

So:

$$H_0: \mu = 2$$

Tip: The manager's null hypothesis is that the time customers spend queuing between 1 pm and 2 pm is the same as at other times.

b) Write down a suitable alternative hypothesis.

The manager wants to test for **any** difference (rather than just an increase or just a decrease).

So:

$$H_1: \mu \neq 2$$

c) State whether this test is one- or two-tailed.

The alternative hypothesis only specifies that μ is not equal to 2, so the test is two-tailed.

Exercise 2.1

Q1 Meryl's Bakery has taken on a new pastry chef. Previously the lengths of the bakery's chocolate croissants had a mean of 12 cm. Meryl suspects that the new pastry chef is baking shorter croissants, and wants to test her suspicion.

a) Write down the quantity that Meryl is investigating.

b) Write down a suitable null hypothesis.

c) Write down a suitable alternative hypothesis.

d) State whether this test is one-tailed or two-tailed.

Q2 In recent years, the mean length of time per subject that students at a particular school spend revising before an exam has been 65.7 hours. The head wants to test whether this year's students revise more than in the past.

a) Write down the quantity that is being investigated.

b) Write down a suitable null hypothesis.

c) Write down a suitable alternative hypothesis.

d) State whether this test is one- or two-tailed.

Q3 Customers normally queue for a particular theme park for a mean time of 0.45 hours. The theme park has built a new 'Invisible-Track' ride and increased its ticket price for entry into the park. The managers want to test whether this will affect queuing times.

a) Write down the quantity that is being investigated.

b) Formulate the null and alternative hypotheses, H_0 and H_1.

c) State whether this test is one- or two-tailed.

Q4 The mean weight of lobster meat that Layton sells on his fish counter per day is 2.5 kg. He decreases the price and wants to test whether he sells more lobster meat.

a) Write down the quantity that is being investigated.

b) Formulate the null and alternative hypotheses, H_0 and H_1.

c) State whether this test is one- or two-tailed.

Q5 Simon knows the players at his local golf club take a mean time of 3.7 hours to play 18 holes. Jules is a new member of the golf club and wants to test whether she plays at a different rate.

Write down suitable null and alternative hypotheses.

Q6 The mean time taken by Katie's toaster to toast a slice of bread is 33.2 seconds. She buys a new toaster and wants to test whether it toasts at a different rate. Write down suitable null and alternative hypotheses.

Significance levels

- You've seen that you would reject H_0 if the data you collect is 'really unlikely' under H_0. But you need to decide exactly **how unlikely** your results will need to be before you decide to reject H_0.
- The **significance level** of a test shows how far you're prepared to believe that unlikely results are just down to **chance**, rather than because the assumption in H_0 is wrong.

> The **significance level** of a test (α) determines **how unlikely** your data needs to be under the null hypothesis (H_0) before you reject H_0.

Tip: If your results under H_0 have a probability lower than α, then you can say that your results are **significant**.

- For example, your significance level could be $\alpha = 0.05$ (or 5%). This would mean that you would **only** reject H_0 if your observed data fell into the **most extreme 5%** of possible outcomes.
- You'll usually be told what significance level to use, but the most common values are $\alpha = 0.05$ (or 5%) and $\alpha = 0.01$ (or 1%).

Tip: Significance levels can be written as percentages or decimals.

- The value of α also determines the strength of the evidence that the test has provided if you reject H_0 — the **lower** the value of α, the **stronger the evidence** you have that H_0 is false.
  - For example, if you use $\alpha = 0.05$ and your data lets you reject H_0, then you have evidence that H_0 is false.
  - But if you use $\alpha = 0.01$ and your data lets you reject H_0, then you have **stronger** evidence that H_0 is false.
- Also, the **lower** the value of α, the **lower** the probability of **incorrectly rejecting H_0** when it is in fact **true** — i.e. of getting 'extreme' data due to chance rather than because H_0 was false.

Tip: Incorrectly rejecting H_0 when it is in fact true is called a **Type I error** — see p98.

- But although a **low** value of α sounds like a good thing, there's an important **disadvantage** to using a low significance level — you're **less likely to be able to reject H_0**. This means your experiment is more likely to end up 'failing to reject H_0' and concluding nothing.

Test statistics

To see if your results are **significant**, you need to find their probability under H_0. The way you do this is to '**summarise**' your data in something called a **test statistic**.

> A **test statistic** for a hypothesis test is a statistic calculated from **sample data** which is used to **decide** whether or not to reject H_0.

Tip: Normal distributions were covered in detail in S1. See p83 for more information about t-distributions.

- In S2, the sampling distribution of the test statistics you'll use will be one of the following:
  - a **normal** distribution, $N(\mu, \sigma^2)$
  - a ***t*-distribution** with ν degrees of freedom, $t_{(\nu)}$
- Once you've found your test statistic, you then need to work out the probability of a value **at least as extreme** as this using the parameter in your null hypothesis.
- If this probability is less than the significance level α, you can reject H_0.

Deciding whether or not to reject H_0

1. Comparing the probability of the test statistic with α

Right... back to Milly and her carrots. Let's assume first that Milly is carrying out a **one-tailed test** to check if the mean carrot length (in cm) is **less than 9**.

- For this one-tailed test, Milly's null and alternative hypotheses will be:
  $H_0: \mu = 9$ and $H_1: \mu < 9$
- Milly's going to use a significance level of $\alpha = 0.05$.
- Milly then measures the lengths of a random sample of 50 carrots.
- The individual carrot lengths (X) are normally distributed: $X \sim N(\mu, 2.5)$
  So the sample mean ($\overline{X}$) also has a normal distribution: $\overline{X} \sim N(\mu, \frac{2.5}{50})$
  In fact, under H_0, $\overline{X} \sim N(9, \frac{2.5}{50}) = N(9, 0.05)$.
- Milly can then transform $\overline{X}$ to the standard normal distribution (Z), and use Z as her test statistic where $Z = \frac{\overline{X} - 9}{\sqrt{0.05}} \sim N(0, 1)$.

First suppose Milly got a sample mean of $\bar{x} = 8.64$ — i.e. $z = -1.61$ (2 d.p.)

- The probability of a result **at least as extreme** as $z = -1.61$ is $\mathbf{P(Z \leq -1.61)}$.
  Under H_0, this is $P(Z \geq 1.61) = 1 - P(Z < 1.61) = 1 - 0.94630 = \mathbf{0.05370}$.
- This value of 0.05370 is **not less than** the significance level α, so she **cannot reject H_0**.
- Milly has **no evidence** at the 5% level of significance that the mean carrot length is less than 9 cm.

Suppose now Milly got a sample mean of $\bar{x} = 8.63$ — i.e. $z = -1.65$ (2 d.p.)

- The probability of a result **at least as extreme** as $z = -1.65$ is $\mathbf{P(Z \leq -1.65)}$.
  Under H_0, this is $1 - P(Z < 1.65) = 1 - 0.95053 = \mathbf{0.04947}$.
- This value of 0.04947 is **less than** the significance level α, so she **can reject H_0**.
- Milly has **evidence** at the 5% level of significance that the mean carrot length is less than 9 cm.

Before moving on, look at the p.d.f., f(z), of the test statistic.

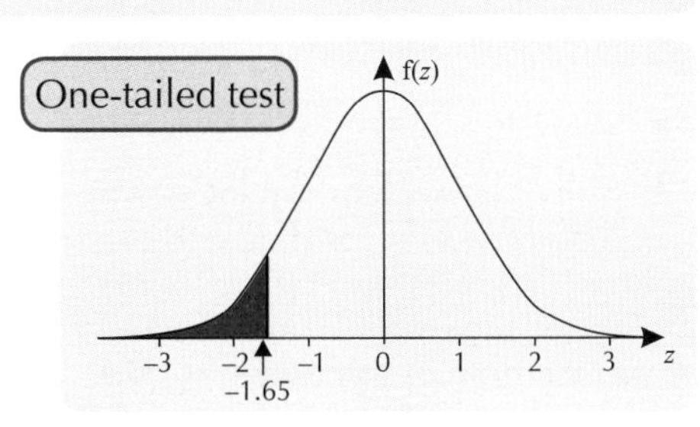

- The red area forms the 'one tail' of the test statistic's distribution containing values that would lead Milly to reject H_0 in favour of H_1.
- Notice how these values are at the 'low' end of the distribution — this is because H_1 was $H_1: \mu < 9$ (meaning very low values of Z are more likely under H_1 than under H_0).
- If Milly had chosen her alternative hypothesis to be $H_1: \mu > 9$, then the values that would lead her to reject H_0 would be at the 'high' end.

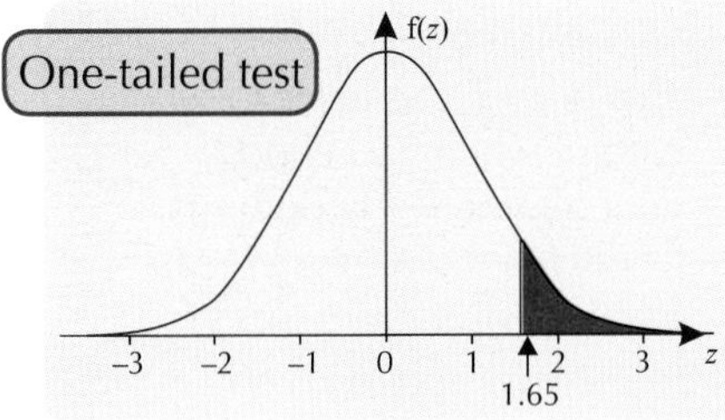

Tip: Remember... Milly knows that the population variance (σ^2) is 2.5 — see p89.

Tip: Remember... if $X \sim N(\mu, \sigma^2)$, then $\overline{X} \sim N(\mu, \frac{\sigma^2}{n})$.

Tip: Remember... to transform a normally distributed random variable to the standard normal distribution (Z), subtract the mean (μ) and divide by the standard deviation (σ).

Tip: A result 'at least as extreme as −1.61' means '−1.61 or less' here. See below for more details.

Tip: Remember...
$P(Z \leq -1.61)$
$= P(Z \geq 1.61)$
$= 1 - P(Z < 1.61)$

Tip: In fact, any value for z of −1.65 or less (equivalent to any value of $\bar{x}$ of approximately 8.63 or less) would lead Milly to reject H_0.

Tip: The red areas show the critical regions. See p97 for more information.

Tip: If Milly's alternative hypothesis had been $H_1: \mu > 9$, then by symmetry she would reject H_0 for values of Z equal to 1.65 or more (equivalent to any value of $\bar{x}$ of approximately 9.37 or more).

Now assume that Milly is carrying out a **two-tailed test** to check if the mean is different from 9 cm (**either** greater than 9 cm **or** less than 9 cm).

Most of what follows is the same as for the one-tailed test, but there's one important difference.

- For this two-tailed test, Milly's null and alternative hypotheses will be: $H_0: \mu = 9$ and $H_1: \mu \neq 9$
- Milly's going to use the same significance level of $\alpha = 0.05$.
- Milly then measures the lengths of a random sample of 50 carrots.
- Again, $X \sim N(\mu, 2.5)$, so $\overline{X} \sim N(\mu, \frac{2.5}{50})$.
  So under H_0, $\overline{X} \sim N(9, 0.05)$.
- Again, her test statistic will be $Z = \frac{\overline{X} - 9}{\sqrt{0.05}}$, where $Z \sim N(0, 1)$.

Tip: You **do** need to write down all these pieces of information for **every** hypothesis test you do — it's worth loads of marks.

So up to this point, things are pretty much identical to the one-tailed test.

But now think about which 'extreme' outcomes for the test statistic would favour H_1 over H_0.

- This time, extreme outcomes at **either** the 'high' end **or** the 'low' end of the distribution would favour your alternative hypothesis, $H_1: \mu \neq 9$.
- But the significance level is the **total** probability of the results that would lead to you reject H_0. So for a two-tailed test, you have to **divide α by 2** and use half of the significance level ($\frac{\alpha}{2} = 0.025$) at each end of the distribution.

Tip: Testing for significance is slightly different for one- and two-tailed tests. You just need to compare the probability to a different number.

First suppose that Milly got a sample mean of $\bar{x} = 8.57$, so $z = -1.92$ (2 d.p.).

- The probability of a result **at least as extreme** as $z = -1.92$ is $\mathbf{P(Z \leq -1.92)}$.
  Under H_0, this is $P(Z \geq 1.92) = 1 - P(Z < 1.92) = 1 - 0.97257 = \mathbf{0.02743}$.
- This value of 0.02743 is **not less than** $\frac{\alpha}{2}$, so she **cannot reject H_0**.
- Milly has **no evidence** at the 5% level of significance that the mean carrot length is not equal to 9 cm.

Tip: Always state the significance level in your conclusion.

Suppose instead Milly got a sample mean of $\bar{x} = 8.56$, so $z = -1.97$ (2 d.p.).

- The probability of a result **at least as extreme** as $z = -1.97$ is $\mathbf{P(Z \leq -1.97)}$.
  Under H_0, this is $P(Z \geq 1.97) = 1 - P(Z < 1.97) = 1 - 0.97558 = \mathbf{0.02442}$.
- This value of 0.02442 is **less than** $\frac{\alpha}{2}$, so she **can reject H_0**.
- Milly has **evidence** at the 5% level of significance that the mean carrot length is not equal to 9 cm.

Tip: The values of Z at the 'high' end that would lead Milly to reject H_0 are symmetrical to those at the low end.
So $z = 1.97$ (equivalent roughly to $\bar{x} = 9.44$ cm) would lead Milly to reject H_0, but $z = 1.92$ (equivalent roughly to $\bar{x} = 9.43$ cm) would **not** lead Milly to reject H_0.

- Notice how in this two-tailed test, a sample mean of 8.63 cm is **not** low enough to reject H_0, whereas in the one-tailed test, it was.
- This is why you need to be careful when you choose your alternative hypothesis. Choosing the wrong H_1 can make it harder to reject H_0.

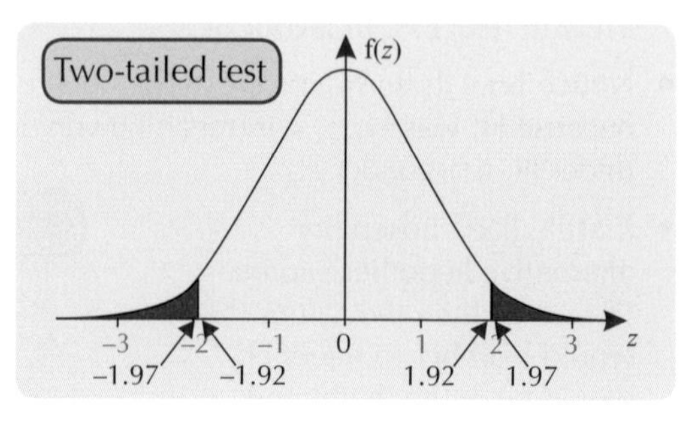

Tip: Remember... values of z in the red zone would lead Milly to reject H_0.

2. Finding the critical region and critical values

When Milly was deciding whether to reject H_0 or not reject H_0, she:

1. worked out her test statistic using her data,
2. then calculated the probability (under H_0) of getting a value for the test statistic at least as extreme as the value she had found.

Finding the **critical region** is another way of doing a hypothesis test. It involves working out in advance all the values of the test statistic that would lead you to reject H_0.

> The **critical region** (CR) is the **set** of all values of the **test statistic** that would cause you to **reject H_0**.

Similarly...

> The **acceptance region** is the **set** of all values of the **test statistic** that mean you **fail to reject H_0**.

Using a critical region is like doing things the other way round, because you:

1. work out all the values that would make you reject H_0,
2. then work out the value of your test statistic using your data, and check if it is in the critical region (and if it is, then reject H_0).

So if you find the **critical region** first, you can quickly say whether any observed value of the test statistic is **significant**.

Critical values are the values on the borderline of the critical region — if your test statistic is at least as extreme as a critical value, then you can reject H_0.

- Since **one-tailed tests** have a **single critical region** (containing either the highest or lowest values), there is only **one critical value**.
  - If your alternative hypothesis is of the form H_1: $\mu < k$ (for some value of k) then you need to find z such that $\mathbf{P(Z \leq z) = \alpha}$.
  - If your alternative hypothesis is of the form H_1: $\mu > k$ (for some value of k) then you need to find z such that $\mathbf{P(Z \geq z) = \alpha}$.

- For Milly's **one-tailed** test (with H_1: $\mu < 9$), you can find the critical value by solving $P(Z \leq z) = 0.05$.
- Using the percentage-points table, $P(Z \leq z) = 0.95$ for $z = 1.6449$. So $P(Z \leq -1.6449) = 0.05$.
- This means the critical region is $\mathbf{Z \leq -1.6449}$.

- Here's the graph from page 95 again — the values of z that fall in the **red** area would all cause you to reject H_0, so they are the values that make up the critical region.

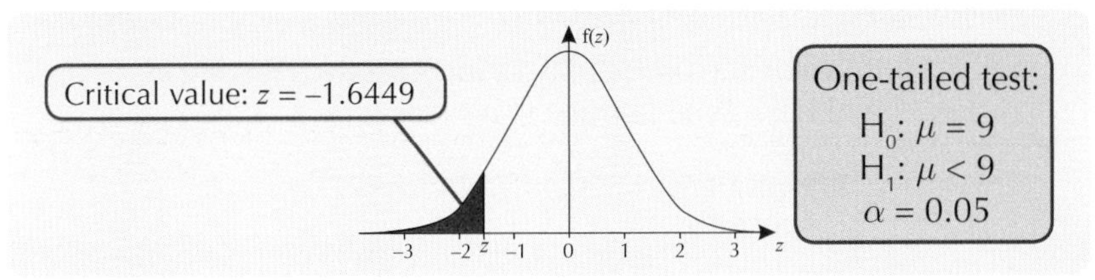

Tip: The critical region is just a set of values that your test statistic can take which fall far enough away from what's expected under the null hypothesis to allow you to reject it.

Tip: Hypothesis tests for the mean of a normal distribution are usually done using this critical region method.

Tip: Remember... Milly's significance level is $\alpha = 0.05$.

Tip: 0.05 is less than 0.5, so you can't use the tables to find z with $P(Z \leq z) = 0.05$ directly.
Instead use the symmetry of the normal distribution to solve $P(Z \geq z) = 0.05$, i.e. $P(Z < z) = 0.95$. This gives $z = 1.6449$.
So by symmetry, $P(Z \leq -1.6449) = 0.05$

Tip: If the alternative hypothesis had been H_1: $\mu > 9$, then by symmetry the critical value would have been $z = 1.6449$.

- A **two-tailed test** has a **critical region** that's split into two 'tails' — one tail at each end of the distribution. This means there are **two critical values**. Because the distribution is symmetrical, the two critical values will be the same distance either side of $z = 0$.

  - The distribution is **symmetric** about $z = 0$, so once you've found one critical value, the other will just be its **negative**.
  - You need to find the value of z with $\mathbf{P(Z \geq z) = \frac{\alpha}{2}}$ and $\mathbf{P(Z \leq -z) = \frac{\alpha}{2}}$

  - For Milly's **two-tailed** test (with $H_1: \mu \neq 9$), find z with $P(Z \leq z) = 0.025$.
  - Using the percentage points table, $P(Z \leq z) = 0.975$ for $z = 1.9600$. So $P(Z \leq -1.9600) = 0.025$.
  - This means the critical region is $\mathbf{Z \leq -1.9600}$ **and** $\mathbf{Z \geq 1.9600}$.

- Here's the graph from p96 again. Values of z in the two **red** areas make up the two parts of the critical region.

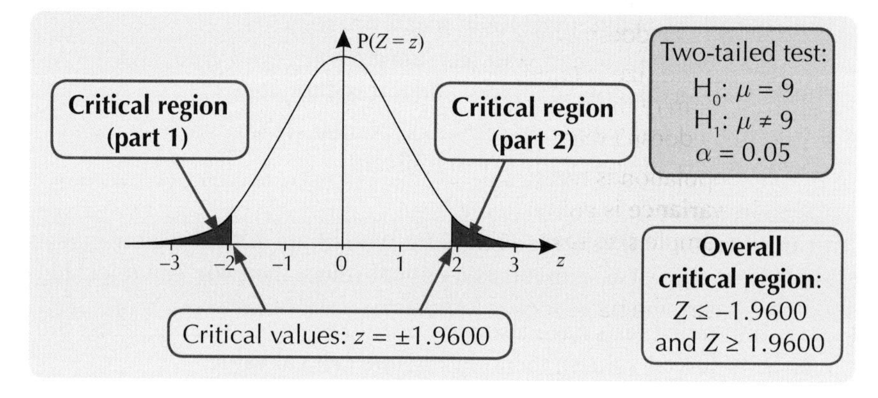

Tip: Remember... use a two-tailed test if you're testing for a difference from the value in H_0, but you're not sure how it'll differ (i.e. whether it will be bigger or smaller).

Type I and Type II errors

A hypothesis test allows you to say that you have significant **evidence** to reject H_0, but remember... your results are based on the 'balance of probabilities' (see p91) — so mistakes are possible.

There are two different kinds of mistakes — **Type I** errors and **Type II** errors.

Type I error — reject H_0 when H_0 is in fact **true**
Type II error — fail to reject H_0 when H_0 is **not true**

In the exam you could be asked to find the **probability** of making a **Type I** error — this is actually dead easy.

- The significance level (α) of a test is the **probability of rejecting H_0** (assuming H_0 is true).
- So it must also be the probability of **incorrectly rejecting H_0** — i.e. of making a Type I error.

P(Type I error) = significance level (α)

Tip: You won't be asked to calculate the probability of making a Type II error in your exam.

3. Hypothesis Tests of the Mean of a Population

In the previous section, you saw all the general theory of hypothesis testing. This section will go through lots more examples of tests in particular circumstances, and there'll be loads of practice too. There's not too much to actually learn here — it's mostly just applying what you already know.

Learning Objective:

- Be able to conduct hypothesis tests about population means using a normal or t-distribution when:
  i. the population is normally distributed with known variance.
  ii. the population is not necessarily normal but the sample size is large ($n \geq 30$).
  iii. the population is normal but the variance is unknown and the sample size is small ($n < 30$).

Setting up the test

In S2 you'll be carrying out hypothesis tests of the **mean** of different distributions, based on a **random sample** of ***n* observations** from the population.

Using your sample data, you'll be able to calculate the **sample mean**, $\overline{X}$. You'll then be able to find the value of your **test statistic**.

There are actually three different situations you'll need to be ready for:

- The population is **normally distributed** with **known variance**. Sample size doesn't matter here.
- The sample size is **large** ($n \geq 30$).
  - The form of the distribution doesn't matter here.
  - It also doesn't matter whether the variance is known or unknown.
- The population is **normally distributed**, but:
  - the **variance** is **unknown**,
  - the sample size is **small** ($n < 30$).

Tip: These are the same three situations you've seen how to find confidence intervals for (in S1 and earlier in this chapter).

In all three cases, the basic method is the same.

- Identify the **population parameter**
  — it's always μ, the mean of the population.
- Write down the **null** hypothesis (H_0)
  — H_0: $\mu = a$ for some constant a.
- Write down the **alternative** hypothesis (H_1)
  — H_1 will either be $H_1: \mu < a$ or $H_1: \mu > a$ (one-tailed test)
  or $H_1: \mu \neq a$ (two-tailed test)
- State the **significance level, α**
  — you'll usually be given this.
- Find the value of the **test statistic**
  — in the first two cases above, this will be: $Z = \dfrac{\overline{X} - \mu}{\sigma/\sqrt{n}} \sim N(0, 1)$
  (or $Z = \dfrac{\overline{X} - \mu}{S/\sqrt{n}} \sim N(0, 1)$ if you estimate σ using a large sample)
  — in the third case above, this will be: $T = \dfrac{\overline{X} - \mu}{S/\sqrt{n}} \sim t_{(n-1)}$
- Use **normal tables** or ***t*-tables** to test for significance, either by:
  — finding the **probability** of your test statistic taking a value **at least as extreme** as your observed value, and comparing it to α,
  — finding the **critical value(s)** of the test statistic and seeing if your observed value lies in the critical region.

Tip: Remember... the critical value(s) depend on the significance level α, and whether it's a one-tailed or a two-tailed test (see p97-98).

Hypothesis tests of a population mean — normal population with known variance

If your population follows a **normal distribution** with **known variance**, then:

- Your null hypothesis is $H_0: \mu = a$
- Your alternative hypothesis is $H_1: \mu < a$ or $H_1: \mu > a$ (one-tailed test) or $H_1: \mu \neq a$ (two-tailed test)
- The test statistic is: $Z = \dfrac{\overline{X} - \mu}{\sigma/\sqrt{n}}$
- Under H_0, $Z \sim N(0, 1)$.

Tip: Use the value of μ that you're assuming for the mean — i.e. the one in H_0.

Tip: Remember... if $X \sim N(\mu, \sigma^2)$, then $\overline{X} \sim N(\mu, \frac{\sigma^2}{n})$.

Or, to put that another way... if $X \sim N(\mu, \sigma^2)$, then $\dfrac{\overline{X} - \mu}{\sigma/\sqrt{n}} \sim N(0, 1)$.

Example 1

The times, in minutes, taken by the athletes in a running club to complete a certain run have been found to follow an N(12, 4) distribution. The coach increases the number of training sessions per week, and a random sample of 20 times run since the increase has a mean of 11.2 minutes. Assuming that the variance has remained unchanged, test at the 5% level whether there is evidence that the average time has decreased.

- Let μ = mean time (in minutes) since the increase in training sessions.
- Then the **hypotheses** are: $H_0: \mu = 12$, $H_1: \mu < 12$

  Assume that there's been no change in the value of μ.

  You're testing to see if there's been a decrease.

  So this is a **one-tailed** test.
- The **significance level** is 5%, so $\alpha = 0.05$.
- Now find the value of your test statistic:

  $\bar{x} = 11.2$, so $z = \dfrac{\bar{x} - \mu}{\sigma/\sqrt{n}} = \dfrac{11.2 - 12}{2/\sqrt{20}} = -1.7888... = -1.79$ (to 2 d.p.)
- All that's left is to test for significance. Here are the **two methods**...

Tip: $\sigma^2 = 4$, so $\sigma = 2$.

Tip: Under H_0, $X \sim (12, 4)$, so $\overline{X} \sim N(12, \frac{4}{20}) = N(12, 0.2)$.

So under H_0, $Z = \dfrac{\overline{X} - 12}{\sqrt{0.2}} \sim N(0, 1)$

Method 1: Finding P(test statistic at least as extreme as observed value)

- Work out the probability of the test statistic (Z) being at least as extreme as the observed value of $z = -1.79$.
- This is a **one-tailed test** and values more likely to occur under the alternative hypothesis (H_1) are at the **lower end** of the distribution. So 'at least as extreme as the observed value' means '–1.79 or lower'.
- $P(Z \leq -1.79) = P(Z \geq 1.79) = 1 - P(Z < 1.79)$
  $= 1 - 0.96327$
  $= \mathbf{0.03673 < 0.05}$ ← $\alpha = 0.05$
- So the result is **significant**.

Tip: You'll need to round your value of z to 2 decimal places to use the table for the normal distribution function.

Method 2: Finding the critical region

- This is a **one-tailed test** and the critical region will be at the **lower end** of the distribution.
  So the critical value is z such that $\mathbf{P(Z < z) = 0.05}$.
- Using the **percentage-points** table, $P(Z < 1.6449) = 0.95$, which means $P(Z < -1.6449) = 0.05$.
- So the critical value is $z = -1.6449$,
  meaning the critical region is $Z < -1.6449$.

$P(Z < -1.6449) = 0.05$

P(Z = z)

−1.6449 0 z

- Since $z = -1.7888... < -1.6449$, the observed value of the test statistic lies in the critical region.
- So the result is **significant**.

- All you need to do now is write your conclusion.

  There is evidence at the 5% level of significance to **reject H_0** and to suggest that the average time has decreased.

Example 2

The volume (in ml) of a cleaning fluid dispensed in each operation by a machine is normally distributed with mean μ and standard deviation 3. Out of a random sample of 20 measured volumes, the mean volume dispensed was 30.9 ml.

a) Does this data provide evidence at the 1% level of significance that the machine is dispensing a mean volume that is different from 30 ml?

- Let μ = mean volume (in ml) dispensed in all possible operations of the machine (i.e. μ is the mean volume of the 'population').
- Your hypotheses will be: H_0: $\mu = 30$ and H_1: $\mu \neq 30$
- The **significance level** is 1%, so $\alpha = 0.01$.
- Now find the value of your test statistic:

  $\bar{x} = 30.9$, so $z = \dfrac{\bar{x} - \mu}{\sigma/\sqrt{n}} = \dfrac{30.9 - 30}{3/\sqrt{20}} = 1.3416... = 1.34$ (to 2 d.p.)
- This is a **two-tailed** test, so you need to check whether the probability of the test statistic being at least as extreme as the observed value is less than $\frac{\alpha}{2} = 0.005$.

  $P(Z \geq 1.34) = 1 - P(Z < 1.34) = 1 - 0.90988 = 0.09012 > \frac{\alpha}{2}$.

  This means this result is **not significant** at this level.
- This data does **not** provide evidence at the 1% level to support the claim that the machine is dispensing a mean volume different from 30 ml.

b) It is later found that the mean volume of fluid dispensed by the machine really is less than 30 ml. State whether the result above is a type I error or a type II error. Give a reason for your answer.

- The null hypothesis was not rejected when it was actually untrue, so this is a type II error.

Tip: Under H_0, $X \sim (30, 3^2)$, so $\bar{X} \sim N(30, \frac{3^2}{20})$. So under H_0, $Z = \dfrac{\bar{X} - 30}{3/\sqrt{20}} \sim N(0, 1)$

Tip: This is a **two-tailed** test. The critical region is given by $P(Z > z) = \frac{\alpha}{2} = 0.005$ or $P(Z < -z) = \frac{\alpha}{2} = 0.005$.

Using the percentage-points table, this gives a value for z of 2.5758.

So the critical region is $Z > 2.5758$ or $Z < -2.5758$.

Exercise 3.1

Q1 The weight of plums in grams from a tree over previous years is known to follow the distribution N(42,16). It is suggested that the weight of plums has increased this year. A random sample of 25 plums gives a mean weight of 43.5 grams.

Assuming the variance has remained unchanged, test this claim at:

a) the 5% significance level

b) the 1% significance level

Q2 Bree plays cards with her friends, and the amount of money she wins each week is normally distributed with a mean, μ, of £24 and standard deviation, σ, of £2. A new friend has joined the game and Bree thinks this will change the amount she wins. In a random sample of 12 weeks the sample mean, $\bar{x}$, was found to be £22.50.

Test Bree's claim at the 1% level.

Q3 In previous years, the marks obtained in a language test by students in a city's schools have followed a normal distribution with mean 70 and variance 64. A teacher suspects that this year the mean score is lower. A sample of 40 students is taken and the mean score is 67.7.

a) Assuming the variance remains unchanged, test the teacher's claim at the 5% level of significance.

b) In fact, the mean score for the year really was 70.
Is the above result a Type I error, Type II error or neither?
Give a reason for your answer.

Q4 The weights (in grams) of pigeons in a city centre are normally distributed with mean 300 and standard deviation 45. The council claims that this year the city's pigeons are, on average, heavier. A random sample of 25 pigeons gives a mean of 314 g.

a) State the null hypothesis and the alternative hypothesis.

b) State whether it is a one- or two-tailed test.

c) Assuming the variance remains unchanged, use a 1% level of significance to test the hypothesis.

d) It is later found that the mean weight of the pigeons has in fact gone up. Is this a Type I error, a Type II error or neither?
Give a reason for your answer.

Q5 The number of hours that Kyle spends each week building his time machine has always followed a normal distribution with mean 32 and standard deviation 5. Kyle is close to finishing the machine and believes that over the last year the mean amount of time spent building it each week has gone up. In a random sample of 20 weeks over the past year, the mean number of hours spent building the time machine was recorded as 34.

Use both a 5% and a 1% level to test Kyle's belief.
Comment on your answers.

Hypothesis tests for a large sample

The method on the last few pages worked because the **population** was **normally distributed** with mean μ and variance σ^2, so the **sampling distribution of the mean** followed the distribution $\overline{X} \sim N(\mu, \frac{\sigma^2}{n})$.

This meant you could use as your test statistic the quantity $Z = \frac{\overline{X} - \mu}{\sigma/\sqrt{n}}$, as this would follow the standard normal distribution N(0, 1).

But if you have a large sample size ($n \geq 30$), then the **Central Limit Theorem** tells you that however the **population** is distributed, the **sampling distribution of the mean** will still (approximately) follow $\overline{X} \sim N(\mu, \frac{\sigma^2}{n})$. So the same method still works in these circumstances.

Also, it doesn't matter whether you know the population variance (σ^2) here.

- If you **know** the population variance (σ^2), then the quantity $Z = \frac{\overline{X} - \mu}{\sigma/\sqrt{n}}$ will follow the standard normal distribution N(0, 1). So you can use this as your test statistic.
- If you **don't know** the population variance (σ^2), the large sample means the sample variance (S^2) should be a good estimate, and $Z = \frac{\overline{X} - \mu}{S/\sqrt{n}}$ will follow the standard normal distribution N(0, 1) pretty well. So you can use this as your test statistic.

Tip: Remember... if $X \sim N(\mu, \sigma^2)$, then $\overline{X} \sim N(\mu, \frac{\sigma^2}{n})$.

Or, to put that another way... if $X \sim N(\mu, \sigma^2)$, then $\frac{\overline{X} - \mu}{\sigma/\sqrt{n}} \sim N(0, 1)$.

So if you have a **large sample** ($n \geq 30$), you can carry out a hypothesis test of the mean of a population like this:

- Your null hypothesis is $H_0: \mu = a$
- Your alternative hypothesis is $H_1: \mu < a$ or $H_1: \mu > a$ (one-tailed test) or $H_1: \mu \neq a$ (two-tailed test)
- If the population variance (σ^2) is **known**, the test statistic is: $Z = \frac{\overline{X} - \mu}{\sigma/\sqrt{n}}$

  If the population variance (σ^2) is **unknown**, the test statistic is: $Z = \frac{\overline{X} - \mu}{S/\sqrt{n}}$
- Under H_0, $Z \sim N(0, 1)$.

Tip: Remember...

$$S^2 = \frac{\sum(X_i - \overline{X})^2}{n-1} = \frac{n}{n-1}\left[\frac{\sum X_i^2}{n} - \left(\frac{\sum X_i}{n}\right)^2\right]$$

Example 1

The mean volume of the drinks dispensed by a drinks machine is claimed to be 250 ml. An engineer measures the volumes, x, of a random sample of 40 drinks from the machine and calculates the following:

$$\sum x = 9800 \quad \text{and} \quad \sum(x - \overline{x})^2 = 3900$$

Carry out a two-tailed test of this claim at the 5% level of significance.

- You don't know how the volumes are distributed, but since n is large (≥ 30), you can apply the Central Limit Theorem and use a z-test with σ estimated by s.
- The average volume is assumed to be 250 ml, so the hypotheses are:

$$H_0: \mu = 250 \quad \text{and} \quad H_1: \mu \neq 250$$

Tip: A 'z-test' means a hypothesis test where the test statistic is $Z \sim N(0, 1)$.

- The significance level is 5%, so $\alpha = 0.05$.

  But the test is **two-tailed**, so you'll need to use $\frac{\alpha}{2} = 0.025$ at either end.

  So to find the critical values, you need to look for z such that $P(Z \leq -z) = 0.025$ and $P(Z \geq z) = 0.025$. Use the normal percentage-points table to find the critical values are $z = \pm 1.9600$.

  This means the **critical region** is $Z < -1.9600$ or $Z > 1.9600$.

- Find the **sample mean** and **estimate** the **population variance**:

$$\bar{x} = \frac{\sum x}{n} = \frac{9800}{40} = 245\,\text{ml} \quad \text{and} \quad s^2 = \frac{\sum(x-\bar{x})^2}{n-1} = \frac{3900}{39} = 100$$

- Now find the value of your **test statistic**:

$$z = \frac{\bar{x}-\mu}{s/\sqrt{n}} = \frac{245-250}{10/\sqrt{40}} = -3.1622...$$

- Since $z = -3.1622 < -1.9600$, the result is **significant**.

  There is evidence at the 5% level of significance to **reject H_0** and to suggest that the mean volume does not equal 250 ml.

Example 2

The mean length of pickle forks made in a workshop is claimed to be 22 cm, while the standard deviation is known to be 0.3 cm.
A customer suspects that the mean length is actually shorter.

The lengths (x cm) of a random sample of 45 pickle forks were measured and it was found that $\sum x = 985.5$

a) Test the claim about the mean at the 1% level of significance.

- You don't know how the lengths are distributed. But since n is large, you can apply the Central Limit Theorem and use a z-test.
- The hypotheses are: $H_0: \mu = 22$ and $H_1: \mu < 22$
- The significance level is 1%, so $\alpha = 0.01$.

  To find the critical values, you need to find z with $P(Z \leq z) = 0.01$. Use the normal percentage-points table to find the critical value is $z = -2.3263$.

  This means the **critical region** is $Z < -2.3263$.

- Find the **sample mean**: $\bar{x} = \frac{\sum x}{n} = \frac{985.5}{45} = 21.9$
- Now find the value of your **test statistic**:

$$z = \frac{\bar{x}-\mu}{\sigma/\sqrt{n}} = \frac{21.9-22}{0.3/\sqrt{45}} = -2.2360...$$

- Since this value for z is not in the critical region, this result is **not significant**, and so you cannot reject H_0.

  There is **no evidence** at the 1% level of significance to conclude that the mean length of the pickle forks is less than 22 cm.

b) Using later results, based on a much larger sample, it is found that the average length of the pickle forks really was less than 22 cm. State whether the result of the test carried out above is a Type I or Type II error. Give a reason for your answer.

- The null hypothesis was not rejected when it was actually untrue, so this is a **Type II error**.

Exercise 3.2

Q1 A company produces fluorescent light bulbs and claims that the mean lifetime is 1400 hours. To investigate this claim, the lifetimes of a random sample of 100 bulbs are measured. The mean lifetime of this sample is 1380 hours. If the population standard deviation is known to be $\sigma = 80$ hours, test the company's claim at the 5% level.

Q2 A manufacturer produces high-strength cables. The cables' breaking strengths have a mean of 700 kg and a variance of 6400 kg^2.

A different technique is used to manufacture a new batch of cables and it is claimed that the breaking strength is greater.
A random sample of 40 cables has a mean strength of 725 kg.

Assuming the variance of the breaking strengths remains unchanged:
a) test this claim at the 5% level
b) test the claim at the 1% level

Q3 Tiger plays darts and averages a score of 57 with each set of darts. Tiger starts to use the energy drinks made by a particular company and claims that his score with each set of darts has increased.

A random sample of 40 of Tiger's scores (x) are recorded.
The scores have the following summary statistics:

$$\sum x = 2316 \text{ and } \sum(x - \bar{x})^2 = 351.$$

a) Calculate an estimate, s^2, of the population variance.

b) Test Tiger's claim at the 5% level of significance.

Q4 A robot can cover 100 metres in an average time of 10.1 seconds. The robot's inventor attaches some rockets and a random sample of 35 of its times (t, in seconds) over 100 m then gives the results below:

$$\sum t = 346.5 \text{ and } \sum(t - \bar{t})^2 = 34.51$$

The inventor claims that this provides evidence that the times have fallen.

a) Calculate an estimate, s^2, of the variance of the robot's times.

b) Test the inventor's claim at the 1% level.

c) It is later found that the rockets do make a significant difference to the times. Explain whether the above test resulted in a type I or type II error.

Hypothesis tests of a population mean — normal population / unknown σ^2 / small n

Tip: See p83 for more on t-distributions.

On p83, you saw that if $X \sim N(\mu, \sigma^2)$ but:

(i) you don't know the population variance (σ^2),

and (ii) n is **small**,

the quantity $\frac{\overline{X} - \mu}{S/\sqrt{n}}$ doesn't follow the standard normal distribution N(0, 1).

Instead it follows a ***t*-distribution** with **(n – 1) degrees of freedom**.

You can use this fact to carry out a hypothesis test of the mean of a **normally distributed** population with **unknown variance** using only a **small sample**.

Tip: Remember...

$$S^2 = \frac{\sum(X_i - \overline{X})^2}{n-1} = \frac{n}{n-1}\left[\frac{\sum X_i^2}{n} - \left(\frac{\sum X_i}{n}\right)^2\right]$$

- Your null hypothesis is $H_0: \mu = a$
- Your alternative hypothesis is $H_1: \mu < a$ or $H_1: \mu > a$ (one-tailed test) or $H_1: \mu \neq a$ (two-tailed test)

  The test statistic is: $T = \frac{\overline{X} - \mu}{S/\sqrt{n}}$
- Under H_0, $T \sim t_{(n-1)}$.

Example 1

A random sample of 8 observations from a normal distribution with mean μ and variance σ^2 produces the following results: $\overline{x} = 9.5$ and $s^2 = 2.25$. Test at the 1% level of significance the claim that $\mu > 9$.

- The null and alternative hypotheses are: $H_0: \mu = 9$ and $H_1: \mu > 9$
- The significance level is 1%, so $\alpha = 0.01$.
- σ^2 is unknown and $n = 8$, so you need to use a ***t*-test**, where your test statistic will have **7 degrees of freedom** (i.e. $\nu = 7$).

  This means that under H_0, $T = \frac{\overline{X} - 9}{S/\sqrt{n}} \sim t_{(7)}$.
- The test is **one-tailed**, so the critical value is t such that $\mathbf{P(T > t) = 0.01}$ — this means looking up $P(T < t) = 0.99$ in the t-tables with $\nu = 7$.

  You find that $P(T < 2.998) = 0.99$, and so the critical region is $T > 2.998$
- Work out the value of your test statistic: $t = \frac{9.5 - 9}{1.5/\sqrt{8}} = 0.943$ (3 d.p.)
- Since $t = 0.943 < 2.998$, the result is **not significant**.

  There is insufficient evidence at the 5% level to reject the null hypothesis in support of the claim that $\mu > 9$.

Tip: A 't-test' means a hypothesis test where the test statistic is $T \sim t_{(\nu)}$.

Tip: $s^2 = 2.25$, so $s = 1.5$

Example 2

An ostrich farmer believes that the mean weight of eggs produced by his ostriches is less than 1.4 kg. A random sample of 10 eggs is selected and their weights (x kg) measured. The results are summarised below:

$$\sum x = 13.7 \qquad \sum x^2 = 18.8$$

Assuming that the weights of the ostrich eggs are normally distributed, test the farmer's claim at the 5% level.

- The null and alternative hypotheses are: $H_0: \mu = 1.4$ and $H_1: \mu < 1.4$
- The significance level is 5%, so $\alpha = 0.05$.
- Calculate the sample mean $\bar{x}$ and the sample variance (s^2):

$$\bar{x} = \frac{\sum x}{n} = \frac{13.7}{10} = 1.37 \text{ and } s^2 = \frac{n}{n-1}\left[\frac{\sum x^2}{n} - \left(\frac{\sum x}{n}\right)^2\right]$$
$$= \frac{10}{9}\left[\frac{18.8}{10} - \left(\frac{13.7}{10}\right)^2\right] = 0.00344...$$

- Since the sample size is small, you need to use a t-test. $n = 10$, so the test statistic (T) will have 9 degrees of freedom (i.e. $\nu = 9$).
- Under H_0, $T = \frac{\bar{X} - \mu}{S/\sqrt{n}} \sim t_{(9)}$.

  The test is one-tailed, so the critical value is t such that $P(T < t) = 0.05$ — this gives $t = -1.833$. So the critical region is $T < -1.833$.
- Your test statistic is $t = \frac{1.37 - 1.4}{\sqrt{0.00344...}/\sqrt{10}} = -1.616$ (3 d.p.)
- Since $t = -1.616 > -1.833$, the result is **not significant**.

  There is insufficient evidence at the 5% level to reject H_0 and support the claim that the ostrich eggs have a mean weight less than 1.4 kg.

Exercise 3.3

Q1 A company fitting new digital aerials states that the mean time for fitting is 35 minutes. It is claimed by a customer that the mean time is longer than this, based on his own random sample of 6 aerial fittings. The times (in minutes) he recorded are:

37 34 36 39 38 34

a) Calculate the sample mean ($\bar{x}$) and the sample variance (s^2).

b) Assuming that the fitting times are normally distributed, test this customer's claim at the 5% level.

Q2 A sweet shop claims the mean length of its jelly worms is 12 cm. The lengths are assumed to be normally distributed.

a) A customer claims that the lengths are shorter than claimed and measures the lengths of a random sample of 6 jelly worms. The lengths (in cm) are: 11.3 12.1 11.7 10.5 10.9 11.4 Use this data to test the customer's claim at the 5% level.

b) The sweet shop takes a random sample of 20 of its jelly worms and records the following summary statistics:

$$\sum x = 236, \sum (x - \bar{x})^2 = 5.1.$$

Use this data to test the customer's claim at the 5% level.

Review Exercise — Chapter 4

Q1 A random sample of 12 observations is taken from a population with unknown mean, μ, and unknown variance, σ^2.

a) Karl wants to construct a confidence interval for μ, using the data from this sample. What assumption does he need to make about the population?

b) Write down the confidence-interval formula that Karl should use.

c) Find a 95% confidence interval for μ if the sample mean is 50 and $s^2 = 0.7$.

Q2 A 99% confidence interval for the mean of a normal population is found to be (4.2, 8.7). Comment on the claim that the mean value is 9.

Q3 a) For each of the following, state whether a one-tailed or a two-tailed hypothesis test should be used:

i) Salma wants to test whether the average height of the students at her college is greater than 160 cm.

ii) An investigation into the diameter of the metal discs produced by a machine found that the mean diameter was 2.2 cm. Joy wants to test the claim that the mean diameter has changed since the investigation was done.

b) Define suitable null and alternative hypotheses for each test above.

Q4 Andrew carries out a hypothesis test concerning the mean of a normal distribution. His conclusion is to reject the null hypothesis that $\mu = 10$. If it turned out that the mean was actually 10, what type of error would Andrew have made?

Q5 Explain when you would use a t-test to test the mean of a population.

Q6 Carry out the following test of the mean, μ, of a normal distribution with variance $\sigma^2 = 9$.

A random sample of 16 observations from the distribution was taken and the sample mean ($\overline{x}$) calculated.

Test H_0: $\mu = 45$ against H_1: $\mu < 45$, at the 5% significance level, using $\overline{x} = 42$.

Q7 A random sample of 10 observations is taken from a normal distribution with unknown mean μ and unknown variance σ^2. The results are shown below.

20.1, 18.5, 19.6, 21.1, 20.7, 20.2, 19.5, 19.7, 20.2, 18.2

a) Calculate the value of the sample mean and an unbiased estimate of the population variance.

b) Test at the 5% level of significance the claim that $\mu < 20$.

Exam-Style Questions — Chapter 4

1 Samir claims that the average time it takes an employee in his department to travel to work is less than 17 minutes.

The times in minutes (x) taken by 45 randomly selected employees to travel to work are recorded and give the results $\bar{x} = 16.55$ and $s^2 = 2.3$.

Investigate Samir's claim at the 5% level of significance.

(6 marks)

2 A garden centre sells bags of soil. The volume of these bags is known to follow a normal distribution with unknown mean μ and variance σ^2. The garden centre wishes to advertise the mean volume, μ litres, of their bags of soil on the packaging.

Marion is asked to select a random sample of 36 bags of soil from the garden centre's supply and calculate a confidence interval for μ with a width of 1 litre. She correctly calculates the sample standard deviation to be 1.52982 and the confidence interval to be (49.20, 50.20).

a) (i) Calculate the sample mean.

(1 mark)

(ii) Find the percentage confidence level for this interval.

(3 marks)

(iii) The manager of the garden centre chooses to advertise the mean volume of the bags as 50 litres. Comment on this claim.

(2 marks)

The manager of the garden centre decides that the confidence interval that Marion calculated is too large. He finds the volumes (x, in litres) of a new random sample of 8 bags of soil with the following results:

$$\sum x = 395 \quad \sum x^2 = 19503.4$$

b) (i) Construct a 99% confidence interval for μ, based on the manager's sample.

(6 marks)

(ii) Comment on the claim that the mean volume of the bags is 50 litres, using evidence from part b) (i).

(2 marks)

3 Joe claims that, on average, it takes him 15 minutes to walk to work. He records his journey times, x minutes, on 20 randomly selected days and calculates the following:

$$\sum x = 324 \quad \text{and} \quad \sum (x - \bar{x})^2 = 19.2$$

a) Find a 95% confidence interval for the mean journey time, stating any assumption you make. *(7 marks)*

b) Comment on Joe's claim that, on average, it takes him 15 minutes to walk to work. *(1 mark)*

4 The heights of trees in an area of woodland are known to be normally distributed with a mean of 5.1 m. A random sample of 100 trees from a second area of woodland is selected and the heights, X, of the trees are measured giving the following results:

$$\sum x = 490 \text{ and } \sum x^2 = 2421$$

a) Calculate the sample mean, $\bar{x}$, and the sample variance, s^2. *(3 marks)*

b) Test at the 1% level of significance whether the trees in the second area of woodland have a different mean height from the trees in the first area. *(6 marks)*

5 The manufacturer of a particular brand of chilli flakes claims, on the packaging, that the average weight of a jar is 28 grams. Ceara thinks that the mean is actually 26 g, and finds the weights in grams of a random sample of 9 jars of chilli flakes. She records the following results:

27 29 31 26 32 31 29 23 27

a) (i) Construct a 99% confidence interval for the mean weight of the jars of chilli flakes. State any assumptions that you need to make. *(6 marks)*

(ii) Comment on Ceara's claim that the mean is actually 26 g. *(2 marks)*

b) Megan thinks that the mean weight of the jars of chilli flakes is more than 26 g.
Test her belief at a 5% level of significance.
State any assumptions that you need to make. *(7 marks)*

c) Ceara writes a letter to the producer of the chilli flakes.
They investigate the mean weight and find that it **is** in fact 26 g.

State with a reason what type of error, if any, has been made in the investigation in part b). *(2 marks)*

1. Chi-Squared Contingency Table Tests

In this chapter you'll be introduced to another type of hypothesis test and a new distribution — the chi-squared (χ^2) distribution. You'll use the χ^2 test to find out whether two variables are independent or linked.

Learning Objectives:
- Be able to carry out a χ^2 contingency table test.
- Be able to interpret the results of a χ^2 contingency table test.
- Be able to use Yates' correction in tests of 2 × 2 contingency tables.

Contingency tables

- Suppose you've got a sample of size n, and you're interested in two different **variables** for each of the n members — where each variable can be **classified** into **different categories**.
- For example, one variable might be **eye colour** — with the categories 'blue', 'brown', 'green' and 'hazel'. And the other might be **age** in whole years — with the categories '20-40', 41-60' and '61-80'.
- You can show this data in a **contingency table**, like the one below. Use the **columns** to show the **categories** for one of the variables, and the **rows** to show the other. Fill in each **cell** in the table with the **number of sample members** that fit that particular **combination** of categories. For example, the highlighted cell shows the number of sample members who have brown eyes **and** are between the ages of 41 and 60.

	Blue	Brown	Green	Hazel	Total
20-40	5	7	3	3	18
41-60	8	8	3	1	20
61-80	3	5	3	1	12
Total	16	20	9	5	50

Observed and expected frequencies

- Using the data in a contingency table, you can do a **hypothesis test** of whether the two variables are **linked** or **independent**. So for the table above, you can test whether there is an **association** between eye colour and age.
- The **null hypothesis** for this test is that the two variables are **independent**. We'll get on to the hypothesis test itself on page 114, but before you can carry out the test, you need to work out what you would **expect** to happen **assuming the variables are independent**.
- For each **observed frequency** in the table, you need to work out the corresponding **expected frequency**, assuming that the variables are independent.

Tip: An association means that eye colour and age go together in some way.

Tip: See page 89 for more about hypotheses.

Tip: Working out what you'd expect to happen gives you something to compare the observed data to.

So, looking at the **eye colour** and **age** data...

- If eye colour and age are **independent**, then the **proportion** with blue eyes in the 20-40 age group should be **the same** as the proportion with blue eyes in the 41-60 and 61-80 age groups.
- And the best estimate of this proportion is the proportion of the whole sample with blue eyes — i.e. $\frac{16}{50}$ of each age group should have blue eyes.
- Similarly, $\frac{20}{50}$ of each age group should have brown eyes, $\frac{9}{50}$ should have green eyes and $\frac{5}{50}$ should have hazel eyes.
- So if we take the first row of the contingency table on the previous page — the **20-40 age group**...

Tip: In other words, the ratio of the four eye colours should be 16 : 20 : 9 : 5 in each age group.

$\frac{16}{50} \times 18 = \mathbf{5.76}$ is the expected frequency for **blue** eyes,

$\frac{20}{50} \times 18 = \mathbf{7.2}$ is the expected frequency for **brown** eyes,

$\frac{9}{50} \times 18 = \mathbf{3.24}$ is the expected frequency for **green** eyes, and

$\frac{5}{50} \times 18 = \mathbf{1.8}$ is the expected frequency for **hazel** eyes.

So for **row 1** you have the following expected frequencies:

	Blue	Brown	Green	Hazel	Total
20-40	5.76	7.2	3.24	1.8	18

And going through the same process to find the expected frequencies for rows 2 and 3 gives the following table:

	Blue	Brown	Green	Hazel	Total
20-40	5.76	7.2	3.24	1.8	18
41-60	6.4	8	3.6	2	20
61-80	3.84	4.8	2.16	1.2	12
Total	16	20	9	5	50

Tip: Notice that the expected frequencies give the same row and column totals as the observed frequencies.

Now then, the above method for finding the expected frequency, E_{ij}, in the cell in row i and column j of the contingency table, can be summarised by the handy formula below.

If R_i = the total of row i, C_j = the total of column j and T = the total number of observations, then:

$$E_{ij} = \frac{R_i \times C_j}{T}$$

Tip: You have to learn this formula — it won't be on the exam formula sheet. You can see that it's just a different way of writing the working above. E.g.

$$E_{21} = \frac{R_2 \times C_1}{T} = \frac{20 \times 16}{50} = 6.4$$

So to find the expected frequency for a particular cell, you multiply the total frequency in its row by the total frequency in its column, and divide by the total number of observations.

Using this formula, it's easy to find the expected frequencies for a set of observations. There's an example on the next page.

Example

This table shows soil pH and plant growth for a sample of 100 plants.

Find the expected frequencies assuming that plant growth is independent of soil pH.

	Poor growth	Average growth	Good growth	Total
Acidic soil	12	16	4	32
Neutral soil	3	13	14	30
Alkaline soil	3	10	25	38
Total	18	39	43	100

- Starting with row 1: $R_1 = 32$, so using the formula $E_{ij} = \frac{R_i \times C_j}{T}$, the expected frequencies for row 1 are:

$$\boldsymbol{E_{11}} = \frac{R_1 \times C_1}{T} = \frac{32 \times 18}{100} = \mathbf{5.76}$$

$$\boldsymbol{E_{12}} = \frac{R_1 \times C_2}{T} = \frac{32 \times 39}{100} = \mathbf{12.48}$$

$$\boldsymbol{E_{13}} = \frac{R_1 \times C_3}{T} = \frac{32 \times 43}{100} = \mathbf{13.76}$$

- Working out the frequencies for rows 2 and 3 in the same way gives this table of expected frequencies:

	Poor growth	Average growth	Good growth	Total
Acidic soil	5.76	12.48	13.76	32
Neutral soil	5.4	11.7	12.9	30
Alkaline soil	6.84	14.82	16.34	38
Total	18	39	43	100

Exercise 1.1

Q1 A survey of 100 households is carried out to determine whether house value is associated with the number of books in a house. Here are the results:

	House value < £100 000	House value ≥ £100 000	Total
< 100 books	23	7	30
≥ 100 books	42	28	70
Total	65	35	100

Draw a table of expected frequencies under the null hypothesis that there is no association between house value and number of books.

Q2 A school wants to know if grades achieved in Maths are linked to grades achieved in English. Use these results to draw a table of expected frequencies, under the assumption that there is no link between grades achieved in Maths and English.

		Maths grades		
		High	Medium	Low
English grades	High	20	15	5
	Medium	16	19	15
	Low	12	9	14

Q3 80 male and 120 female college students are asked to choose a sport to play in their recreational period. The table below shows the percentage of male and female students choosing each sport.

	Table tennis	Snooker	Badminton
Male	50%	35%	15%
Female	40%	20%	40%

a) Draw a contingency table showing the numbers of male and female students choosing each sport.

b) Work out the expected frequencies under the hypothesis that the choice of sport is independent of gender.

Chi-squared (χ^2) contingency table tests

The chi-squared (χ^2) contingency table test of independence is used to determine whether there is an association between the two variables in a contingency table. It's a hypothesis test, so the first stage is to define **null** and **alternative hypotheses**.

Tip: See Chapter 4 for more on hypothesis testing.

The **null hypothesis** is that there is **no association** between the two variables, so you can define the following hypotheses:

H_0: the variables are **independent**
H_1: the variables are **not independent**

To decide whether or not to reject H_0, you need to find the value of a test statistic, and that's where the idea of expected frequencies comes in.

The chi-squared test statistic (X^2)

As with the other hypothesis tests you've seen, the **evidence** for rejecting or failing to reject H_0 is provided by the value of a **test statistic**. The statistic you need in this case is given by:

Tip: X is the upper case Greek letter 'chi'.

$$X^2 = \sum \frac{(O_i - E_i)^2}{E_i}$$

Here O_i is the observed frequency for cell i in the contingency table and E_i is the expected frequency for cell i, assuming H_0 is true.

To carry out the test, you need to find the **sampling distribution** of X^2, assuming that H_0 is true. Then, if your observed value of X^2 is unlikely enough under H_0, you'll have evidence to reject the null hypothesis.

Tip: Remember, a sampling distribution is a statistic's probability distribution.

The χ^2 distribution

Assuming that H_0 is true, the test statistic, X^2, **approximately** follows a χ^2 (**chi-squared**) distribution.

(That's as long as all the **expected frequencies** (E_i) are **greater than 5** — if not, the approximation may not be **valid**.)

Tip: χ is the lower case Greek letter 'chi', and ν is the lower case Greek letter 'nu'.

- The χ^2 p.d.f. contains just **one parameter**, ν, called the **degrees of freedom**. A χ^2 distribution with ν degrees of freedom is written $\chi^2_{(\nu)}$.
- χ^2 distributions follow the sort of shape shown by the curves below.
- The diagram shows the shapes of the $\chi^2_{(5)}$ and $\chi^2_{(10)}$ distributions. As ν increases, the distributions become more widely spread and more symmetrical, but they all have tails on the right-hand side.

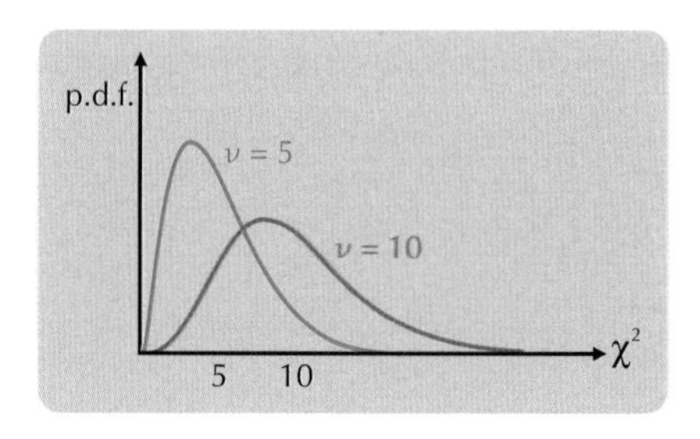

The sampling distribution of X^2

So you know that under H_0 your X^2 test statistic approximately follows a χ^2 distribution, but to be able to define the sampling distribution exactly, you need to know **how many degrees of freedom** the distribution has.
The value of ν depends on **how many rows and columns** there are in the contingency table.

You work it out using this **formula**:

$$\nu = (\text{number of rows} - 1) \times (\text{number of columns} - 1)$$

Tip: Again, you need to learn this formula for ν.

So under H_0, the sampling distribution of X^2 is approximately $\chi^2_{(\nu)}$, where ν is calculated using the formula above.

Testing for significance

Okay, so you've defined your hypotheses, calculated the expected frequencies under H_0, worked out the value of X^2 and found its sampling distribution. Now you're ready to **test** your value of X^2 for **significance**.

- Remember, you have evidence to **reject** the null hypothesis if your observed test statistic is **unlikely enough** under H_0. And the **significance level** (α) of the test tells you **how unlikely** it needs to be.
- The values of the test statistic that would cause you to reject H_0 make up the **critical region** of the distribution.
- For this χ^2 test, it only makes sense to reject H_0 for **large** values of X^2. That's because if the observed data fits the hypothesis of independence, then the differences $(O_i - E_i)$ will be small, and so $\sum \frac{(O_i - E_i)^2}{E_i}$ will also be small.
- This means you need to use a **one-tailed test** with **one critical region** at the **upper** end of the distribution.

  For example, the graph below shows the critical region for a test statistic (labelled X here) with a $\chi^2_{(5)}$ distribution, at the 5% level of significance. The **critical value** is x, where $P(X > x)$ = the significance level, α.

Tip: See pages 94-98 for more about testing for significance.

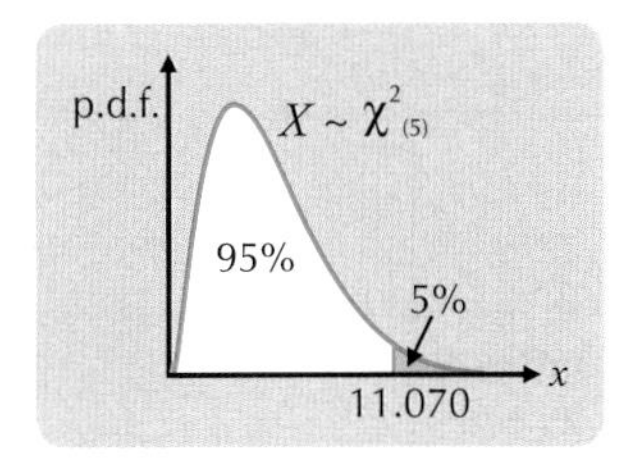

- If your value of the test statistic is **greater** than the critical value, then reject H_0.

  So if your test statistic followed $\chi^2_{(5)}$, you would reject H_0 at the 5% level for values greater than 11.070.

To find the critical value for your test, you need to use the '**percentage points of the χ^2 distribution**' table. The full table is given on page 128, but the top-right corner of it is shown below.

- Each row shows the values of x for which $P(X \le x) = p$, where X is a random variable with a $\chi^2_{(\nu)}$ distribution and p is the probability shown in the column heading.
- So to find the value exceeded by 5% of the $\chi^2_{(5)}$ distribution, you look along the row for $\nu = 5$ to find x such that $P(X \le x) = 0.95$ — i.e. $x = 11.070$.

Tip: If $P(X > x) = 0.05$, then $P(X \le x) = 0.95$.

Tip: You only need to use the right-hand part of the table because it's only the right-hand tail of the distribution that you're interested in.

0.1	0.9	0.95	0.975	0.99	0.995	p
						ν
0.016	2.706	3.841	5.024	6.635	7.879	1
0.211	4.605	5.991	7.378	9.210	10.597	2
0.584	6.251	7.815	9.348	11.345	12.838	3
1.064	7.779	9.488	11.143	13.277	14.860	4
1.610	9.236	11.070	12.833	15.086	16.750	5

Here's the example from page 113 again. Now we're going to carry out a χ^2 test to determine whether plant growth is independent of soil pH.

Example 1

This table shows soil pH and plant growth for a sample of 100 plants.

Use a χ^2 test at the 5% level of significance to determine whether there is an association between soil pH and plant growth.

	Poor growth	Average growth	Good growth	Total
Acidic soil	12	16	4	32
Neutral soil	3	13	14	30
Alkaline soil	3	10	25	38
Total	18	39	43	100

- Start by defining the **hypotheses**:

  H_0: no association between soil pH and plant growth
  H_1: an association between soil pH and plant growth

- Next make a table of the **observed frequencies** (O_i) and the **expected frequencies** (E_i), assuming H_0 is true, for each cell in the table.

  Using the formula $E_{ij} = \frac{R_i \times C_j}{T}$ gives the expected frequencies we found on page 113. Putting those values together with the observed frequencies above gives you this table:

- Calculate the values of $\frac{(O_i - E_i)^2}{E_i}$, which you'll sum to find the value of X^2. Add a third column to put them in.

- So your value of X^2

  $= \sum \frac{(O_i - E_i)^2}{E_i} =$ **24.294** (3 d.p.)

Observed frequency (O_i)	Expected Frequency (E_i)	$\frac{(O_i - E_i)^2}{E_i}$
12	5.76	6.7600
3	5.4	1.0667
3	6.84	2.1558
16	12.48	0.9928
13	11.7	0.1444
10	14.82	1.5676
4	13.76	6.9228
14	12.9	0.0938
25	16.34	4.5897
100	100	24.294

Tip: Putting the values of O_i and E_i together in the same table will make it easier to calculate the test statistic. It doesn't matter what order they go in as long as you match up the pairs correctly.

- Now you can define the **sampling distribution**.
  Under H_0, the sampling distribution of X^2 is approximately $\chi^2_{(\nu)}$, where ν = (no. of rows – 1) × (no. of columns – 1) = (3 – 1) × (3 – 1) = **4**.
  So X^2 approximately follows a $\chi^2_{(4)}$ distribution.

- The **significance level is 5%**, so look up the 5% point of $\chi^2_{(4)}$ in the table. You want to find the value x such that $P(X > x) = 0.05$, which means looking up $P(X \leq x) = 0.95$.
  Using the table on page 128 (or the previous page), you find that $P(X \leq x) = 0.95$ for $x = 9.488$, so the **critical value** is **9.488** .

- Since 24.294 > 9.488, the data is **significant** at the 5% level.
  There is evidence to reject H_0 and to suggest that there is an association between soil pH and plant growth.

Tip: Remember, it's the number of rows and columns (not including the 'total' row and 'total' column) in the original contingency table.

You might also be asked to comment on the observed data...

Example 2

A manufacturing company produces items at two different factories. A survey is carried out to determine whether there is an association between the quality of items and the factory they're made in. A sample of 100 items gives the following results:

	Unsatisfactory quality	Satisfactory quality	Good quality	Total
Factory A	8	25	21	54
Factory B	4	27	15	46
Total	12	52	36	100

a) Use a χ^2 test at the 1% level of significance to determine whether there is an association between the quality of items and the factory they're made in.

- The **hypotheses** are:
  H_0: no association between quality and factory
  H_1: an association between quality and factory

- The table of **observed frequencies** (O_i), **expected frequencies** (E_i), assuming H_0 is true, and values of $\frac{(O_i - E_i)^2}{E_i}$ looks like this:

Observed frequency (O_i)	Expected Frequency (E_i)	$\frac{(O_i - E_i)^2}{E_i}$
8	6.48	0.3565
4	5.52	0.4186
25	28.08	0.3378
27	23.92	0.3966
21	19.44	0.1252
15	16.56	0.1470
100	100	1.782

- So your value of X^2
  $= \sum \frac{(O_i - E_i)^2}{E_i} =$ **1.782** (3 d.p.)

- Under H_0, the sampling distribution of X^2 is approximately $\chi^2_{(\nu)}$, where $\nu = (2 - 1) \times (3 - 1) = \mathbf{2}$.
  So X^2 approximately follows a $\chi^2_{(2)}$ distribution.

- The **significance level is 1%**, so look up the 1% point of $\chi^2_{(2)}$ in the table. You want to find the value x such that $P(X > x) = 0.01$, which means looking up $P(X \leq x) = 0.99$.

  Using the table on page 128 (or page 116), you find that $P(X \leq x) = 0.99$ for $x = 9.210$, so the **critical value** is **9.210**.

- Since $1.782 < 9.210$, the data is **not significant** at the 1% level.

  There is no evidence to reject H_0 at the 1% level.
  There is no evidence at this level to suggest an association between the quality of items and the factory they're made in.

b) Comment on the number of items made in factory B that were rated as being of satisfactory quality.

You need to compare the number of observed items in the cell 'Factory B and Satisfactory quality' with the number of expected items.

There were more items of satisfactory quality made in factory B than expected.

c) Comment on the validity of the χ^2 approximation used in part a).

All of the expected frequencies are greater than 5, so the approximation is valid.

Exercise 1.2

Q1 A supermarket chain wants to know what people in a particular town think about its plan to open a new supermarket there. They carry out a survey, with the results shown below.

		In favour of plan	Against plan
Age of resident	16-21	4	10
	22-49	7	23
	50-64	93	87
	65 or over	17	14

a) Assuming that there is no association between a resident's age and their attitude to the plan, draw a table showing the observed and expected frequencies.

b) Work out the value of the test statistic, X^2, which could be used to test for independence of the variables.

Q2 Three χ^2 contingency table tests were carried out, producing the values of the test statistic shown below.

By comparing each value to the χ^2 distribution given, test whether there is evidence of an association at the given level of significance.

a) $\chi^2 = 7.213$. Test against $\chi^2_{(3)}$ at the 5% level of significance.

b) $\chi^2 = 18.147$. Test against $\chi^2_{(6)}$ at the 1% level of significance.

c) $\chi^2 = 15.655$. Test against $\chi^2_{(9)}$ at the 10% level of significance.

Q3 The table below shows the results for some music students who passed exams in both the piano and the violin.

		Violin			
		Pass	Merit	Distinction	Total
Piano	Pass	32	54	12	98
	Merit	24	98	43	165
	Distinction	17	34	65	116
	Total	73	186	120	379

Use a χ^2 test, at the 1% level of significance, to decide whether there is an association between the performance in the piano exam and the performance in the violin exam.

Q4 The manager of a leisure centre wants to know if longer opening hours in the evening would be popular with its members. He carries out a survey of the members, with the results shown below.

		In favour of longer hours	Against longer hours
Age of member	16-20	3	8
	21-25	9	26
	26-30	72	87
	31-45	31	37
	46 or over	4	2

a) Draw a table of expected frequencies under the null hypothesis that there is no association between age and attitude to longer opening hours.

b) Explain why some of the age categories should be grouped together for a χ^2 approximation to be valid. Draw a new contingency table showing the above results in 3 age categories.

c) Use a χ^2 test, at the 5% level of significance, to decide whether there is an association between the age of members and their attitude to longer opening hours.

d) Interpret your result in part c) in terms of the 26-30 age group.

Q4 d) Hint: This is just asking you to compare the observed frequencies in the 26-30 age group with those expected under H_0.

2 × 2 contingency tables

If your contingency table has **2 rows** and **2 columns**, you can improve the χ^2 approximation by using **Yates' continuity correction**.

The **test statistic** for a **2 × 2** table using Yates' correction is:

$$X^2 = \sum \frac{(|O_i - E_i| - 0.5)^2}{E_i}$$

Tip: You have to **learn** the formula for Yates' correction.

Since there are 2 rows and 2 columns in the table, X^2 will approximately follow a χ^2 distribution with $\nu = (2 - 1) \times (2 - 1) = \mathbf{1}$ degree of freedom — i.e. $\chi^2_{(1)}$.

Apart from using a different test statistic, the method for carrying out a χ^2 test of the data in a 2 × 2 table is just the same as you've seen over the last few pages.

Tip: Since the sample is random, it should be valid to apply the results from this test to the population of newts.

Tip: All the expected frequencies are greater than 5, so the approximation you use below should be valid.

Example

This contingency table was produced after studying a random sample of 100 newts.

Carry out a χ^2 test at the 1% level of significance to determine whether length is independent of colour.

	Red colour	Green colour	Total
Long	12	29	41
Short	29	30	59
Total	41	59	100

- Start by defining the **hypotheses**:

  $\mathbf{H_0}$: no association between the length of newts and their colour
  $\mathbf{H_1}$: an association between the length of newts and their colour

- Next make a table of the **observed frequencies** (O_i) and the **expected frequencies** (E_i), assuming H_0 is true, for each cell in the table.

  Using the formula $E_{ij} = \frac{R_i \times C_j}{T}$:

  $E_{11} = \frac{41 \times 41}{100} = 16.81$

  E_{12} and $E_{21} = \frac{41 \times 59}{100} = 24.19$

  $E_{22} = \frac{59 \times 59}{100} = 34.81$

Observed frequency (O_i)	Expected Frequency (E_i)
12	16.81
29	24.19
29	24.19
30	34.81
100	100

- This is a 2 × 2 table, so your test statistic includes **Yates' continuity correction**. Add a third column containing values of $\frac{(|O_i - E_i| - 0.5)^2}{E_i}$.

  ***i* = 1:**

  $\frac{(|12 - 16.81| - 0.5)^2}{16.81} = 1.1051$

  ***i* = 2 and *i* = 3:**

  $\frac{(|29 - 24.19| - 0.5)^2}{24.19} = 0.7679$

  ***i* = 4:**

  $\frac{(|30 - 34.81| - 0.5)^2}{34.81} = 0.5336$

Observed frequency (O_i)	Expected Frequency (E_i)	$\frac{(\lvert O_i - E_i \rvert - 0.5)^2}{E_i}$
12	16.81	1.1051
29	24.19	0.7679
29	24.19	0.7679
30	34.81	0.5336
100	100	3.175

- So your value of $X^2 = \sum \frac{(|O_i - E_i| - 0.5)^2}{E_i}$ = **3.175** (3 d.p.)

- Under H_0, the sampling distribution of X^2 is approximately $\chi^2_{(\nu)}$, where $\nu = (2 - 1) \times (2 - 1) = \mathbf{1}$.
  So X^2 approximately follows a $\chi^2_{(1)}$ distribution.

- The **significance level is 1%**, so look up the 1% point of $\chi^2_{(1)}$ in the table. You want to find the value x such that $P(X > x) = 0.01$, which means looking up $P(X \leq x) = 0.99$.

  Using the table on page 128 (or page 116), you find that $P(X \leq x) = 0.99$ for $x = 6.635$, so the **critical value** is **6.635**.

- Since 3.175 < 6.635, the data is **not significant** at the 1% level.

  There is no evidence at the 1% level to reject H_0.
  There is no evidence to suggest an association between the length of newts and their colour.

Exercise 1.3

Q1 200 dogs complete obedience and agility tests. Their results are shown in the table opposite.

		Obedience	
		Pass	Fail
Agility	Pass	103	44
	Fail	22	31

a) Assuming that there is no association between performance in the obedience test and performance in the agility test, draw a table showing the observed and expected frequencies.

b) Use Yates' continuity correction to find the value of the test statistic, X^2, which could be used to test for independence.

Q2 The organisers of a cookery course are interested in whether there is a link between the gender of people who do the course and whether or not they are vegetarian. A random sample of people doing the course is taken. 12 out of the 47 men sampled are vegetarian, and 22 out of the 43 women sampled are vegetarian.

a) Show the above information in a 2×2 contingency table.

b) Work out the value of the test statistic, X^2, which could be used to test for a link between the variables.

Q3 A gymnastics coach claims there is an association between a gymnast's height and their score on vault for the female gymnasts at her club. The table below shows the heights and average vault scores of 100 female gymnasts at the club.

		Vault score		
		Less than 15	15 or higher	Total
Height	Less than 150 cm	16	26	42
	150 cm or taller	20	38	58
	Total	36	64	100

Use a χ^2 test, at the 1% level of significance, to test the coach's claim.

Q4 A study is being done to find out if a new exercise programme can help to improve sleep. The table below shows the quality of sleep of two similar groups of people over a two-week period — where one group did the exercise programme each day and the other didn't.

	Good sleep	Poor sleep
Did exercise programme	58	22
Didn't do exercise programme	43	37

a) Use a χ^2 test, at the 5% level of significance, to determine whether there is an association between doing the exercise programme and quality of sleep.

b) Comment on the number of people who didn't do the exercise programme and had good sleep.

c) Would your conclusion from part a) be different if you tested at the 1% level of significance? Explain why.

Review Exercise — Chapter 5

Q1 For each of the contingency tables below, draw a table showing the expected frequencies under the null hypothesis that the variables are independent.

a)

	Result of first driving test		
	Pass	Fail	Total
Male	29	11	40
Female	35	25	60
Total	64	36	100

b)

		Colour of cat		
		Black	White	Tabby
Length of tail	Long	14	15	31
	Short	19	11	10

Q2 The tables below show the observed frequencies and expected frequencies, under H_0, for three χ^2 contingency table tests. For each table, say whether it would be valid to carry out a χ^2 test on the given data. If the test is valid, find the value of the test statistic X^2.

a)

Observed frequency (O_i)	Expected Frequency (E_i)
12	12
18	18
7	9.2
16	13.8
21	18.8
26	28.2
100	100

b)

Observed frequency (O_i)	Expected Frequency (E_i)
3	4
7	6
5	6
10	9
12	10
13	15
50	50

c)

Observed frequency (O_i)	Expected Frequency (E_i)
45	49.8
38	33.2
75	70.2
42	46.8
200	200

Q3 A χ^2 contingency table test produces the test statistic 8.3. By comparing this value to the $\chi^2_{(4)}$ distribution, test at the 1% level whether there is evidence of an association between the variables.

Q4 A farmer is growing potato plants in two different fields. He wants to know if the potato yield per plant differs between the two fields. The yields of 150 potato plants are given below.

		Yield per plant			
		Low	Average	High	Total
Field	A	22	26	12	60
	B	14	30	46	90
	Total	36	56	58	150

a) Assuming that there is no association between potato yield and the field the plants are grown in, draw a table showing the observed and expected frequencies.

b) Use your table to work out the value of the test statistic X^2.

c) Using a χ^2 test at the 10% level of significance, determine whether there is a difference in potato yield between the two fields.

Q5 Courtney claims there is an association between gender and liking olives. She asks a random sample of 100 people if they like or dislike olives, with the results shown in the table below.

	Likes olives	Dislikes olives
Male	22	18
Female	30	30

Use a χ^2 test, at the 5% level of significance, to test Courtney's claim.

Exam-Style Questions — Chapter 5

1 A random sample of 100 shoppers is surveyed to determine whether age is associated with favourite flavour of ice cream. The results are shown in the table below.

		Age in full years		
		0 – 40	41 +	Total
Favourite flavour of ice cream	Vanilla	10	14	24
	Chocolate	24	26	50
	Strawberry	7	4	11
	Mint choc chip	7	8	15
	Total	48	52	100

Use a χ^2 test, at the 5% level of significance, to examine whether there is an association between age and favourite flavour of ice cream.

(9 marks)

2 Data was recorded about the trains arriving at three different stations on a particular day. The table shows the numbers of trains arriving on time and late at each station.

		Arrival time		
		On time	Late	Total
Station	1	40	20	60
	2	56	19	75
	3	24	41	65
	Total	120	80	200

a) Use a χ^2 test, at the 1% level of significance, to determine whether there is an association between a train arriving on time and the station it arrives at.

(9 marks)

b) Interpret your conclusion from part a) in terms of the numbers of trains arriving on time and late at Station 3.

(2 marks)

3 All 200 members of a film club were asked to rate a particular film as 'enjoyable' or 'not enjoyable'. A random sample of 200 other people were also asked to rate the same film. The percentage of each group of people giving each rating is shown in the table below.

	Film rating	
	Enjoyable	Not enjoyable
Club members	56%	44%
Others	64%	36%

a) Draw a contingency table to represent this data. *(2 marks)*

b) Use a χ^2 test, at the 5% level of significance, to determine whether the film rating given is independent of whether or not a person belongs to the film club. *(9 marks)*

c) Comment on the number of people belonging to the film club who rated the film as 'enjoyable'. *(1 mark)*

4 A survey was carried out to find out how common a particular species of bumblebee is. The table below shows the numbers of all types of bumblebees observed in conservation areas in three different counties, and how many of them were of the species being studied.

		Species of bumblebee		
		Species being studied	Other	Total
County	Cumbria	115	305	420
	Lancashire	75	205	280
	Yorkshire	60	240	300
	Total	250	750	1000

a) Use a χ^2 test, at the 10% level of significance, to determine whether there is an association between the proportion of this particular species of bumblebee and the location of the conservation area. *(9 marks)*

b) Comment on the number of bumblebees of the species being studied observed in Yorkshire. *(1 mark)*

c) Use the value of the test statistic you calculated in part a) to test whether there is an association at the 5% level of significance. *(2 marks)*

S2 Statistical Tables

The normal distribution function

This table gives the probability, p, that the random variable $Z \sim N(0, 1)$ is less than or equal to z.

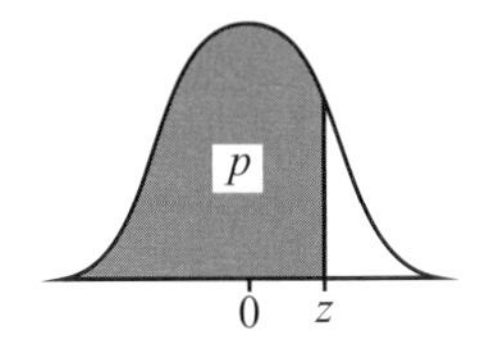

z	0.00	0.01	0.02	0.03	0.04	0.05	0.06	0.07	0.08	0.09	z
0.0	0.50000	0.50399	0.50798	0.51197	0.51595	0.51994	0.52392	0.52790	0.53188	0.53586	**0.0**
0.1	0.53983	0.54380	0.54776	0.55172	0.55567	0.55962	0.56356	0.56749	0.57142	0.57535	**0.1**
0.2	0.57926	0.58317	0.58706	0.59095	0.59483	0.59871	0.60257	0.60642	0.61026	0.61409	**0.2**
0.3	0.61791	0.62172	0.62552	0.62930	0.63307	0.63683	0.64058	0.64431	0.64803	0.65173	**0.3**
0.4	0.65542	0.65910	0.66276	0.66640	0.67003	0.67364	0.67724	0.68082	0.68439	0.68793	**0.4**
0.5	0.69146	0.69497	0.69847	0.70194	0.70540	0.70884	0.71226	0.71566	0.71904	0.72240	**0.5**
0.6	0.72575	0.72907	0.73237	0.73565	0.73891	0.74215	0.74537	0.74857	0.75175	0.75490	**0.6**
0.7	0.75804	0.76115	0.76424	0.76730	0.77035	0.77337	0.77637	0.77935	0.78230	0.78524	**0.7**
0.8	0.78814	0.79103	0.79389	0.79673	0.79955	0.80234	0.80511	0.80785	0.81057	0.81327	**0.8**
0.9	0.81594	0.81859	0.82121	0.82381	0.82639	0.82894	0.83147	0.83398	0.83646	0.83891	**0.9**
1.0	0.84134	0.84375	0.84614	0.84849	0.85083	0.85314	0.85543	0.85769	0.85993	0.86214	**1.0**
1.1	0.86433	0.86650	0.86864	0.87076	0.87286	0.87493	0.87698	0.87900	0.88100	0.88298	**1.1**
1.2	0.88493	0.88686	0.88877	0.89065	0.89251	0.89435	0.89617	0.89796	0.89973	0.90147	**1.2**
1.3	0.90320	0.90490	0.90658	0.90824	0.90988	0.91149	0.91309	0.91466	0.91621	0.91774	**1.3**
1.4	0.91924	0.92073	0.92220	0.92364	0.92507	0.92647	0.92785	0.92922	0.93056	0.93189	**1.4**
1.5	0.93319	0.93448	0.93574	0.93699	0.93822	0.93943	0.94062	0.94179	0.94295	0.94408	**1.5**
1.6	0.94520	0.94630	0.94738	0.94845	0.94950	0.95053	0.95154	0.95254	0.95352	0.95449	**1.6**
1.7	0.95543	0.95637	0.95728	0.95818	0.95907	0.95994	0.96080	0.96164	0.96246	0.96327	**1.7**
1.8	0.96407	0.96485	0.96562	0.96638	0.96712	0.96784	0.96856	0.96926	0.96995	0.97062	**1.8**
1.9	0.97128	0.97193	0.97257	0.97320	0.97381	0.97441	0.97500	0.97558	0.97615	0.97670	**1.9**
2.0	0.97725	0.97778	0.97831	0.97882	0.97932	0.97982	0.98030	0.98077	0.98124	0.98169	**2.0**
2.1	0.98214	0.98257	0.98300	0.98341	0.98382	0.98422	0.98461	0.98500	0.98537	0.98574	**2.1**
2.2	0.98610	0.98645	0.98679	0.98713	0.98745	0.98778	0.98809	0.98840	0.98870	0.98899	**2.2**
2.3	0.98928	0.98956	0.98983	0.99010	0.99036	0.99061	0.99086	0.99111	0.99134	0.99158	**2.3**
2.4	0.99180	0.99202	0.99224	0.99245	0.99266	0.99286	0.99305	0.99324	0.99343	0.99361	**2.4**
2.5	0.99379	0.99396	0.99413	0.99430	0.99446	0.99461	0.99477	0.99492	0.99506	0.99520	**2.5**
2.6	0.99534	0.99547	0.99560	0.99573	0.99585	0.99598	0.99609	0.99621	0.99632	0.99643	**2.6**
2.7	0.99653	0.99664	0.99674	0.99683	0.99693	0.99702	0.99711	0.99720	0.99728	0.99736	**2.7**
2.8	0.99744	0.99752	0.99760	0.99767	0.99774	0.99781	0.99788	0.99795	0.99801	0.99807	**2.8**
2.9	0.99813	0.99819	0.99825	0.99831	0.99836	0.99841	0.99846	0.99851	0.99856	0.99861	**2.9**
3.0	0.99865	0.99869	0.99874	0.99878	0.99882	0.99886	0.99889	0.99893	0.99896	0.99900	**3.0**
3.1	0.99903	0.99906	0.99910	0.99913	0.99916	0.99918	0.99921	0.99924	0.99926	0.99929	**3.1**
3.2	0.99931	0.99934	0.99936	0.99938	0.99940	0.99942	0.99944	0.99946	0.99948	0.99950	**3.2**
3.3	0.99952	0.99953	0.99955	0.99957	0.99958	0.99960	0.99961	0.99962	0.99964	0.99965	**3.3**
3.4	0.99966	0.99968	0.99969	0.99970	0.99971	0.99972	0.99973	0.99974	0.99975	0.99976	**3.4**
3.5	0.99977	0.99978	0.99978	0.99979	0.99980	0.99981	0.99981	0.99982	0.99983	0.99983	**3.5**
3.6	0.99984	0.99985	0.99985	0.99986	0.99986	0.99987	0.99987	0.99988	0.99988	0.99989	**3.6**
3.7	0.99989	0.99990	0.99990	0.99990	0.99991	0.99991	0.99992	0.99992	0.99992	0.99992	**3.7**
3.8	0.99993	0.99993	0.99993	0.99994	0.99994	0.99994	0.99994	0.99995	0.99995	0.99995	**3.8**
3.9	0.99995	0.99995	0.99996	0.99996	0.99996	0.99996	0.99996	0.99996	0.99997	0.99997	**3.9**

Percentage points of the normal distribution

The table gives the values of z satisfying $P(Z \le z) = p$, where $Z \sim N(0, 1)$.

p	0.00	0.01	0.02	0.03	0.04	0.05	0.06	0.07	0.08	0.09	p
0.5	0.0000	0.0251	0.0502	0.0753	0.1004	0.1257	0.1510	0.1764	0.2019	0.2275	**0.5**
0.6	0.2533	0.2793	0.3055	0.3319	0.3585	0.3853	0.4125	0.4399	0.4677	0.4959	**0.6**
0.7	0.5244	0.5534	0.5828	0.6128	0.6433	0.6745	0.7063	0.7388	0.7722	0.8064	**0.7**
0.8	0.8416	0.8779	0.9154	0.9542	0.9945	1.0364	1.0803	1.1264	1.1750	1.2265	**0.8**
0.9	1.2816	1.3408	1.4051	1.4758	1.5548	1.6449	1.7507	1.8808	2.0537	2.3263	**0.9**
p	**0.000**	**0.001**	**0.002**	**0.003**	**0.004**	**0.005**	**0.006**	**0.007**	**0.008**	**0.009**	p
0.95	1.6449	1.6546	1.6646	1.6747	1.6849	1.6954	1.7060	1.7169	1.7279	1.7392	**0.95**
0.96	1.7507	1.7624	1.7744	1.7866	1.7991	1.8119	1.8250	1.8384	1.8522	1.8663	**0.96**
0.97	1.8808	1.8957	1.9110	1.9268	1.9431	1.9600	1.9774	1.9954	2.0141	2.0335	**0.97**
0.98	2.0537	2.0749	2.0969	2.1201	2.1444	2.1701	2.1973	2.2262	2.2571	2.2904	**0.98**
0.99	2.3263	2.3656	2.4089	2.4573	2.5121	2.5758	2.6521	2.7478	2.8782	3.0902	**0.99**

The Poisson cumulative distribution function

This table gives the probability $P(X \leq x)$, where the random variable $X \sim Po(\lambda)$.

λ / x	0.10	0.20	0.30	0.40	0.50	0.60	0.70	0.80	0.90	1.0	1.2	1.4	1.6	1.8	x
0	0.9048	0.8187	0.7408	0.6703	0.6065	0.5488	0.4966	0.4493	0.4066	0.3679	0.3012	0.2466	0.2019	0.1653	0
1	0.9953	0.9825	0.9631	0.9384	0.9098	0.8781	0.8442	0.8088	0.7725	0.7358	0.6626	0.5918	0.5249	0.4628	1
2	0.9998	0.9989	0.9964	0.9921	0.9856	0.9769	0.9659	0.9526	0.9371	0.9197	0.8795	0.8335	0.7834	0.7306	2
3	1.0000	0.9999	0.9997	0.9992	0.9982	0.9966	0.9942	0.9909	0.9865	0.9810	0.9662	0.9463	0.9212	0.8913	3
4		1.0000	1.0000	0.9999	0.9998	0.9996	0.9992	0.9986	0.9977	0.9963	0.9923	0.9857	0.9763	0.9636	4
5				1.0000	1.0000	1.0000	0.9999	0.9998	0.9997	0.9994	0.9985	0.9968	0.9940	0.9896	5
6							1.0000	1.0000	1.0000	0.9999	0.9997	0.9994	0.9987	0.9974	6
7										1.0000	1.0000	0.9999	0.9997	0.9994	7
8												1.0000	1.0000	0.9999	8
9														1.0000	9

λ / x	2.0	2.2	2.4	2.6	2.8	3.0	3.2	3.4	3.6	3.8	4.0	4.5	5.0	5.5	x
0	0.1353	0.1108	0.0907	0.0743	0.0608	0.0498	0.0408	0.0334	0.0273	0.0224	0.0183	0.0111	0.0067	0.0041	0
1	0.4060	0.3546	0.3084	0.2674	0.2311	0.1991	0.1712	0.1468	0.1257	0.1074	0.0916	0.0611	0.0404	0.0266	1
2	0.6767	0.6227	0.5697	0.5184	0.4695	0.4232	0.3799	0.3397	0.3027	0.2689	0.2381	0.1736	0.1247	0.0884	2
3	0.8571	0.8194	0.7787	0.7360	0.6919	0.6472	0.6025	0.5584	0.5152	0.4735	0.4335	0.3423	0.2650	0.2017	3
4	0.9473	0.9275	0.9041	0.8774	0.8477	0.8153	0.7806	0.7442	0.7064	0.6678	0.6288	0.5321	0.4405	0.3575	4
5	0.9834	0.9751	0.9643	0.9510	0.9349	0.9161	0.8946	0.8705	0.8441	0.8156	0.7851	0.7029	0.6160	0.5289	5
6	0.9955	0.9925	0.9884	0.9828	0.9756	0.9665	0.9554	0.9421	0.9267	0.9091	0.8893	0.8311	0.7622	0.6860	6
7	0.9989	0.9980	0.9967	0.9947	0.9919	0.9881	0.9832	0.9769	0.9692	0.9599	0.9489	0.9134	0.8666	0.8095	7
8	0.9998	0.9995	0.9991	0.9985	0.9976	0.9962	0.9943	0.9917	0.9883	0.9840	0.9786	0.9597	0.9319	0.8944	8
9	1.0000	0.9999	0.9998	0.9996	0.9993	0.9989	0.9982	0.9973	0.9960	0.9942	0.9919	0.9829	0.9682	0.9462	9
10		1.0000	1.0000	0.9999	0.9998	0.9997	0.9995	0.9992	0.9987	0.9981	0.9972	0.9933	0.9863	0.9747	10
11				1.0000	1.0000	0.9999	0.9999	0.9998	0.9996	0.9994	0.9991	0.9976	0.9945	0.9890	11
12						1.0000	1.0000	0.9999	0.9999	0.9998	0.9997	0.9992	0.9980	0.9955	12
13								1.0000	1.0000	1.0000	0.9999	0.9997	0.9993	0.9983	13
14											1.0000	0.9999	0.9998	0.9994	14
15												1.0000	0.9999	0.9998	15
16													1.0000	0.9999	16
17														1.0000	17

λ / x	6.0	6.5	7.0	7.5	8.0	8.5	9.0	9.5	10.0	11.0	12.0	13.0	14.0	15.0	x
0	0.0025	0.0015	0.0009	0.0006	0.0003	0.0002	0.0001	0.0001	0.0000	0.0000	0.0000	0.0000	0.0000	0.0000	0
1	0.0174	0.0113	0.0073	0.0047	0.0030	0.0019	0.0012	0.0008	0.0005	0.0002	0.0001	0.0000	0.0000	0.0000	1
2	0.0620	0.0430	0.0296	0.0203	0.0138	0.0093	0.0062	0.0042	0.0028	0.0012	0.0005	0.0002	0.0001	0.0000	2
3	0.1512	0.1118	0.0818	0.0591	0.0424	0.0301	0.0212	0.0149	0.0103	0.0049	0.0023	0.0011	0.0005	0.0002	3
4	0.2851	0.2237	0.1730	0.1321	0.0996	0.0744	0.0550	0.0403	0.0293	0.0151	0.0076	0.0037	0.0018	0.0009	4
5	0.4457	0.3690	0.3007	0.2414	0.1912	0.1496	0.1157	0.0885	0.0671	0.0375	0.0203	0.0107	0.0055	0.0028	5
6	0.6063	0.5265	0.4497	0.3782	0.3134	0.2562	0.2068	0.1649	0.1301	0.0786	0.0458	0.0259	0.0142	0.0076	6
7	0.7440	0.6728	0.5987	0.5246	0.4530	0.3856	0.3239	0.2687	0.2202	0.1432	0.0895	0.0540	0.0316	0.0180	7
8	0.8472	0.7916	0.7291	0.6620	0.5925	0.5231	0.4557	0.3918	0.3328	0.2320	0.1550	0.0998	0.0621	0.0374	8
9	0.9161	0.8774	0.8305	0.7764	0.7166	0.6530	0.5874	0.5218	0.4579	0.3405	0.2424	0.1658	0.1094	0.0699	9
10	0.9574	0.9332	0.9015	0.8622	0.8159	0.7634	0.7060	0.6453	0.5830	0.4599	0.3472	0.2517	0.1757	0.1185	10
11	0.9799	0.9661	0.9467	0.9208	0.8881	0.8487	0.8030	0.7520	0.6968	0.5793	0.4616	0.3532	0.2600	0.1848	11
12	0.9912	0.9840	0.9730	0.9573	0.9362	0.9091	0.8758	0.8364	0.7916	0.6887	0.5760	0.4631	0.3585	0.2676	12
13	0.9964	0.9929	0.9872	0.9784	0.9658	0.9486	0.9261	0.8981	0.8645	0.7813	0.6815	0.5730	0.4644	0.3632	13
14	0.9986	0.9970	0.9943	0.9897	0.9827	0.9726	0.9585	0.9400	0.9165	0.8540	0.7720	0.6751	0.5704	0.4657	14
15	0.9995	0.9988	0.9976	0.9954	0.9918	0.9862	0.9780	0.9665	0.9513	0.9074	0.8444	0.7636	0.6694	0.5681	15
16	0.9998	0.9996	0.9990	0.9980	0.9963	0.9934	0.9889	0.9823	0.9730	0.9441	0.8987	0.8355	0.7559	0.6641	16
17	0.9999	0.9998	0.9996	0.9992	0.9984	0.9970	0.9947	0.9911	0.9857	0.9678	0.9370	0.8905	0.8272	0.7489	17
18	1.0000	0.9999	0.9999	0.9997	0.9993	0.9987	0.9976	0.9957	0.9928	0.9823	0.9626	0.9302	0.8826	0.8195	18
19		1.0000	1.0000	0.9999	0.9997	0.9995	0.9989	0.9980	0.9965	0.9907	0.9787	0.9573	0.9235	0.8752	19
20				1.0000	0.9999	0.9998	0.9996	0.9991	0.9984	0.9953	0.9884	0.9750	0.9521	0.9170	20
21					1.0000	0.9999	0.9998	0.9996	0.9993	0.9977	0.9939	0.9859	0.9712	0.9469	21
22						1.0000	0.9999	0.9999	0.9997	0.9990	0.9970	0.9924	0.9833	0.9673	22
23							1.0000	0.9999	0.9999	0.9995	0.9985	0.9960	0.9907	0.9805	23
24								1.0000	1.0000	0.9998	0.9993	0.9980	0.9950	0.9888	24
25										0.9999	0.9997	0.9990	0.9974	0.9938	25
26										1.0000	0.9999	0.9995	0.9987	0.9967	26
27											0.9999	0.9998	0.9994	0.9983	27
28											1.0000	0.9999	0.9997	0.9991	28
29												1.0000	0.9999	0.9996	29
30													0.9999	0.9998	30
31													1.0000	0.9999	31
32														1.0000	32

Percentage points of the χ^2 distribution

The table shows values of x satisfying $P(X \le x) = p$,
where X has the χ^2 distribution with ν degrees of freedom.

p / ν	0.005	0.01	0.025	0.05	0.1	0.9	0.95	0.975	0.99	0.995	p / ν
1	0.00004	0.0002	0.001	0.004	0.016	2.706	3.841	5.024	6.635	7.879	1
2	0.010	0.020	0.051	0.103	0.211	4.605	5.991	7.378	9.210	10.597	2
3	0.072	0.115	0.216	0.352	0.584	6.251	7.815	9.348	11.345	12.838	3
4	0.207	0.297	0.484	0.711	1.064	7.779	9.488	11.143	13.277	14.860	4
5	0.412	0.554	0.831	1.145	1.610	9.236	11.070	12.833	15.086	16.750	5
6	0.676	0.872	1.237	1.635	2.204	10.645	12.592	14.449	16.812	18.548	6
7	0.989	1.239	1.690	2.167	2.833	12.017	14.067	16.013	18.475	20.278	7
8	1.344	1.646	2.180	2.733	3.490	13.362	15.507	17.535	20.090	21.955	8
9	1.735	2.088	2.700	3.325	4.168	14.684	16.919	19.023	21.666	23.589	9
10	2.156	2.558	3.247	3.940	4.865	15.987	18.307	20.483	23.209	25.188	10
11	2.603	3.053	3.816	4.575	5.578	17.275	19.675	21.920	24.725	26.757	11
12	3.074	3.571	4.404	5.226	6.304	18.549	21.026	23.337	26.217	28.300	12
13	3.565	4.107	5.009	5.892	7.042	19.812	22.362	24.736	27.688	29.819	13
14	4.075	4.660	5.629	6.571	7.790	21.064	23.685	26.119	29.141	31.319	14
15	4.601	5.229	6.262	7.261	8.547	22.307	24.996	27.488	30.578	32.801	15
16	5.142	5.812	6.908	7.962	9.312	23.542	26.296	28.845	32.000	34.267	16
17	5.697	6.408	7.564	8.672	10.085	24.769	27.587	30.191	33.409	35.718	17
18	6.265	7.015	8.231	9.390	10.865	25.989	28.869	31.526	34.805	37.156	18
19	6.844	7.633	8.907	10.117	11.651	27.204	30.144	32.852	36.191	38.582	19
20	7.434	8.260	9.591	10.851	12.443	28.412	31.410	34.170	37.566	39.997	20
21	8.034	8.897	10.283	11.591	13.240	29.615	32.671	35.479	38.932	41.401	21
22	8.643	9.542	10.982	12.338	14.041	30.813	33.924	36.781	40.289	42.796	22
23	9.260	10.196	11.689	13.091	14.848	32.007	35.172	38.076	41.638	44.181	23
24	9.886	10.856	12.401	13.848	15.659	33.196	36.415	39.364	42.980	45.559	24
25	10.520	11.524	13.120	14.611	16.473	34.382	37.652	40.646	44.314	46.928	25
26	11.160	12.198	13.844	15.379	17.292	35.563	38.885	41.923	45.642	48.290	26
27	11.808	12.879	14.573	16.151	18.114	36.741	40.113	43.195	46.963	49.645	27
28	12.461	13.565	15.308	16.928	18.939	37.916	41.337	44.461	48.278	50.993	28
29	13.121	14.256	16.047	17.708	19.768	39.087	42.557	45.722	49.588	52.336	29
30	13.787	14.953	16.791	18.493	20.599	40.256	43.773	46.979	50.892	53.672	30
31	14.458	15.655	17.539	19.281	21.434	41.422	44.985	48.232	52.191	55.003	31
32	15.134	16.362	18.291	20.072	22.271	42.585	46.194	49.480	53.486	56.328	32
33	15.815	17.074	19.047	20.867	23.110	43.745	47.400	50.725	54.776	57.648	33
34	16.501	17.789	19.806	21.664	23.952	44.903	48.602	51.996	56.061	58.964	34
35	17.192	18.509	20.569	22.465	24.797	46.059	49.802	53.203	57.342	60.275	35
36	17.887	19.223	21.336	23.269	25.643	47.212	50.998	54.437	58.619	61.581	36
37	18.586	19.960	22.106	24.075	26.492	48.363	52.192	55.668	59.892	62.883	37
38	19.289	20.691	22.878	24.884	27.343	49.513	53.384	56.896	61.162	64.181	38
39	19.996	21.426	23.654	25.695	28.196	50.660	54.572	58.120	62.428	65.476	39
40	20.707	22.164	24.433	26.509	29.051	51.805	55.758	59.342	63.691	66.766	40
45	24.311	25.901	28.366	30.612	33.350	57.505	61.656	65.410	69.957	73.166	45
50	27.991	29.707	32.357	34.764	37.689	63.167	67.505	71.420	76.154	79.490	50
55	31.735	33.570	36.398	38.958	42.060	68.796	73.311	77.380	82.292	85.749	55
60	35.534	37.485	40.482	43.188	46.459	74.397	79.082	83.298	88.379	91.952	60
65	39.383	41.444	44.603	47.450	50.883	79.973	84.821	89.177	94.422	98.105	65
70	43.275	45.442	48.758	51.739	55.329	85.527	90.531	95.023	100.425	104.215	70
75	47.206	49.475	52.942	56.054	59.795	91.061	96.217	100.839	106.393	110.286	75
80	51.172	53.540	57.153	60.391	64.278	96.578	101.879	106.629	112.329	116.321	80
85	55.170	57.634	61.389	64.749	68.777	102.079	107.522	112.393	118.236	122.325	85
90	59.196	61.754	65.647	69.126	73.291	107.565	113.145	118.136	124.116	128.299	90
95	63.250	65.898	69.925	73.520	77.818	113.038	118.752	123.858	129.973	134.247	95
100	67.328	70.065	74.222	77.929	82.358	118.498	124.342	129.561	135.807	140.169	100

Percentage points of the Student's *t*-distribution

The table shows values of x satisfying $P(X \leq x) = p$,
where X has the Student's t-distribution with ν degrees of freedom.

p / v	0.9	0.95	0.975	0.99	0.995
1	3.078	6.314	12.706	31.821	63.657
2	1.886	2.920	4.303	6.965	9.925
3	1.638	2.353	3.182	4.541	5.841
4	1.533	2.132	2.776	3.747	4.604
5	1.476	2.015	2.571	3.365	4.032
6	1.440	1.943	2.447	3.143	3.707
7	1.415	1.895	2.365	2.998	3.499
8	1.397	1.860	2.306	2.896	3.355
9	1.383	1.833	2.262	2.821	3.250
10	1.372	1.812	2.228	2.764	3.169
11	1.363	1.796	2.201	2.718	3.106
12	1.356	1.782	2.179	2.681	3.055
13	1.350	1.771	2.160	2.650	3.012
14	1.345	1.761	2.145	2.624	2.977
15	1.341	1.753	2.131	2.602	2.947
16	1.337	1.746	2.120	2.583	2.921
17	1.333	1.740	2.110	2.567	2.898
18	1.330	1.734	2.101	2.552	2.878
19	1.328	1.729	2.093	2.539	2.861
20	1.325	1.725	2.086	2.528	2.845
21	1.323	1.721	2.080	2.518	2.831
22	1.321	1.717	2.074	2.508	2.819
23	1.319	1.714	2.069	2.500	2.807
24	1.318	1.711	2.064	2.492	2.797
25	1.316	1.708	2.060	2.485	2.787
26	1.315	1.706	2.056	2.479	2.779
27	1.314	1.703	2.052	2.473	2.771
28	1.313	1.701	2.048	2.467	2.763

Answers

Chapter 1: Discrete Random Variables

1. Probability Distributions

Exercise 1.1 — Probability distributions and functions

Q1 a) (i) The discrete random variable X is 'number of tails'.

(ii) x could be 0, 1, 2, 3 or 4.

b) (i) The discrete random variable X is 'number of orange balls selected'.

(ii) x could be 0, 1 or 2.

c) (i) The discrete random variable X is 'sum of the two dice scores'.

(ii) x could be 2, 3, 4, 5, 6, 7 or 8.

Q2 a)

a	1	2	3	4	5	6
$P(A = a)$	$\frac{1}{6}$	$\frac{1}{6}$	$\frac{1}{6}$	$\frac{1}{6}$	$\frac{1}{6}$	$\frac{1}{6}$

b) The probability of the score being even is $\frac{3}{6} = \frac{1}{2}$ and the probability of 'otherwise' (the score being odd) is the same. The probability distribution is:

b	0	1
$P(B = b)$	$\frac{1}{2}$	$\frac{1}{2}$

c) C can take 6 values, $c = 5, 10, 15, 20, 25, 30$ (each score × 5) and each one will have probability $\frac{1}{6}$. The probability distribution is:

c	5	10	15	20	25	30
$P(C = c)$	$\frac{1}{6}$	$\frac{1}{6}$	$\frac{1}{6}$	$\frac{1}{6}$	$\frac{1}{6}$	$\frac{1}{6}$

Q3 a) (i) $\sum_{\text{all}\,x} P(X = x) = 0.2 + 0.4 + 0.1 + a = 1$

So, $a = 1 - 0.2 - 0.4 - 0.1 = 0.3$

(ii) $P(X \geq 2) = P(X = 2) + P(X = 3) + P(X = 4)$
$= 0.4 + 0.1 + 0.3 = 0.8$

b) (i) $\sum_{\text{all}\,x} P(X = x) = 6k = 1$

So, $k = \frac{1}{6}$.

(ii) $P(X \geq 5)$
$= P(X = 9) + P(X = 16) + P(X = 25) + P(X = 36)$
$= 4k = \frac{4}{6} = \frac{2}{3}$.

(iii) $P(X \geq 10) = P(X = 16) + P(X = 25) + P(X = 36)$
$= 3k = \frac{3}{6} = \frac{1}{2}$.

(iv) $P(3 \leq X \leq 15) = P(X = 4) + P(X = 9)$
$= 2k = \frac{2}{6} = \frac{1}{3}$.

(v) $P(X \text{ is divisible by } 3) = P(X = 9 \text{ or } 36)$
$= P(X = 9) + P(X = 36)$
$= 2k = \frac{2}{6} = \frac{1}{3}$.

Q4 a) (i) $\sum_{\text{all}\,x} P(X = x) = k + 4k + 9k = 14k = 1$

So $k = \frac{1}{14}$.

(ii)

x	1	2	3
$P(X = x)$	$\frac{1}{14}$	$\frac{2}{7}$	$\frac{9}{14}$

b) (i) $\sum_{\text{all}\,x} P(X = x) = k + \frac{k}{2} + \frac{k}{3} = \frac{11k}{6} = 1$

So $k = \frac{6}{11}$.

(ii)

x	1	2	3
$P(X = x)$	$\frac{6}{11}$	$\frac{3}{11}$	$\frac{2}{11}$

c) (i) $\sum_{\text{all}\,x} P(X = x) = k + 2k + 3k + 4k + 3k + 2k + k = 1$

So $16k = 1$ so $k = \frac{1}{16}$.

(ii)

x	1	2	3	4	5	6	7
$P(X = x)$	$\frac{1}{16}$	$\frac{1}{8}$	$\frac{3}{16}$	$\frac{1}{4}$	$\frac{3}{16}$	$\frac{1}{8}$	$\frac{1}{16}$

Q5 a) Draw a sample-space diagram to show all the possible outcomes:

Score on dice 1 (columns); Score on dice 2 (rows)

×	1	2	3	4
1	1	2	3	4
2	2	4	6	8
3	3	6	9	12
4	4	8	12	16

So the possible values that X can take are 1, 2, 3, 4, 6, 8, 9, 12 and 16.

To find the probability of X taking each value, count the number of outcomes that give the value and divide by the total number, 16.

$P(X = 1) = \frac{1}{16}$, $P(X = 2) = \frac{2}{16} = \frac{1}{8}$,

$P(X = 3) = \frac{2}{16} = \frac{1}{8}$, $P(X = 4) = \frac{3}{16}$,

$P(X = 6) = \frac{2}{16} = \frac{1}{8}$, $P(X = 8) = \frac{2}{16} = \frac{1}{8}$,

$P(X = 9) = \frac{1}{16}$, $P(X = 12) = \frac{2}{16} = \frac{1}{8}$,

$P(X = 16) = \frac{1}{16}$

So the probability distribution looks like this:

x	1	2	3	4	6	8	9	12	16
P(X = x)	$\frac{1}{16}$	$\frac{1}{8}$	$\frac{1}{8}$	$\frac{3}{16}$	$\frac{1}{8}$	$\frac{1}{8}$	$\frac{1}{16}$	$\frac{1}{8}$	$\frac{1}{16}$

b) The probability function is:

$$P(X = x) = \begin{cases} \frac{1}{8} & x = 2, 3, 6, 8, 12 \\ \frac{3}{16} & x = 4 \\ \frac{1}{16} & x = 1, 9, 16 \end{cases}$$

c) $P(3 < X \leq 10)$
$= P(X = 4) + P(X = 6) + P(X = 8) + P(X = 9)$
$= \frac{3}{16} + \frac{1}{8} + \frac{1}{8} + \frac{1}{16} = \frac{1}{2}$

2. Expected Values, Mean and Variance

Exercise 2.1 — The expected value

Q1 a) $E(X) = [0 \times 0.2] + [1 \times 0.2] + [2 \times 0.2] + [3 \times 0.2] + [4 \times 0.2] = 2$

b) $E(X) = \left[1 \times \frac{1}{14}\right] + \left[2 \times \frac{4}{14}\right] + \left[3 \times \frac{9}{14}\right]$
$= \frac{36}{14} = \frac{18}{7} = 2.57$ to 3 s.f.

c) $E(X) = [2 \times 0.1] + [3 \times 0.4] + [1 \times 0.5] = 1.9$

d) $E(X) = [-2 \times 0.1] + [-1 \times 0.2] + [1 \times 0.2] + [2 \times 0.2] + [0 \times 0.3] = 0.2$

e) First work out the value of k:
The probabilities add up to 1 so
$3k + 4k + 5k + 6k + 7k = 1$
$25k = 1 \Rightarrow k = \frac{1}{25}$.
Now you can work out E(X):

$$E(X) = \left[1 \times \tfrac{1}{25}(1 + 2)\right] + \left[2 \times \tfrac{1}{25}(2 + 2)\right] + \left[3 \times \tfrac{1}{25}(3 + 2)\right] + \left[4 \times \tfrac{1}{25}(4 + 2)\right] + \left[5 \times \tfrac{1}{25}(5 + 2)\right]$$
$$= \frac{17}{5} = 3.4$$

f) First work out the value of k:
The probabilities add up to 1 so

$$\frac{k}{1} + \frac{k}{2} + \frac{k}{3} + \frac{k}{4} + \frac{k}{5} = 1$$
$$\Rightarrow k\left(\frac{1}{1} + \frac{1}{2} + \frac{1}{3} + \frac{1}{4} + \frac{1}{5}\right) = 1$$
$$\Rightarrow k\left(\frac{137}{60}\right) = 1$$
$$\Rightarrow k = \frac{60}{137}$$

$$E(X) = \left[1 \times \frac{\left(\frac{60}{137}\right)}{1}\right] + \left[2 \times \frac{\left(\frac{60}{137}\right)}{2}\right] + \left[3 \times \frac{\left(\frac{60}{137}\right)}{3}\right] + \left[4 \times \frac{\left(\frac{60}{137}\right)}{4}\right] + \left[5 \times \frac{\left(\frac{60}{137}\right)}{5}\right]$$
$$= \frac{300}{137} = 2\tfrac{26}{137} \text{ (or 2.19 to 3 s.f.)}$$

Q2 a) $E(X) = [2 \times 0.2] + [5 \times 0.3] + [6 \times 0.1] + [p \times 0.4]$
$= 2.5 + 0.4p$
So $6.5 = 2.5 + 0.4p \Rightarrow p = 10$.

b) The probabilities add up to 1 so
$0.5 + 0.2 + a + 0.2 = 1 \Rightarrow a = 0.1$
$E(X) = [4 \times 0.5] + [8 \times 0.2] + [p \times a] + [15 \times 0.2]$
$= 6.6 + 0.1p$
So $7.5 = 6.6 + 0.1p \Rightarrow p = 9$.

Q3 a) The sum of the probabilities is 1 so
$0.2 + a + 0.1 + b = 1 \Rightarrow a + b = 0.7$
E(X) is 2.5 so
$0.2 + 2a + 0.3 + 4b = 2.5$
$\Rightarrow 2a + 4b = 2 \Rightarrow a + 2b = 1$
Rearranging the second equation to get $a = 1 - 2b$ and substituting this into the first equation we get:
$(1 - 2b) + b = 0.7 \Rightarrow b = 0.3$
and putting $b = 0.3$ into the first equation we get $a = 0.4$.

b) The sum of the probabilities is 1 so
$0.1 + a + b + 0.1 = 1 \Rightarrow a + b = 0.8$
E(X) is 7.8 so
$0.3 + 7a + 8b + 1.2 = 7.8 \Rightarrow 7a + 8b = 6.3$
From the first equation, $a = 0.8 - b$, and substituting this into the second equation, we get:
$7(0.8 - b) + 8b = 6.3$
$\Rightarrow 5.6 - 7b + 8b = 6.3$
$\Rightarrow 5.6 + b = 6.3$
$\Rightarrow b = 0.7$
Now the first equation is $a + b = 0.8$, and substituting in $b = 0.7$ we get $a = 0.1$.

Q4 a) (i) $E(X) = [1 \times 0.2] + [2 \times 0.1] + [3 \times 0.25] + [4 \times 0.25] + [5 \times 0.2]$
$= 3.15$

(ii) $E(X^2) = [1 \times 0.2] + [4 \times 0.1] + [9 \times 0.25] + [16 \times 0.25] + [25 \times 0.2]$
$= 11.85$

b) (i) $E(X) = [-3 \times 0.2] + [-2 \times 0.1] + [-1 \times 0.25] + [0 \times 0.25] + [1 \times 0.2]$
$= -0.85$

(ii) $E(X^2) = [9 \times 0.2] + [4 \times 0.1] + [1 \times 0.25] + [0 \times 0.25] + [1 \times 0.2]$
$= 2.65$

c) (i) $E(X) = [3 \times 0.1] + [4 \times 0.25] + [5 \times 0.15] + [7 \times 0.3] + [9 \times 0.2] = 5.95$

(ii) $E(X^2) = [9 \times 0.1] + [16 \times 0.25] + [25 \times 0.15] + [49 \times 0.3] + [81 \times 0.2] = 39.55$

Exercise 2.2 — Variance

Q1 a) $E(X) = [1 \times 0.2] + [2 \times 0.1] + [3 \times 0.2] + [4 \times 0.1] + [5 \times 0.4] = 3.4$

$E(X^2) = [1 \times 0.2] + [4 \times 0.1] + [9 \times 0.2] + [16 \times 0.1] + [25 \times 0.4] = 14$

So $\text{Var}(X) = E(X^2) - (E(X))^2 = 14 - 3.4^2 = 2.44$

b) $E(X) = [1 \times \frac{1}{2}] + [3 \times \frac{1}{4}] + [6 \times \frac{1}{8}] + [8 \times \frac{1}{16}] + [9 \times \frac{1}{32}] + [10 \times \frac{1}{32}]$

$= \frac{99}{32}$ (= 3.09 to 3 s.f.)

$E(X^2) = [1 \times \frac{1}{2}] + [9 \times \frac{1}{4}] + [36 \times \frac{1}{8}] + [64 \times \frac{1}{16}] + [81 \times \frac{1}{32}] + [100 \times \frac{1}{32}]$

$= \frac{541}{32}$ (= 16.9 to 3 s.f.)

So $\text{Var}(X) = E(X^2) - (E(X))^2$

$= \frac{541}{32} - \left(\frac{99}{32}\right)^2 = \frac{7511}{1024}$ (= 7.33 to 3 s.f.)

c) $E(X) = [-2 \times 0.2] + [-1 \times 0.1] + [0 \times 0.2] + [1 \times 0.1] + [2 \times 0.4] = 0.4$

$E(X^2) = [4 \times 0.2] + [1 \times 0.1] + [0 \times 0.2] + [1 \times 0.1] + [4 \times 0.4] = 2.6$

So $\text{Var}(X) = E(X^2) - (E(X))^2 = 2.6 - 0.4^2 = 2.44$

Q2 a) $E(X) = [1 \times \frac{1}{5}] + [2 \times \frac{1}{5}] + [3 \times \frac{1}{5}] + [4 \times \frac{1}{5}] + [5 \times \frac{1}{5}] = 3$

$E(X^2) = [1 \times \frac{1}{5}] + [4 \times \frac{1}{5}] + [9 \times \frac{1}{5}] + [16 \times \frac{1}{5}] + [25 \times \frac{1}{5}] = 11$

So $\text{Var}(X) = E(X^2) - (E(X))^2 = 11 - 3^2 = 2$

b) $E(X) = [1 \times \frac{1}{30}] + [2 \times \frac{4}{30}] + [3 \times \frac{9}{30}] + [4 \times \frac{16}{30}] = \frac{10}{3}$

$E(X^2) = [1 \times \frac{1}{30}] + [4 \times \frac{4}{30}] + [9 \times \frac{9}{30}] + [16 \times \frac{16}{30}] = \frac{59}{5}$

So $\text{Var}(X) = E(X^2) - (E(X))^2 = \frac{59}{5} - \left(\frac{10}{3}\right)^2$

$= \frac{31}{45}$ (= 0.689 to 3 s.f.)

Q3 a) (i) The probabilities must add up to 1:
$0.2 + a + 0.4 + 0.1 = 1 \Rightarrow a = 0.3$.

(ii) $E(X) = [1 \times 0.2] + [2 \times 0.3] + [3 \times 0.4] + [4 \times 0.1] = 2.4$

$E(X^2) = [1 \times 0.2] + [4 \times 0.3] + [9 \times 0.4] + [16 \times 0.1] = 6.6$

$\text{Var}(X) = 6.6 - 2.4^2 = 0.84$

Standard deviation $= \sqrt{0.84} = 0.917$ (3 s.f.)

b) (i) The probabilities must add up to 1:
$a + 0.3 + a + 0.1 = 1 \Rightarrow a = 0.3$.

(ii) $E(X) = [-3 \times 0.3] + [-2 \times 0.3] + [-1 \times 0.3] + [0 \times 0.1] = -1.8$

$E(X^2) = [9 \times 0.3] + [4 \times 0.3] + [1 \times 0.3] + [0 \times 0.1] = 4.2$

$\text{Var}(X) = 4.2 - (-1.8)^2 = 0.96$

Standard deviation $= \sqrt{0.96} = 0.980$ (3 s.f.)

Q4 a) (i) $E(X) = [3 \times 0.2] + [4 \times 0.3] + [6 \times 0.1] + 0.4p = 2.4 + 0.4p$

$5.2 = 2.4 + 0.4p \Rightarrow p = 7$.

(ii) $E(X^2) = [9 \times 0.2] + [16 \times 0.3] + [36 \times 0.1] + [49 \times 0.4]$

$= 29.8$

So $\text{Var}(X) = 29.8 - 5.2^2 = 2.76$

And standard deviation $= \sqrt{2.76} = 1.66$ (3 s.f.)

b) The probabilities add up to 1:
$0.2 + a + 0.4 + 0.3 = 1 \Rightarrow a = 0.1$

$E(X) = [1 \times 0.2] + [4 \times 0.1] + 0.4p + [9 \times 0.3] = 3.3 + 0.4p$

$5.7 = 3.3 + 0.4p \Rightarrow p = 6$

$E(X^2) = [1 \times 0.2] + [16 \times 0.1] + [36 \times 0.4] + [81 \times 0.3] = 40.5$

$\text{Var}(X) = 40.5 - 5.7^2 = 8.01$

Q5 a) (i) All the probabilities add up to 1:
$9k + 16k + 25k = 1$

$50k = 1 \Rightarrow k = \frac{1}{50}$

(ii) $E(X) = \left[3 \times \frac{1}{50} \times 3^2\right] + \left[4 \times \frac{1}{50} \times 4^2\right] + \left[5 \times \frac{1}{50} \times 5^2\right] = 4.32$

(iii) $E(X^2) = \left[9 \times \frac{1}{50} 3^2\right] + \left[16 \times \frac{1}{50} 4^2\right] + \left[25 \times \frac{1}{50} 5^2\right] = 19.24$

So $\text{Var}(X) = 19.24 - 4.32^2 = 0.5776$

b) (i) All the probabilities add up to 1:

$\frac{k}{3}+\frac{k}{4}+\frac{k}{5}+\frac{k}{6}=1$

$\Rightarrow k\left(\frac{1}{3}+\frac{1}{4}+\frac{1}{5}+\frac{1}{6}\right)=1$

$\Rightarrow \frac{19}{20}k=1$

$\Rightarrow k=\frac{20}{19}$

(ii) $E(X)=\left[3\times\frac{\left(\frac{20}{19}\right)}{3}\right]+\left[4\times\frac{\left(\frac{20}{19}\right)}{4}\right]+\left[5\times\frac{\left(\frac{20}{19}\right)}{5}\right]+\left[6\times\frac{\left(\frac{20}{19}\right)}{6}\right]$

$=\frac{80}{19}=4.21$ to 3 s.f.

Notice that the numbers cancel in each bracket so you're just left to add together four lots of $\frac{20}{19}$.

(iii) $E(X^2)=\left[9\times\frac{\left(\frac{20}{19}\right)}{3}\right]+\left[16\times\frac{\left(\frac{20}{19}\right)}{4}\right]+\left[25\times\frac{\left(\frac{20}{19}\right)}{5}\right]+\left[36\times\frac{\left(\frac{20}{19}\right)}{6}\right]$

$=\left[\frac{20}{19}\times3\right]+\left[\frac{20}{19}\times4\right]+\left[\frac{20}{19}\times5\right]+\left[\frac{20}{19}\times6\right]$

$=\frac{360}{19}$ (= 18.9 to 3 s.f.)

So $\text{Var}(X)=\frac{360}{19}-\left(\frac{80}{19}\right)^2=\frac{440}{361}$

(= 1.22 to 3 s.f.)

Exercise 2.3 — Expected value and variance of a function of X

Q1 a) $E(X^2)=\sum x_i^2p_i=(1^2\times0.2)+(2^2\times0.3)+(3^2\times0.4)+(4^2\times0.1)=0.2+1.2+3.6+1.6=6.6$

b) $E(2X^2-3)=2E(X^2)-3=(2\times6.6)-3=10.2$

You could do part b) by calculating $\sum(2x_i^2-3)p_i$ *— but it's much easier if you notice that you can use the formula for the expected value of a linear function and your answer to part a).*

c) $\text{Var}(X^2)=E((X^2)^2)-[E(X)^2]^2=E(X^4)-[E(X)^2]^2.$

$=\sum x_i^4p_i-[6.6]^2=[(1^4\times0.2)+(2^4\times0.3)+(3^4\times0.4)+(4^4\times0.1)]-[6.6]^2$

$=[0.2+4.8+32.4+25.6]-[6.6]^2$

$=63-43.56=19.44$

d) $\text{Var}(2X^2-3)=2^2\text{Var}(X^2)=4\times19.44=77.76.$

Again, you can use the rule $\text{Var}(aX+b)=a^2\text{Var}(X)$ *but replace* X *with* X^2.

Q2 a) The sum of the probabilities is 1 so

$\frac{3}{k}+\frac{4}{k}+\frac{5}{k}=1\Rightarrow\frac{12}{k}=1\Rightarrow k=12$

b) $E(3X^2+2)=3E(X^2)+2$

$=3\left[\left(3^2\times\frac{3}{12}\right)+\left(4^2\times\frac{4}{12}\right)+\left(5^2\times\frac{5}{12}\right)\right]+2$

$=3[18]+2$

$=56$

c) $\text{Var}(3X^2+2)=9\text{Var}(X^2)$

$\text{Var}(X^2)=E((X^2)^2)-[E(X^2)]^2=E(X^4)-[18]^2$

$=\left[\left(3^4\times\frac{3}{12}\right)+\left(4^4\times\frac{4}{12}\right)+\left(5^4\times\frac{5}{12}\right)\right]-[18]^2$

$=366-324=42$

So $\text{Var}(3X^2+2)=9\times42=378.$

Q3 a) $E(X^2)=17.1$ so $(0^2\times0.1)+(1^2\times0.1)+(2^2\times0.3)+(a^2\times0.2)+(6^2\times0.3)=17.1,$

$\Rightarrow 12.1+0.2a^2=17.1\Rightarrow0.2a^2=5\Rightarrow a^2=25$

$\Rightarrow a=5$

a must be a positive constant.

b) $\text{Var}(3X^2)=9\,\text{Var}(X^2)=9[E((X^2)^2)-(E(X^2))^2]$

$=9[E(X^4)-(17.1)^2]$

$=9[(0^4\times0.1)+(1^4\times0.1)+(2^4\times0.3)+(5^4\times0.2)+(6^4\times0.3)-(17.1)^2]$

$=9[518.7-(17.1)^2]=9[518.7-292.41]$

$=2036.61$

Q4 a) $E(Y)=E(X+3)=E(X)+3=4+3=7$

$\text{Var}(Y)=\text{Var}(X+3)=1^2\times\text{Var}(X)=3$

b) $E(Z)=E(5X)=5E(X)=5\times4=20$

$\text{Var}(Z)=\text{Var}(5X)=5^2\times\text{Var}(X)=25\times3=75$

c) $E(W)=E(2X-7)=2E(X)-7=(2\times4)-7=1$

$\text{Var}(W)=\text{Var}(2X-7)=2^2\times\text{Var}(X)=4\times3=12$

d) $E(V)=E(7-2X)=7-2E(X)=7-(2\times4)=-1$

$\text{Var}(V)=\text{Var}(7-2X)=(-2)^2\times\text{Var}(X)=4\times3=12$

Q5 a) (i) $Y=3X+4$

y	7	10	13	16	19
$P(Y=y)$	0.1	0.2	0.3	0.2	0.2

(ii) $E(Y)=[7\times0.1]+[10\times0.2]+[13\times0.3]+[16\times0.2]+[19\times0.2]=13.6$

$E(Y^2)=[49\times0.1]+[100\times0.2]+[169\times0.3]+[256\times0.2]+[361\times0.2]=199$

$\text{Var}(Y)=199-13.6^2=14.04$

(iii) $E(Y)=E(3X+4)=3E(X)+4=(3\times3.2)+4=13.6$

$\text{Var}(Y)=\text{Var}(3X+4)=9\text{Var}(X)=9\times1.56=14.04$

Notice that you get the same values for the mean and variance in parts (ii) and (iii).

b) (i) $Z=3X-4$

z	–1	2	5	8	11
$P(Z=z)$	0.1	0.2	0.3	0.2	0.2

(ii) $E(Z)=[-1\times0.1]+[2\times0.2]+[5\times0.3]+[8\times0.2]+[11\times0.2]=5.6$

$E(Z^2)=[1\times0.1]+[4\times0.2]+[25\times0.3]+[64\times0.2]+[121\times0.2]=45.4$

$\text{Var}(Z)=45.4-5.6^2=14.04$

(iii) $E(Z)=E(3X-4)=3E(X)-4=(3\times3.2)-4=5.6$

$\text{Var}(Z)=\text{Var}(3X-4)=9\text{Var}(X)=9\times1.56=14.04$

c) (i) $V = 20 - 3X$

v	17	14	11	8	5
$P(V = v)$	0.1	0.2	0.3	0.2	0.2

(ii) $E(V) = [17 \times 0.1] + [14 \times 0.2]$
$+ [11 \times 0.3] + [8 \times 0.2] + [5 \times 0.2] = 10.4$

$E(V^2) = [289 \times 0.1] + [196 \times 0.2]$
$+ [121 \times 0.3] + [64 \times 0.2] + [25 \times 0.2]$
$= 122.2$

$Var(V) = 122.2 - 10.4^2 = 14.04$

(iii) $E(V) = E(20 - 3X) = 20 - 3E(X) = 20 - (3 \times 3.2)$
$= 10.4$
$Var(V) = Var(20 - 3X) = 9Var(X) = 9 \times 1.56$
$= 14.04$

d) (i) $W = 20 + 3X$

w	23	26	29	32	35
$P(W = w)$	0.1	0.2	0.3	0.2	0.2

(ii) $E(W) = [23 \times 0.1] + [26 \times 0.2]$
$+ [29 \times 0.3] + [32 \times 0.2] + [35 \times 0.2] = 29.6$

$E(W^2) = [529 \times 0.1] + [676 \times 0.2]$
$+ [841 \times 0.3] + [1024 \times 0.2]$
$+ [1225 \times 0.2]$
$= 890.2$

$Var(W) = 890.2 - 29.6^2 = 14.04$

(iii) $E(W) = E(20 + 3X) = 20 + 3E(X)$
$= 20 + (3 \times 3.2) = 29.6$
$Var(W) = Var(20 + 3X) = 9Var(X) = 9 \times 1.56$
$= 14.04$

Q6 a) $E(X) = [10 \times 0.2] + [12 \times 0.3] + [13 \times 0.1]$
$+ [15 \times 0.3] + [16 \times 0.1] = 13$
$E(X^2) = [100 \times 0.2] + [144 \times 0.3] + [169 \times 0.1]$
$+ [225 \times 0.3] + [256 \times 0.1] = 173.2$
$Var(X) = 173.2 - 13^2 = 4.2$

b) $E(Y) = E(26 - mX) = 26 - mE(X) = 26 - 13m$
So $0 = 26 - 13m \Rightarrow m = 2$.
$Var(Y) = Var(26 - mX) = (-m)^2 Var(X) = 4 \times 4.2$
$= 16.8$

c) $E(Z) = E(3X - c) = 3E(X) - c = (3 \times 13) - c = 39 - c$
So $30 = 39 - c \Rightarrow c = 9$
$Var(Z) = Var(3X - c) = 9Var(X) = 9 \times 4.2 = 37.8$

Review Exercise — Chapter 1

Q1 a) All the probabilities have to add up to 1.
So $0.5 + k + k + 3k = 0.5 + 5k = 1$, i.e. $5k = 0.5$,
i.e. $k = 0.1$.

b) $P(Y < 2) = P(Y = 0) + P(Y = 1) = 0.5 + 0.1 = 0.6$.

Q2 a) $E(X) = (1 \times 0.6) + (2 \times 0.3) + (3 \times 0.1) = 1.5$

b) $E(X^2) = (1 \times 0.6) + (4 \times 0.3) + (9 \times 0.1) = 2.7$

$Var(X) = E(X^2) - [E(X)]^2 = 2.7 - 2.25 = 0.45$

c) $E\left(\frac{3}{X}\right) = \sum \frac{3}{x_i} p_i$

$= \left(\frac{3}{1} \times 0.6\right) + \left(\frac{3}{2} \times 0.3\right) + \left(\frac{3}{3} \times 0.1\right) = 2.35$

d) $E\left(\left(\frac{3}{X}\right)^2\right) = \sum \frac{9}{x_i^2} p_i$

$= \left(\frac{9}{1} \times 0.6\right) + \left(\frac{9}{4} \times 0.3\right) + \left(\frac{9}{9} \times 0.1\right) = 6.175$

$Var\left(\frac{3}{X}\right) = E\left(\left(\frac{3}{X}\right)^2\right) - \left[E\left(\frac{3}{X}\right)\right]^2$
$= 6.175 - 2.35^2 = 0.6525$

Q3 a) As always, the probabilities have to add up to 1:
$k = 1 - \left(\frac{1}{6} + \frac{1}{2} + \frac{5}{24}\right) = 1 - \frac{21}{24} = \frac{3}{24} = \frac{1}{8}$

b) $E(X) = \left(1 \times \frac{1}{6}\right) + \left(2 \times \frac{1}{2}\right)$
$+ \left(3 \times \frac{1}{8}\right) + \left(4 \times \frac{5}{24}\right)$
$= \frac{4 + 24 + 9 + 20}{24} = \frac{57}{24} = \frac{19}{8}$

$E(X^2) = \left(1^2 \times \frac{1}{6}\right) + \left(2^2 \times \frac{1}{2}\right)$
$+ \left(3^2 \times \frac{1}{8}\right) + \left(4^2 \times \frac{5}{24}\right)$
$= \frac{4 + 48 + 27 + 80}{24} = \frac{159}{24} = \frac{53}{8}$

$Var(X) = E(X^2) - [E(X)]^2 = \frac{53}{8} - \left(\frac{19}{8}\right)^2$
$= \frac{424 - 361}{64} = \frac{63}{64}$

c) $E(2X - 1) = 2E(X) - 1$
$= 2 \times \frac{19}{8} - 1 = \frac{30}{8} = \frac{15}{4}$

$Var(2X - 1) = 2^2 Var(X) = 4 \times \frac{63}{64} = \frac{63}{16}$

Q4 a) $E(X) = (1 \times 0.1) + (2 \times 0.2) + (3 \times 0.25)$
$+ (4 \times 0.2) + (5 \times 0.1) + (6 \times 0.15) = 3.45$

b) $Var(X) = E(X^2) - (E(X))^2$
$E(X^2) = (1 \times 0.1) + (4 \times 0.2) + (9 \times 0.25)$
$+ (16 \times 0.2) + (25 \times 0.1) + (36 \times 0.15) = 14.25$
So $Var(X) = 14.25 - 3.45^2 = 2.3475$

Q5 a) (i) $E(X) = [8 \times 0.2] + [10 \times 0.3]$
$+ [15 \times 0.1] + [20 \times 0.4]$
$= 14.1$

$E(X^2) = [64 \times 0.2] + [100 \times 0.3]$
$+ [225 \times 0.1] + [400 \times 0.4]$
$= 225.3$

$Var(X) = 225.3 - 14.1^2 = 26.49$

(ii) $E(Y) = E(4X + 3) = 4E(X) + 3$
$= (4 \times 14.1) + 3 = 59.4$
$Var(Y) = Var(4X + 3) = 16Var(X) = 16 \times 26.49$
$= 423.84$

(iii) $E(Z) = E(50 - 2X) = 50 - 2E(X)$
$= 50 - (2 \times 14.1) = 21.8$
$Var(Z) = Var(50 - 2X) = (-2)^2 Var(X)$
$= 4 \times 26.49 = 105.96$

b) (i) $E(X) = [-4 \times \frac{1}{2}] + [-1 \times \frac{1}{4}] + [0 \times \frac{1}{8}]$
$+ [2 \times \frac{1}{16}] + [5 \times \frac{1}{32}] + [6 \times \frac{1}{32}]$
$= -\frac{57}{32} = -1.78$ to 3 s.f.
$E(X^2) = [16 \times \frac{1}{2}] + [1 \times \frac{1}{4}] + [0 \times \frac{1}{8}]$
$+ [4 \times \frac{1}{16}] + [25 \times \frac{1}{32}] + [36 \times \frac{1}{32}]$
$= \frac{333}{32} = 10.4$ to 3 s.f.
$\text{Var}(X) = \frac{333}{32} - \left(-\frac{57}{32}\right)^2 = \frac{7407}{1024}$
$= 7.23$ to 3 s.f.

(ii) $E(Y) = E(7 - 2X) = 7 - 2E(X)$
$= 7 - \left(2 \times \left(-\frac{57}{32}\right)\right) = \frac{169}{16} = 10.5625$
$\text{Var}(Y) = \text{Var}(7 - 2X) = (-2)^2\text{Var}(X) = 4 \times \frac{7407}{1024}$
$= \frac{7407}{256} = 28.9$ to 3 s.f.

(iii) $E(Z) = E(7 + 2X) = 7 + 2E(X)$
$= 7 + \left(2 \times \left(-\frac{57}{32}\right)\right) = \frac{55}{16} = 3.4375$
$\text{Var}(Z) = \text{Var}(7 + 2X) = (+2)^2\text{Var}(X) = 4 \times \frac{7407}{1024}$
$= \frac{7407}{256} = 28.9$ to 3 s.f.

Exam-Style Questions — Chapter 1

1 a) The probability of getting 3 heads is:
$\frac{1}{2} \times \frac{1}{2} \times \frac{1}{2} = \frac{1}{8}$ ***[1 mark]***
The probability of getting 2 heads is:
$3 \times \frac{1}{2} \times \frac{1}{2} \times \frac{1}{2} = \frac{3}{8}$ (multiply by 3 because any of the three coins could be the tail — the order in which the heads and the tail occur isn't important). ***[1 mark]***
Similarly the probability of getting 1 head is:
$3 \times \frac{1}{2} \times \frac{1}{2} \times \frac{1}{2} = \frac{3}{8}$
And the probability of getting no heads is:
$\frac{1}{2} \times \frac{1}{2} \times \frac{1}{2} = \frac{1}{8}$
So the probability of 1 or no heads
$= \frac{3}{8} + \frac{1}{8} = \frac{1}{2}$ ***[1 mark]***
Hence the probability distribution of X is:

x	20p	10p	*nothing*
$P(X = x)$	$\frac{1}{8}$	$\frac{3}{8}$	$\frac{1}{2}$

[1 mark]

b) You need the probability that $X > 10\text{p}$ ***[1 mark]***
This is just $P(X = 20\text{p}) = \frac{1}{8}$ ***[1 mark]***

2 a) All the probabilities must add up to 1, so $2k + 3k + k + k = 1$, i.e. $7k = 1$, and so $k = \frac{1}{7}$. ***[1 mark]***

b) (i) $E(X) = (0 \times \frac{2}{7}) + (1 \times \frac{3}{7}) + (2 \times \frac{1}{7}) + (3 \times \frac{1}{7})$ ***[1 mark]***
$= \frac{8}{7} = 1.14$ (3 s.f.) ***[1 mark]***

(ii) $E(X^2) = (0 \times \frac{2}{7}) + (1 \times \frac{3}{7}) + (4 \times \frac{1}{7}) + (9 \times \frac{1}{7})$
$= \frac{16}{7}$ ***[1 mark]***
$\text{Var}(X) = E(X^2) - [E(X)]^2$
$= \frac{16}{7} - \left(\frac{8}{7}\right)^2$ ***[1 mark]***
$= \frac{48}{49} = 0.980$ (3 s.f.) ***[1 mark]***

c) $\text{Var}(Y) = \text{Var}\left(\frac{2X^2 + 3X}{X}\right) = \text{Var}(2X + 3)$
$= 4\text{Var}(X)$ ***[1 mark]***
$= 4 \times \frac{48}{49} = \frac{192}{49} = 3.92$ (3 s.f.) ***[1 mark]***

d) (i) $P(X < 2) = P(X = 0) + P(X = 1)$
$= \frac{2}{7} + \frac{3}{7} = \frac{5}{7}$ ***[1 mark]***

(ii) $P(Y > 3 \mid X < 2) = \frac{P(Y > 3 \text{ and } X < 2)}{P(X < 2)}$ ***[1 mark]***
But $Y > 3$ means $X > 0$ (since $Y = 2X + 3$).
So $P(Y > 3 \mid X < 2) = \frac{P(X > 0 \text{ and } X < 2)}{P(X < 2)}$
$= \frac{P(X = 1)}{P(X < 2)}$ ***[1 mark]***
$= \frac{3/7}{5/7} = \frac{3}{5}$ ***[1 mark]***

3 a) $E\left(\frac{1}{X}\right) = \left(\frac{1}{1} \times \frac{1}{4}\right) + \left(\frac{1}{2} \times \frac{2}{4}\right) + \left(\frac{1}{3} \times \frac{3}{48}\right)$
$+ \left(\frac{1}{4} \times \frac{4}{48}\right) + \left(\frac{1}{5} \times \frac{5}{48}\right)$
$= \frac{9}{16} = 0.5625$ ***[1 mark]***
$E\left(\left(\frac{1}{X}\right)^2\right) = E\left(\frac{1}{X^2}\right)$
$= \left(\frac{1}{1^2} \times \frac{1}{4}\right) + \left(\frac{1}{2^2} \times \frac{2}{4}\right)$
$+ \left(\frac{1}{3^2} \times \frac{3}{48}\right) + \left(\frac{1}{4^2} \times \frac{4}{48}\right)$
$+ \left(\frac{1}{5^2} \times \frac{5}{48}\right)$ ***[1 mark]***
$= \frac{1127}{2880} = 0.3913$ (4 s.f.) ***[1 mark]***
$\text{Var}\left(\frac{1}{X}\right) = E\left(\left(\frac{1}{X}\right)^2\right) - \left[E\left(\frac{1}{X}\right)\right]^2$
$= \frac{1127}{2880} - \left(\frac{9}{16}\right)^2$ ***[1 mark]***
$= \frac{863}{11520} = 0.0749$ (3 s.f.) ***[1 mark]***

b) Perimeter of the square, $P = \frac{4}{X} \times 4 = \frac{16}{X}$ ***[1 mark]***.
$E(P) = E\left(\frac{16}{X}\right) = 16E\left(\frac{1}{X}\right)$
$= 16 \times \frac{9}{16} = 9$ ***[1 mark]***.
$\text{Var}(P) = \text{Var}\left(\frac{16}{X}\right) = 16^2\text{Var}\left(\frac{1}{X}\right)$
$= 16^2 \times \frac{863}{11520}$ ***[1 mark]***
$= \frac{863}{45} = 19.2$ (3 s.f.) ***[1 mark]***

4 a) $P(X = 1) = a$, $P(X = 2) = 2a$, $P(X = 3) = 3a$.
Therefore the total probability is $3a + 2a + a = 6a$.
This must equal 1, so $a = \frac{1}{6}$. ***[1 mark]***

b) $E(X) = \left(1 \times \frac{1}{6}\right) + \left(2 \times \frac{2}{6}\right) + \left(3 \times \frac{3}{6}\right)$
$= \frac{1 + 4 + 9}{6}$ ***[1 mark]***
$= \frac{7}{3}$ ***[1 mark]***

c) $E(X^2) = \text{Var}(X) + [E(X)]^2$
$= \frac{5}{9} + \left(\frac{7}{3}\right)^2 = \frac{5 + 49}{9}$ ***[1 mark]***
$= \frac{54}{9} = 6$ ***[1 mark]***

d) $E(3X + 4) = 3E(X) + 4 = 3 \times \frac{7}{3} + 4 = 11$ ***[1 mark]***
$\text{Var}(3X + 4) = 3^2\text{Var}(X) = 9 \times \frac{5}{9}$ ***[1 mark]***
$= 5$ ***[1 mark]***

5 a) $E(X) = (0 \times 0.4) + (1 \times 0.3) + (2 \times 0.2) + (3 \times 0.1)$
$= 0 + 0.3 + 0.4 + 0.3$ ***[1 mark]***
$= 1$ ***[1 mark]***

b) $E(6X + 8) = 6E(X) + 8 = 6 + 8$ ***[1 mark]***
$= 14$ ***[1 mark]***

c) The formula for variance is
$\text{Var}(X) = E(X^2) - [E(X)]^2$
So first work out $E(X^2)$:
$E(X^2) = (0^2 \times 0.4) + (1^2 \times 0.3) + (2^2 \times 0.2) + (3^2 \times 0.1)$
$= 0.3 + 0.8 + 0.9$ ***[1 mark]***
$= 2$ ***[1 mark]***
Then complete the formula by using your answer to part a):
$\text{Var}(X) = E(X^2) - [E(X)]^2 = 2 - (1^2)$ ***[1 mark]***
$= 1$ ***[1 mark]***

d) $\text{Var}(aX + b) = a^2\text{Var}(X)$
$\text{Var}(5 - 3X)$
$= (-3)^2\text{Var}(X) = 9\text{Var}(X)$ ***[1 mark]***
$= 9 \times 1$
$= 9$ ***[1 mark]***

6 a) $E(X) = [0 \times a] + [1 \times 5b] + [2 \times b] + [3 \times 0.2]$
$= 7b + 0.6$ ***[1 mark]***
So $1.3 = 7b + 0.6$ ***[1 mark]*** $\Rightarrow b = 0.1$ ***[1 mark]***
All the probabilities must add up to 1 so:
$a + 0.5 + 0.1 + 0.2 = 1$ ***[1 mark]***
$\Rightarrow a = 0.2$ ***[1 mark]***

b) $E(\frac{10}{13}X + 3) = \frac{10}{13}E(X) + 3$ ***[1 mark]***
$= (\frac{10}{13} \times 1.3) + 3 = 4$ ***[1 mark]***

c) $E(X^2) = [0^2 \times 0.2] + [1^2 \times 0.5] + [2^2 \times 0.1] + [3^2 \times 0.2] = 2.7$ ***[1 mark]***
$\text{Var}(X) = E(X^2) - (E(X))^2$ ***[1 mark]***
$= 2.7 - 1.3^2 = 1.01$ ***[1 mark]***

d) $\text{Var}(4 - X) = (-1)^2\text{Var}(X)$ ***[1 mark]***
$= 1.01$ ***[1 mark]***

Chapter 2: The Poisson Distribution

1. Poisson Distributions

Exercise 1.1 — The Poisson distribution

Q1 a) The daisies occur randomly, singly and at a constant average 'rate' of 10 daisies per square metre. So D will follow a Poisson distribution — in fact, $D \sim \text{Po}(10)$.

b) The flaws occur randomly, singly and at a constant average rate of 0.5 flaws per square metre. So F will follow a Poisson distribution — in fact, $F \sim \text{Po}(0.5)$.

c) Because the water has been standing for 24 hours, the gravel particles will not occur randomly throughout the water — they'll have sunk to the bottom. So P does not follow a Poisson distribution.

d) Because the water has just been vigorously stirred, the micro-organisms should be randomly scattered throughout the water. They also occur singly and at a constant average rate of 40 per litre. So M will follow a Poisson distribution — in fact, $M \sim \text{Po}(40)$.

Q2 No, the number of sheep in a randomly chosen square metre of field (X) is unlikely to follow a Poisson distribution. This is because the sheep are probably not randomly scattered, but are likely to be near the corner containing their food.

Exercise 1.2 — Using the Poisson probability function

Q1 a) $P(X = 1) = \frac{e^{-2}2^1}{1!} = 0.271$ (to 3 sig. fig.)

b) $P(X = 0) = \frac{e^{-2}2^0}{0!} = 0.135$ (to 3 sig. fig.)

c) $P(X = 4) = \frac{e^{-2}2^4}{4!} = 0.0902$ (to 3 sig. fig.)

Q2 a) $P(X = 4) = \frac{e^{-3}3^4}{4!} = 0.168$ (to 3 sig. fig.)

b) $P(X \le 1) = P(X = 0) + P(X = 1)$
$= \frac{e^{-3}3^0}{0!} + \frac{e^{-3}3^1}{1!}$
$= 0.04978... + 0.14936...$
$= 0.199$ (to 3 sig. fig.)

c) $P(4 \le X \le 6) = P(X = 4) + P(X = 5) + P(X = 6)$
$= \frac{e^{-3}3^4}{4!} + \frac{e^{-3}3^5}{5!} + \frac{e^{-3}3^6}{6!}$
$= 0.16803... + 0.10081... + 0.05040...$
$= 0.319$ (to 3 sig. fig.)

Q3 a) $P(X = 3) = \frac{e^{-3.8}3.8^3}{3!} = 0.205$ (to 3 sig. fig.)

b) $P(X < 3) = P(X = 0) + P(X = 1) + P(X = 2)$

$$= \frac{e^{-3.8}3.8^0}{0!} + \frac{e^{-3.8}3.8^1}{1!} + \frac{e^{-3.8}3.8^2}{2!}$$

$= 0.02237... + 0.08500... + 0.16151...$

$= 0.26889... = 0.269$ (to 3 sig. fig.)

c) $P(X \geq 3) = 1 - P(X < 3) = 1 - 0.26889...$

$= 0.731$ (to 3 sig. fig.)

Q4 $P(X > 3) = 1 - P(X \leq 3)$

$= 1 - P(X = 0) - P(X = 1) - P(X = 2) - P(X = 3)$

$$= 1 - \frac{e^{-1.4}1.4^0}{0!} - \frac{e^{-1.4}1.4^1}{1!} - \frac{e^{-1.4}1.4^2}{2!} - \frac{e^{-1.4}1.4^3}{3!}$$

$= 1 - 0.24659... - 0.34523... - 0.24166... - 0.11277...$

$= 0.0537$ (to 3 sig. fig.)

Q5 a) The flaws occur randomly, singly and at a constant average rate of 0.2 per metre.
So $X \sim Po(0.2)$.

b) (i) $P(X = 0) = \frac{e^{-0.2}0.2^0}{0!} = 0.819$ (to 3 sig. fig.)

(ii) $P(X < 2) = P(X = 0) + P(X = 1)$

$$= \frac{e^{-0.2}0.2^0}{0!} + \frac{e^{-0.2}0.2^1}{1!}$$

$= 0.81873... + 0.16374...$

$= 0.98247... = 0.982$ (to 3 sig. fig.)

Q6 a) If X represents the number of phone calls arriving at the switchboard in a randomly chosen minute, then $X \sim Po(12)$.

$P(X = 12) = \frac{e^{-12}12^{12}}{12!} = 0.114$ (to 3 sig. fig.)

b) $P(10 \leq X \leq 13) = P(X = 10) + P(X = 11) + P(X = 12) + P(X = 13)$

$$= \frac{e^{-12}12^{10}}{10!} + \frac{e^{-12}12^{11}}{11!} + \frac{e^{-12}12^{12}}{12!} + \frac{e^{-12}12^{13}}{13!}$$

$= 0.10483... + 0.11436... + 0.11436... + 0.10557...$

$= 0.439$ (to 3 sig. fig.)

Exercise 1.3 — Mean and variance of a Poisson distribution

Q1 a) (i) 9 **(ii)** 9

b) (i) 12 **(ii)** 12

c) (i) 4.3 **(ii)** 4.3

Q2 a) $\mu = 9, \sigma^2 = 9$

b) $\sigma = 3$

c) $P(X = \mu + \sigma) = P(X = 12) = \frac{e^{-9}9^{12}}{12!}$

$= 0.0728$ (to 3 sig. fig.)

Q3 a) $\mu = 16, \sigma^2 = 16$

b) $\sigma = 4$

c) $P(X \leq \sigma) = P(X \leq 4)$

$= P(X = 0) + P(X = 1) + P(X = 2) + P(X = 3) + P(X = 4)$

$= 0.00000... + 0.00000... + 0.00001... + 0.00007... + 0.00030...$

$= 0.0004$ (to 4 d.p.)

Q4 a) The mean of this data is $\bar{x} = \frac{\sum fx}{\sum f}$.

And the variance is given by $\frac{\sum fx^2}{\sum f} - \bar{x}^2$

It's easiest if you extend the table as below.

Rentals per week (x)	5	6	7	8	9	10	11	12	13
Frequency (f)	4	6	3	8	16	9	3	2	1
fx	20	36	21	64	144	90	33	24	13
x^2	25	36	49	64	81	100	121	144	169
fx^2	100	216	147	512	1296	900	363	288	169

Find the totals of the 2nd and 3rd rows:
$\sum f = 52$ and $\sum fx = 445$

So $\bar{x} = \frac{445}{52} = 8.557... = 8.56$ (to 3 sig. fig.)

Find the total of the 5th row:
$\sum fx^2 = 3991$

So variance $= \frac{\sum fx^2}{\sum f} - \bar{x}^2 = \frac{3991}{52} - (8.557...)^2$

$= 3.515... = 3.52$ (to 3 sig. fig.)

b) The assumption seems to be wrong. The values probably **don't** follow a Poisson distribution, as the mean and the variance are very different.

Exercise 1.4 — Additive property of the Poisson distribution

Q1 a) $X \sim Po(600)$

b) Since $1 \text{ mm}^2 = 1 \text{ cm}^2 \div 100$, $Y \sim Po(6)$

c) $P(Y = 3) = \frac{e^{-6}6^3}{3!} = 0.0892$ (to 3 sig. fig.)

Q2 If the random variable X represents the number of potholes in 1 km of road, then $X \sim Po(3)$.
So if Y represents the number of potholes in a randomly chosen 8 km stretch of this road, then $Y \sim Po(8 \times 3) = Po(24)$.

$P(20 \leq Y \leq 22) = P(Y = 20) + P(Y = 21) + P(Y = 22)$

$$= \frac{e^{-24}24^{20}}{20!} + \frac{e^{-24}24^{21}}{21!} + \frac{e^{-24}24^{22}}{22!}$$

$= 0.06237... + 0.07128... + 0.07777...$

$= 0.211$ (to 3 sig. fig.)

Q3 a) Let the random variable L represent the number of texts received by Louise in 1 day, and the random variable H represent the number of texts received by Hannah in 1 day. Then $L \sim Po(4)$ and $H \sim Po(2)$.
So the total number of text messages Louise and Hannah receive in 1 day is $L + H$, and $L + H \sim Po(4 + 2) = Po(6)$.

This means that the probability of this total being equal to 5 is $P(L + H = 5) = \frac{e^{-6}6^5}{5!}$

$= 0.161$ (to 3 sig. fig.)

b) The total number of texts received by the two girls in 1 week equals $7(L + H)$, where $7(L + H) \sim Po(7 \times 6) = Po(42)$.
So $P(7(L + H) = 44) = \frac{e^{-42}42^{44}}{44!}$
$= 0.0573$ (to 3 sig. fig.).

Q4 Let the random variable W represent the number of wizard books sold in 1 day, and the random variable B represent the number of celebrity biographies sold in 1 day. Then $W \sim Po(20)$ and $B \sim Po(15)$.
This means the total number of these types of books sold in a day is
$W + B \sim Po(20 + 15) = Po(35)$.
$P(W + B = 40) = \frac{e^{-35}35^{40}}{40!} = 0.0447$ (to 3 sig. fig.)

2. Using Poisson Tables

Exercise 2.1 — Using tables to find probabilities

Q1 Use the column for $\lambda = 2$.

a) $P(X \le 3) = 0.8571$

b) $P(X \le 7) = 0.9989$

c) $P(X < 5) = P(X \le 4) = 0.9473$

Q2 Use the column for $\lambda = 7.5$.

a) $P(X > 6) = 1 - P(X \le 6) = 1 - 0.3782 = 0.6218$

b) $P(X = 9) = P(X \le 9) - P(X \le 8)$
$= 0.7764 - 0.6620 = 0.1144$

c) $P(2 \le X \le 8) = P(X \le 8) - P(X \le 1)$
$= 0.6620 - 0.0047 = 0.6573$

Q3 Use the column for $\lambda = 6$.

a) $P(X > 4) = 1 - P(X \le 4) = 1 - 0.2851 = 0.7149$

b) $P(2 < X \le 5) = P(X \le 5) - P(X \le 2)$
$= 0.4457 - 0.0620 = 0.3837$

c) $P(4 \le X < 9) = P(X \le 8) - P(X \le 3)$
$= 0.8472 - 0.1512 = 0.6960$

Q4 Use the column for $\lambda = 5.5$.

a) $P(X > 2) = 1 - P(X \le 2) = 1 - 0.0884 = 0.9116$

b) $P(X = 4) = P(X \le 4) - P(X \le 3)$
$= 0.3575 - 0.2017 = 0.1558$

c) $P(2 \le X \le 7) = P(X \le 7) - P(X \le 1)$
$= 0.8095 - 0.0266 = 0.7829$

Q5 a) Let X represent the number of telephone calls received in a random minute. Then $X \sim Po(8)$.
Use the Poisson table with $\lambda = 8$.
$P(X = 6) = P(X \le 6) - P(X \le 5)$
$= 0.3134 - 0.1912 = 0.1222$

b) $P(X \ge 3) = 1 - P(X < 3) = 1 - P(X \le 2)$
$= 1 - 0.0138 = 0.9862$

Q6 a) Let X represent the number of tadpoles in 10 cm^3 of water. Then $X \sim Po(0.1)$. So if Y represents the number of tadpoles in 1 litre of water, then $Y \sim Po(100 \times 0.1) = Po(10)$.
So use the Poisson table with $\lambda = 10$.
$P(X < 7) = P(X \le 6) = 0.1301$

b) $P(X > 15) = 1 - P(X \le 15) = 1 - 0.9513 = 0.0487$

Exercise 2.2 — Using tables 'backwards'

Q1 Use the column for $\lambda = 5.5$.

a) If $P(X \le x) = 0.5289$, then $x = 5$.

b) If $P(X < x) = 0.9983$, then $P(X \le x - 1) = 0.9983$.
This means $x - 1 = 13$, i.e. $x = 14$.

Q2 Use the column for $\lambda = 3.4$.

a) If $P(Y > y) = 0.8532$, then $P(Y \le y) = 1 - 0.8532 = 0.1468$. Use tables to find that $y = 1$.

b) If $P(Y \ge y) = 0.1295$, then $P(Y < y) = 1 - 0.1295 = 0.8705$. This means $P(Y \le y - 1) = 0.8705$.
Use tables to find that $y - 1 = 5$, i.e. $y = 6$.

Q3 Use the column for $\lambda = 1.8$.
You need to find the largest value of x for which $P(X < x) \le 0.25$, or $P(X \le x - 1) \le 0.25$.
$P(X \le 0) = 0.1653 < 0.25$, but
$P(X \le 1) = 0.4628 > 0.25$, so the value of x you need is given by $x - 1 = 0$, or $x = 1$.

Q4 $X \sim Po(8)$, so use the column for $\lambda = 8$.
You need to find the smallest value of x for which $P(X \ge x) < 0.05$.
$P(X \le 12) = 0.9362$, so $P(X > 12) = P(X \ge 13)$
$= 1 - 0.9362 = 0.0638 > 0.05$.
$P(X \le 13) = 0.9658$, so $P(X > 13) = P(X \ge 14)$
$= 1 - 0.9658 = 0.0342 < 0.05$.
So the smallest possible value of x where $P(X \ge x) < 0.05$ is $x = 14$.

Q5 If X represents the number of inflatables the company rents out in one hour, then $X \sim Po(6)$.
If the company is to be at least 90% certain of meeting demand, then it needs at least x inflatables, where $P(X > x) < 0.1$.
This means $P(X \le x) = 1 - P(X > x) > 0.9$.
Using the column for $\lambda = 6$: $P(X \le 8) = 0.8472 < 0.9$, but $P(X \le 9) = 0.9161 > 0.9$, so the company needs at least 9 inflatables.

Q6 If X represents the number of breakdowns in one month, then $X \sim Po(0.5)$. So if Y represents the number of breakdowns in four months, then $Y \sim Po(4 \times 0.5) = Po(2)$.
You need to find the minimum value of y for which $P(Y > y) < 0.1$.
Using the column for $\lambda = 2$: $P(Y \le 3) = 0.8571$, and so $P(Y > 3) = 1 - 0.8571 = 0.1429 > 0.1$.
But $P(Y \le 4) = 0.9473$, and so
$P(Y > 4) = 1 - 0.9473 = 0.0527 < 0.1$.
This means that the minimum value of y for which the supplier has a probability of less than 0.1 of paying the penalty is $y = 4$.

Review Exercise — Chapter 2

Q1 **a)** $P(X = 2) = \frac{e^{-3.1} \times 3.1^2}{2!} = 0.21646...$
$= 0.2165$ (to 4 d.p.).

b) $P(X = 1) = \frac{e^{-3.1} \times 3.1}{1!} = 0.13965...$
$= 0.1397$ (to 4 d.p.).

c) $P(X = 0) = \frac{e^{-3.1} \times 3.1^0}{0!} = 0.04504....$
$= 0.0450$ (to 4 d.p.).

d) $P(X < 3) = P(X = 0) + P(X = 1) + P(X = 2)$
$= 0.04504... + 0.13965... + 0.21646...$
$= 0.40116... = 0.4012$ (to 4 d.p.)

e) $P(X \geq 3) = 1 - P(X < 3)$
$= 1 - 0.40116... = 0.5988$ (to 4 d.p.).

Q2 **a)** $P(X = 2) = \frac{e^{-8.7} \times 8.7^2}{2!} = 0.00630...$
$= 0.0063$ (to 4 d.p.).

b) $P(X = 1) = \frac{e^{-8.7} \times 8.7}{1!} = 0.00144...$
$= 0.0014$ (to 4 d.p.).

c) $P(X = 0) = \frac{e^{-8.7} \times 8.7^0}{0!} = 0.00016...$
$= 0.0002$ (to 4 d.p.).

d) $P(X < 3) = P(X = 0) + P(X = 1) + P(X = 2)$
$= 0.00016... + 0.00144... + 0.00630...$
$= 0.00792... = 0.0079$ (to 4 d.p.)

e) $P(X \geq 3) = 1 - P(X < 3)$
$= 1 - 0.00792... = 0.9921$ (to 4 d.p.).

Q3 **a)** $E(X) = Var(X) = 8$
standard deviation $= \sigma = \sqrt{8} = 2.828$ (to 3 d.p.).

b) $E(X) = Var(X) = 12.11$
standard deviation $= \sigma$
$= \sqrt{12.11} = 3.480$ (to 3 d.p.).

c) $E(X) = Var(X) = 84.2227$
standard deviation $= \sigma$
$= \sqrt{84.2227} = 9.177$ (to 3 d.p.).

Q4 Using tables:

a) $P(X \leq \mu) = P(X \leq 9) = 0.5874$
$P(X \leq \mu - \sigma) = P(X \leq 9 - 3) = P(X \leq 6) = 0.2068$

b) $P(X \leq \mu) = P(X \leq 4) = 0.6288$
$P(X \leq \mu - \sigma) = P(X \leq 4 - 2) = P(X \leq 2) = 0.2381$

Q5 **a)** The defective products occur randomly, singly and (on average) at a constant rate, and the random variable represents the number of 'events' (i.e. defective products) within a fixed period, so this would follow a Poisson distribution.

b) There is a fixed number of trials in this situation, and so this situation would be modelled by a binomial distribution. (Or you could say it won't follow a Poisson distribution, as the events don't occur at a constant average rate over the 25 trials.)

c) If the random variable represents the number of people joining the queue within a fixed period, and assuming that the people join the queue randomly, singly and (on average) at a constant rate, then this would follow a Poisson distribution.
You do need to make a couple of assumptions here — the Poisson model wouldn't work if you had, say, big groups of factory workers all coming in together a couple of minutes after the lunchtime hooter sounds.

d) The mistakes occur randomly, singly and (on average) at a constant rate, and the random variable represents the number of mistakes within a fixed 'period' (i.e. the number of pages in the document), so this would follow a Poisson distribution.

Q6 **a)** The number of atoms decaying in an hour would follow the Poisson distribution Po(2000).
So the number decaying in a minute would follow $Po(2000 \div 60) = Po(33\frac{1}{3})$.

b) The number of atoms decaying in a day would follow $Po(2000 \times 24) = Po(48\,000)$.

Q7 **a)** If X represents the number of atoms from the first sample decaying per minute, then $X \sim Po(60)$. And if Y represents the number of atoms from the second sample decaying per minute, then $Y \sim Po(90)$. So $X + Y$ (the total number of atoms decaying per minute) $\sim Po(60 + 90) = Po(150)$.

b) The total number of atoms decaying per hour would be distributed as $Po(150 \times 60) = Po(9000)$.

Q8 **a)** $P(X \leq 2) = 0.0138$

b) $P(X \leq 7) = 0.4530$

c) $P(X \leq 5) = 0.1912$

d) $P(X < 9) = P(X \leq 8) = 0.5925$

e) $P(X \geq 8) = 1 - P(X < 8) = 1 - P(X \leq 7)$
$= 1 - 0.4530 = 0.5470$

f) $P(X > 1) = 1 - P(X \leq 1) = 1 - 0.0030 = 0.9970$

g) $P(X > 7) = 1 - P(X \leq 7) = 1 - 0.4530 = 0.5470$

h) $P(X = 6) = P(X \leq 6) - P(X \leq 5)$
$= 0.3134 - 0.1912 = 0.1222$

i) $P(X = 4) = P(X \leq 4) - P(X \leq 3)$
$= 0.0996 - 0.0424 = 0.0572$

j) $P(X = 3) = P(X \leq 3) - P(X \leq 2)$
$= 0.0424 - 0.0138 = 0.0286$

Q9 If X represents the number of geese in a random square metre of field, then $X \sim Po(1)$ — since the 'rate' at which geese occur is constant, they're randomly scattered, and geese only occur singly.

a) $P(X = 0) = \frac{e^{-1} \times 1^0}{0!} = 0.3679$

b) $P(X = 1) = \frac{e^{-1} \times 1^1}{1!} = 0.3679$

c) $P(X = 2) = \frac{e^{-1} \times 1^2}{2!} = 0.1839$

d) $P(X > 2) = 1 - P(X \leq 2)$
$= 1 - (0.3679 + 0.3679 + 0.1839)$
$= 1 - 0.9197 = 0.0803$
Here, you could use either your Poisson tables or the probability function.

Exam-Style Questions — Chapter 2

1 a) Events need to happen at a constant average rate ***[1 mark]*** and singly ('one at a time') ***[1 mark]***.
You could also have had 'events occur randomly' or 'independently'.

b) (i) If X represents the number of chaffinches visiting the observation spot in an hour, then $X \sim \text{Po}(7)$ ***[1 mark]***.
Using tables, $P(X < 4) = P(X \leq 3) = 0.0818$ ***[1 mark]***.

(ii) $P(X \geq 7) = 1 - P(X < 7) = 1 - P(X \leq 6)$ ***[1 mark]***
$= 1 - 0.4497 = 0.5503$ ***[1 mark]***

(iii) $P(X = 9) = P(X \leq 9) - P(X \leq 8)$ ***[1 mark]***
$= 0.8305 - 0.7291 = 0.1014$ ***[1 mark]***
Or you could work this last one out using the formula: $P(X = 9) = \frac{e^{-7}7^9}{9!} = 0.1014$
— you get the same answer either way.

c) The number of birds of any species visiting per hour would follow the distribution $\text{Po}(22 + 7) = \text{Po}(29)$ ***[1 mark]***. So the total number of birds visiting in a random 15-minute period will follow $\text{Po}(29 \div 4) = \text{Po}(7.25)$ ***[1 mark]***.

$P(X = 3) = \frac{e^{-7.25} \times 7.25^3}{3!}$ ***[1 mark]***
$= 0.045$ (to 3 d.p.) ***[1 mark]***.

2 a) (i) If the mean is 20, then the number of calls per hour follows Po(20). So the number of calls in a random 30-minute period follows $\text{Po}(20 \div 2) = \text{Po}(10)$ ***[1 mark]***.
Using tables for $\lambda = 10$:
$P(X = 8) = P(X \leq 8) - P(X \leq 7)$ ***[1 mark]***
$= 0.3328 - 0.2202 = 0.1126$ ***[1 mark]***
Or you could work this out using the formula:
$P(X = 8) = \frac{e^{-10}10^8}{8!} = 0.1126.$

(ii) $P(X > 8) = 1 - P(X \leq 8)$ ***[1 mark]***
$= 1 - 0.3328 = 0.6672$ ***[1 mark]***

b) In this context, independently means that receiving a phone call at one particular instant does not affect whether or not a call will be received at a different instant ***[1 mark]***.

3 a) (i) Let the random variable X represent the number of errors in the document.
Then since the document contains $4 \times 5 = 20$ lines, $X \sim \text{Po}(4 \times 1) = \text{Po}(4)$ ***[1 mark]***.
$P(X = 0) = \frac{e^{-4}4^0}{0!} = 0.0183$ (to 4 d.p.) ***[1 mark]***.
Or you could use Poisson tables here:
$P(X = 0) = P(X \leq 0) = 0.0183$.

(ii) $P(X > 10) = 1 - P(X \leq 10)$
$= 1 - 0.9972$ ***[1 mark]***
$= 0.0028$ ***[1 mark]***

b) (i) Since the document contains $36 \times 5 = 180$ lines, $Y \sim \text{Po}(36 \times 1) = \text{Po}(36)$ ***[1 mark]***.

(ii) $\text{Var}(Y) = 36$
And so the standard deviation of Y is $\sqrt{36} = 6$ ***[1 mark]***.

4 a) It's assumed that $X \sim \text{Po}(6)$.
$P(4 < X \leq 7) = P(X \leq 7) - P(X \leq 4)$ ***[1 mark]***
$= 0.7440 - 0.2851 = 0.4589$ ***[1 mark]***

b) Let Y be the number of rucksacks sold in a random two-month period.
Then $Y \sim \text{Po}(12)$ ***[1 mark]***.
$P(Y > 14) = 1 - P(Y \leq 14)$ ***[1 mark]***
$= 1 - 0.7720 = 0.2280$ ***[1 mark]***

c) $P(X = 6) = \frac{e^{-6} \times 6^6}{6!}$ ***[1 mark]*** $= 0.1606...$,
so the probability they sell 6 rucksacks in one month is 0.1606...
Assuming each month's sales are independent, the probability they sell 6 in each of 3 consecutive months is $(0.1606...)^3$ ***[1 mark]***
$= 0.00414... = 0.004$ (1 s.f.) ***[1 mark]***.

d) The mean of this sample data is
$\bar{x} = \frac{\sum x}{n} = \frac{48}{8} = 6$ ***[1 mark]***.
For this sample data, the variance is:
$$s^2 = \frac{n}{n-1}\left[\frac{\sum x^2}{n} - \left(\frac{\sum x}{n}\right)^2\right]$$
$$= \frac{8}{7}\left[\frac{394}{8} - (6)^2\right] \textit{ [1 mark]}$$
$$= \frac{8}{7} \times \left(\frac{394}{8} - 36\right) = \frac{8}{7} \times \left(\frac{394}{8} - \frac{288}{8}\right)$$
$$= \frac{8}{7} \times \frac{106}{8} = \frac{106}{7} = 15.1 \text{ (3 s.f.)} \textit{ [1 mark]}$$
If you use the formula $\frac{\sum x^2}{n} - \left(\frac{\sum x}{n}\right)^2$ *to calculate the variance, you won't lose any marks here. Although it's sample data, you're not using the sample variance to estimate the population variance.*

Since the mean and variance of the distribution are very different, the assumption that X follows a Poisson distribution seems to be invalid. ***[1 mark]***

5 a) (i) Let the random variable M represent the number of people mistyping their password in a randomly chosen 10-minute period.
Then $M \sim \text{Po}(30 \div 6) = \text{Po}(5)$ ***[1 mark]***.
Using Poisson tables for $\lambda = 5$:
$P(M > 10) = 1 - P(M \leq 10) = 1 - 0.9863$
$= 0.0137$ ***[1 mark]***.

(ii) $P(10 \leq M \leq 15) = P(M \leq 15) - P(M \leq 9)$ ***[1 mark]***
$= 0.9999 - 0.9682$
$= 0.0317$ ***[1 mark]***

b) (i) Mean $= \frac{\sum x}{n} = \frac{752}{24} = 31.33$ people per hour (to 2 d.p.) ***[1 mark]***.
Variance $= \frac{\sum x^2}{n} - \left(\frac{\sum x}{n}\right)^2 = \frac{24338}{24} - \left(\frac{752}{24}\right)^2$
[1 mark]
So variance $= 32.31$ (to 2 d.p.) ***[1 mark]***.

(ii) The mean is approximately equal to the variance, which means a Poisson distribution is appropriate ***[1 mark]***.

(iii) If X is the number of people mistyping their password in the randomly chosen hour, then $X \sim \text{Po}(31.33)$ ***[1 mark]***.

So $P(X = 30) = \frac{e^{-31.33} \times 31.33^{30}}{30!}$ ***[1 mark]***

$= 0.0706$ (to 3 sig. fig.) ***[1 mark]***.

Chapter 3: Continuous Random Variables

1. Probability Density Functions

Exercise 1.1 — Probability density functions

Q1 a) (i) First check that f(x) cannot be negative.

x^2 is non-negative for all x, so $\frac{1}{2}x^2$ must always be non-negative and $f(x) \geq 0$ for all $x \in \mathbb{R}$.

Now you just need to check that the total probability is 1.

$$\int_{-\infty}^{\infty} f(x)\,dx = \int_{-\infty}^{0} f(x)\,dx + \int_{0}^{2} f(x)\,dx + \int_{2}^{\infty} f(x)\,dx$$

$$= \int_{-\infty}^{0} 0\,dx + \int_{0}^{2} \frac{1}{2}x^2\,dx + \int_{2}^{\infty} 0\,dx$$

$$= \int_{0}^{2} \frac{1}{2}x^2\,dx = \left[\frac{x^3}{2 \times 3}\right]_0^2 = \left[\frac{x^3}{6}\right]_0^2$$

$$= \left(\frac{2^3}{6}\right) - \left(\frac{0^3}{6}\right) = \frac{8}{6} = \frac{4}{3}$$

Okay... I'm not going to write in the integrals where the p.d.f. is zero any more — you can see they're always going to disappear.

So the probability is not equal to 1 and f(x) is not a p.d.f.

(ii) The function is not a p.d.f.

b) (i) x^2 is positive for all x, so $\frac{3}{4}x^2$ must always be positive and $f(x) \geq 0$ for all $x \in \mathbb{R}$.

Now work out the total area:

$$\int_{-\infty}^{\infty} f(x)\,dx = \int_{1}^{2} f(x)\,dx$$

$$= \int_{1}^{2} \frac{3}{4}x^2\,dx$$

$$= \left[\frac{3x^3}{4 \times 3}\right]_1^2 = \left[\frac{x^3}{4}\right]_1^2$$

$$= \left(\frac{2^3}{4}\right) - \left(\frac{1^3}{4}\right) = \frac{7}{4}$$

So the probability is not equal to 1 and f(x) is not a p.d.f.

(ii) The function is not a p.d.f.

c) (i) The graph of $y = 1 - \frac{1}{2}x$ looks like this:

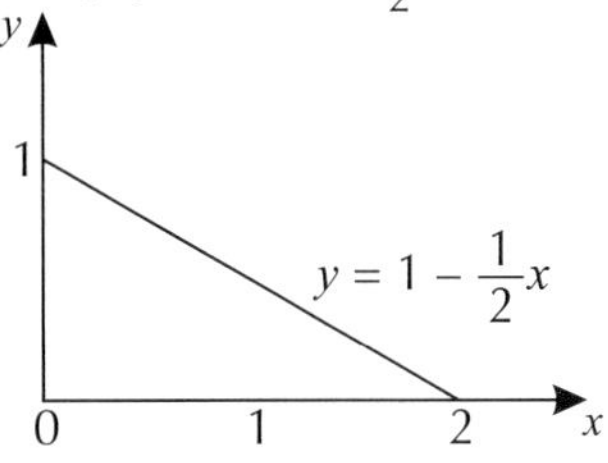

So this function is always non-negative in the range $0 < x < 2$, so $f(x) \geq 0$ for all $x \in \mathbb{R}$.

Work out the total area:

$$\int_{-\infty}^{\infty} f(x)\,dx = \int_{0}^{2} f(x)\,dx$$

$$= \int_{0}^{2} \left(1 - \frac{1}{2}x\right)dx$$

$$= \left[x - \frac{x^2}{4}\right]_0^2$$

$$= \left(2 - \frac{2^2}{4}\right) - \left(0 - \frac{0^2}{4}\right)$$

$$= (2 - 1) - 0 = 1$$

So the total area is 1, and this function is a p.d.f.

(ii)

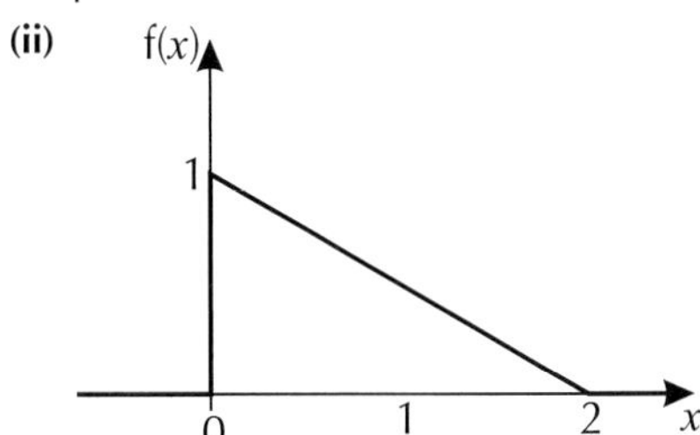

d) (i) When x is non-negative, x^3 is non-negative, so $\frac{1}{4}x^3$ is non-negative for $0 < x < 2$ and $f(x) \geq 0$ for all $x \in \mathbb{R}$.

Work out the total area:

$$\int_{-\infty}^{\infty} f(x)\,dx = \int_{-\infty}^{0} f(x)\,dx + \int_{0}^{2} f(x)\,dx + \int_{2}^{\infty} f(x)\,dx$$

$$= \int_{-\infty}^{0} 1\,dx + \int_{0}^{2} \frac{1}{4}x^3\,dx + \int_{2}^{\infty} 1\,dx$$

$$= [x]_{-\infty}^{0} + \left[\frac{x^4}{16}\right]_0^2 + [x]_2^{\infty}$$

The first and third integrals are both undefined — they are infinite. So the total area is not equal to 1 and this function is not a p.d.f.

(ii) The function is not a p.d.f.

e) (i) x^2 is always non-negative, so $x^2 + 5$ must also always be non-negative and $f(x) \geq 0$ for all $x \in \mathbb{R}$.

Work out the total area:

$$\int_{-\infty}^{\infty} f(x)\,dx = \int_1^2 f(x)\,dx$$
$$= \int_1^2 (x^2 + 5)\,dx$$
$$= \left[\frac{x^3}{3} + 5x\right]_1^2$$
$$= \left(\frac{2^3}{3} + 5(2)\right) - \left(\frac{1^3}{3} + 5(1)\right)$$
$$= \left(\frac{8}{3} + 10\right) - \left(\frac{1}{3} + 5\right) = \frac{22}{3}$$

So the total area is not 1 and this function is not a p.d.f.

(ii) $f(x)$ is not a p.d.f.

f) (i) $y = \frac{2}{9}(3x - x^2) = \frac{2}{9}x(3 - x)$ is a quadratic with negative x^2-coefficient and roots at $x = 0$ and $x = 3$.

So it looks like this:

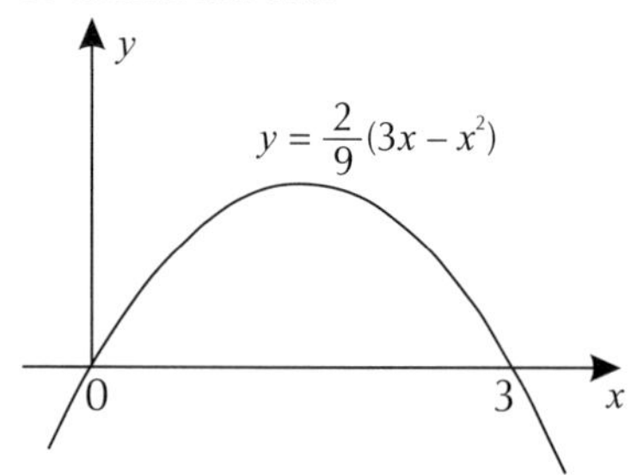

So it is non-negative for $0 < x < 3$, which means $f(x) \geq 0$ for all $x \in \mathbb{R}$.

Work out the total area:

$$\int_{-\infty}^{\infty} f(x)\,dx = \int_0^3 f(x)\,dx$$
$$= \int_0^3 \frac{2}{9}(3x - x^2)\,dx$$
$$= \left[\frac{2}{9}\left(\frac{3x^2}{2} - \frac{x^3}{3}\right)\right]_0^3$$
$$= \left(\frac{2}{9}\left(\frac{3 \times 3^2}{2} - \frac{3^3}{3}\right)\right) - \left(\frac{2}{9}\left(\frac{3 \times 0^2}{2} - \frac{0^3}{3}\right)\right)$$
$$= \left(\frac{2}{9}\left(\frac{27}{2} - \frac{27}{3}\right)\right) - 0 = 1 - 0 = 1$$

So the total area is 1, and this function is a p.d.f.

(ii)

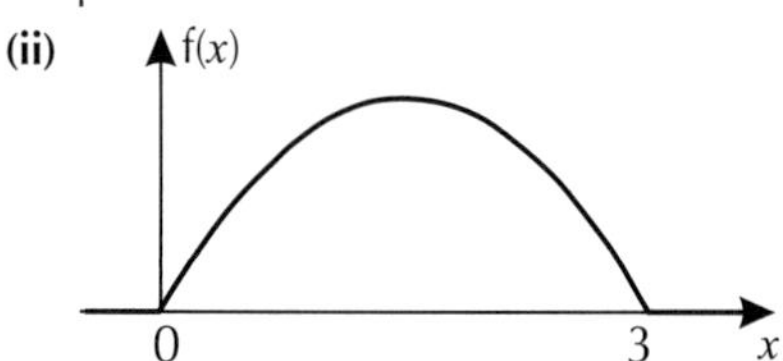

g) (i) The curve with equation $y = x^2 - \frac{5}{3} = \left(x + \sqrt{\frac{5}{3}}\right)\left(x - \sqrt{\frac{5}{3}}\right)$ is a quadratic with positive x^2-coefficient and roots at $\pm\sqrt{\frac{5}{3}}$.

So the graph looks like this:

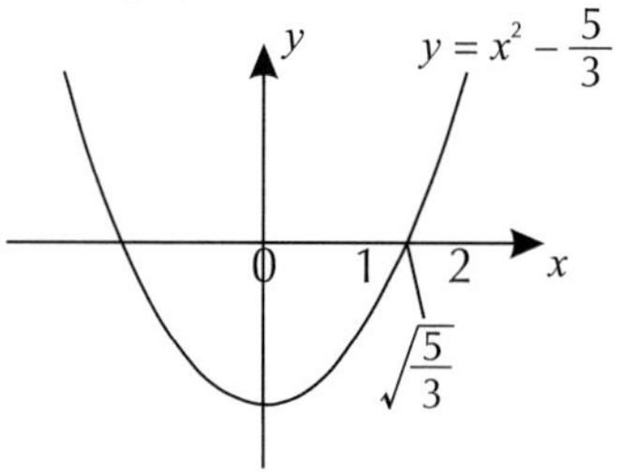

So the function $f(x)$ is negative for $1 \leq x < \sqrt{\frac{5}{3}}$, so the function $f(x)$ is not a p.d.f.

(ii) The function is not a p.d.f.

h) (i) 0.2 is clearly positive and x^2 is non-negative for all x, so $0.5x^2$ is also non-negative. Therefore $f(x) \geq 0$ for all $x \in \mathbb{R}$.

Work out the total area:

$$\int_{-\infty}^{\infty} f(x)\,dx = \int_0^1 f(x)\,dx + \int_1^3 f(x)\,dx$$
$$= \int_0^1 0.2\,dx + \int_1^3 0.5x^2\,dx$$
$$= [0.2x]_0^1 + \left[\frac{0.5x^3}{3}\right]_1^3$$
$$= [0.2 - 0] + \left[\frac{0.5(3)^3}{3} - \frac{0.5(1)^3}{3}\right]$$
$$= 0.2 + \frac{9}{2} - \frac{1}{6} = \frac{68}{15}$$

So the total area is not equal to 1, which means the function is not a p.d.f.

(ii) The function is not a p.d.f.

Q2 a) The total area must be equal to 1, so work the integral out in terms of k and then set it equal to 1 to find k:

$$\int_{-\infty}^{\infty} f(x)\,dx = \int_1^2 f(x)\,dx$$
$$= \int_1^2 kx^2\,dx$$
$$= \left[\frac{kx^3}{3}\right]_1^2$$
$$= \left(\frac{k(2)^3}{3}\right) - \left(\frac{k(1)^3}{3}\right)$$
$$= \frac{8k}{3} - \frac{k}{3} = \frac{7k}{3}$$

So let $\frac{7k}{3} = 1 \Rightarrow k = \frac{3}{7}$.

b) Find the total area:

$$\int_{-\infty}^{\infty} f(x)\,dx = \int_0^2 f(x)\,dx$$
$$= \int_0^2 kx^3\,dx$$
$$= \left[\frac{kx^4}{4}\right]_0^2$$
$$= \left(\frac{k(2)^4}{4}\right) - \left(\frac{k(0)^4}{4}\right)$$
$$= 4k$$

So let $4k = 1 \Rightarrow k = \frac{1}{4}$

c) $$\int_{-\infty}^{\infty} f(x)\,dx = \int_0^1 f(x)\,dx + \int_1^2 f(x)\,dx$$
$$= \int_0^1 k\,dx + \int_1^2 kx\,dx$$
$$= [kx]_0^1 + \left[\frac{kx^2}{2}\right]_1^2$$
$$= [k - 0] + \left[\frac{k(2)^2}{2} - \frac{k(1)^2}{2}\right]$$
$$= k + \left[2k - \frac{k}{2}\right] = \frac{5k}{2}$$

So let $\frac{5k}{2} = 1 \Rightarrow k = \frac{2}{5}$

d) $$\int_{-\infty}^{\infty} f(x)\,dx = \int_0^1 f(x)\,dx + \int_1^2 f(x)\,dx$$
$$= \int_0^1 \frac{1}{3}\,dx + \int_1^2 k(1 - x^2)\,dx$$
$$= \left[\frac{1}{3}x\right]_0^1 + \left[k\left(x - \frac{x^3}{3}\right)\right]_1^2$$
$$= \left[\frac{1}{3} - 0\right] + \left[\left(k\left(2 - \frac{2^3}{3}\right)\right) - \left(k\left(1 - \frac{1^3}{3}\right)\right)\right]$$
$$= \frac{1}{3} + \left[\left(-\frac{2}{3}k\right) - \left(\frac{2}{3}k\right)\right]$$
$$= \frac{1}{3} - \frac{4}{3}k$$

So $\frac{1}{3} - \frac{4}{3}k = 1 \Rightarrow \frac{4}{3}k = -\frac{2}{3} \Rightarrow k = -\frac{2}{4} = -\frac{1}{2}$

Exercise 1.2 — Finding probabilities from probability density functions

Q1 a) $f(x) = 1 - \frac{1}{2}x$ when $0 < x < 1$, so just integrate this expression between the limits.

$$P(0 < X < 1) = \int_0^1 \left(1 - \frac{1}{2}x\right)dx = \left[x - \frac{x^2}{4}\right]_0^1$$
$$= \left(1 - \frac{1^2}{4}\right) - \left(0 - \frac{0^2}{4}\right)$$
$$= \frac{3}{4} - 0 = \frac{3}{4}$$

b) $f(x) = 1 - \frac{1}{2}x$ when $\frac{1}{2} < x < 1$, so:

$$P\left(\frac{1}{2} < X < 1\right) = \int_{\frac{1}{2}}^1 \left(1 - \frac{1}{2}x\right)dx = \left[x - \frac{x^2}{4}\right]_{\frac{1}{2}}^1$$
$$= \left(1 - \frac{1^2}{4}\right) - \left(\frac{1}{2} - \frac{\left(\frac{1}{2}\right)^2}{4}\right)$$
$$= \frac{3}{4} - \frac{7}{16} = \frac{5}{16}$$

Q2 $f(x) = 2(1 - x)$ when $0.25 < x < 0.75$ so:

$$P(0.25 < X < 0.75) = \int_{0.25}^{0.75} 2(1 - x)\,dx$$
$$= \int_{0.25}^{0.75} (2 - 2x)\,dx = [2x - x^2]_{0.25}^{0.75}$$
$$= (2(0.75) - (0.75)^2) - (2(0.25) - (0.25)^2)$$
$$= 0.5$$

Q3 a) $$P(X < 1) = \int_{-\infty}^1 f(x)\,dx = \int_{-\infty}^0 0\,dx + \int_0^1 \frac{1}{4}x^3\,dx$$
$$= \int_0^1 \frac{1}{4}x^3\,dx = \left[\frac{x^4}{16}\right]_0^1 = \left(\frac{1^4}{16}\right) - \left(\frac{0^4}{16}\right)$$
$$= \frac{1}{16}$$

b) $$P(1 < X < 2) = \int_1^2 f(x)\,dx = \int_1^2 \frac{1}{4}x^3\,dx$$
$$= \left[\frac{x^4}{16}\right]_1^2 = \left(\frac{2^4}{16}\right) - \left(\frac{1^4}{16}\right)$$
$$= 1 - \frac{1}{16} = \frac{15}{16}$$

You could do part b) more quickly if you notice that it has to be '1 – answer to part a)' (since the area under the graph between x = 0 and x = 2 has to be 1).

Q4 $$P(1 < X < 2) = \int_1^2 \frac{2}{9}(3x - x^2)\,dx$$
$$= \frac{2}{9}\int_1^2 (3x - x^2)\,dx = \frac{2}{9}\left[\left(\frac{3x^2}{2} - \frac{x^3}{3}\right)\right]_1^2$$
$$= \frac{2}{9}\left[\left(\frac{3(2)^2}{2} - \frac{2^3}{3}\right) - \left(\frac{3(1)^2}{2} - \frac{1^3}{3}\right)\right]$$
$$= \frac{2}{9}\left[\frac{10}{3} - \frac{7}{6}\right] = \frac{2}{9}\left(\frac{13}{6}\right) = \frac{13}{27}$$

Q5 a) $$P(X < 1) = \int_{-\infty}^1 f(x)\,dx = \int_{-\infty}^0 0\,dx + \int_0^1 \frac{2}{5}\,dx$$
$$= \int_0^1 \frac{2}{5}\,dx = \left[\frac{2}{5}x\right]_0^1 = \frac{2}{5} - 0 = \frac{2}{5}$$

If you want, you could do this without integrating — the area you're finding is just the area of a rectangle with width 1 and height 2/5.

b) $$P\left(\frac{1}{2} < X < \frac{3}{2}\right) = \int_{\frac{1}{2}}^{\frac{3}{2}} f(x)\,dx = \int_{\frac{1}{2}}^1 \frac{2}{5}\,dx + \int_1^{\frac{3}{2}} \frac{2}{5}x\,dx$$
$$= \left[\frac{2}{5}x\right]_{\frac{1}{2}}^1 + \left[\frac{x^2}{5}\right]_1^{\frac{3}{2}}$$
$$= \left[\left(\frac{2}{5} \times 1\right) - \left(\frac{2}{5} \times \frac{1}{2}\right)\right] + \left[\left(\frac{\left(\frac{3}{2}\right)^2}{5}\right) - \left(\frac{(1)^2}{5}\right)\right]$$
$$= \frac{1}{5} + \left[\frac{9}{20} - \frac{1}{5}\right] = \frac{9}{20}$$

Notice that we had to split this function into two different integrals and add them together. This is because between $\frac{1}{2}$ and $\frac{3}{2}$ the function is defined differently for different values of x.

Q6 a) $$P(0 < X < 1.5) = \int_0^{1.5} f(x)\,dx$$
$$= \int_0^1 \frac{1}{3}\,dx + \int_1^{1.5} \frac{1}{3}(2x - 1)\,dx$$
$$= \left[\frac{1}{3}x\right]_0^1 + \left[\frac{1}{3}(x^2 - x)\right]_1^{1.5}$$
$$= \left[\frac{1}{3} - 0\right]$$
$$+ \left(\frac{1}{3}((1.5)^2 - (1.5))\right) - \left(\frac{1}{3}(1^2 - 1)\right)$$
$$= \frac{1}{3} + \left[\frac{1}{4} - 0\right] = \frac{7}{12}$$

b) $P(X = 1) = 0$ because the probability of X being equal to an exact value is always 0.

2. Cumulative Distribution Functions

Exercise 2.1 — Cumulative distribution functions

Q1 a) F(x) is not a c.d.f. To be a c.d.f. it must have $0 \le F(x) \le 1$ for all x, but if $x = 2$, $F(2) = -1$.

b) The graph of F(x) looks like this:

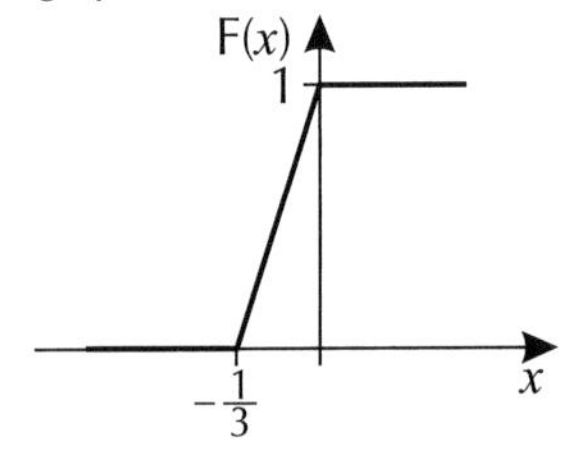

You can see from the graph that it is non-decreasing, it all joins up and it lies between 0 and 1. It satisfies all the properties of a c.d.f., so F(x) is a c.d.f.

c) The graph of F(x) looks like this:

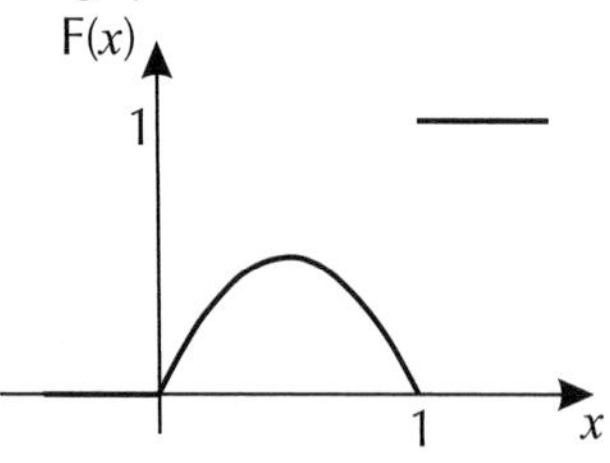

F(x) is decreasing for $0.5 < x < 1$ and it doesn't 'join up' at $x = 1$. So F(x) isn't a c.d.f.

Q2 a) If $x < 0$, $F(x) = 0$ and if $x > 2$, $F(x) = 1$.

For $0 \le x \le 2$:
$$F(x) = \int_{-\infty}^{x} f(t)\,dt = \int_{-\infty}^{0} 0\,dt + \int_0^x \left(1 - \frac{1}{2}t\right)dt$$
$$= 0 + \left[t - \frac{t^2}{4}\right]_0^x = x - \frac{x^2}{4}$$

So
$$F(x) = \begin{cases} 0 & x < 0 \\ x - \frac{x^2}{4} & 0 \le x \le 2 \\ 1 & x > 2 \end{cases}$$

b) If $x < 0$, $F(x) = 0$ and if $x > 1$, $F(x) = 1$.

For $0 \le x \le 1$:
$$F(x) = \int_{-\infty}^{x} f(t)\,dt = \int_{-\infty}^{0} f(t)\,dt + \int_0^x f(t)\,dt$$
$$= \int_{-\infty}^{0} 0\,dt + \int_0^x 2(1 - t)\,dt$$
$$= 0 + \left[2\left(t - \frac{t^2}{2}\right)\right]_0^x = [2t - t^2]_0^x = 2x - x^2$$

So
$$F(x) = \begin{cases} 0 & x < 0 \\ 2x - x^2 & 0 \le x \le 1 \\ 1 & x > 1 \end{cases}$$

c) If $x < 1$, $F(x) = 0$ and if $x > 2$, $F(x) = 1$.

For $1 \le x \le 2$:
$$F(x) = \int_{-\infty}^{x} f(t)\,dt = \int_{-\infty}^{1} f(t)\,dt + \int_1^x f(t)\,dt$$
$$= \int_{-\infty}^{1} 0\,dt + \int_1^x \frac{3}{7}t^2\,dt$$
$$= 0 + \left[\frac{3t^3}{7 \times 3}\right]_1^x = \frac{x^3}{7} - \frac{1}{7}$$

So
$$F(x) = \begin{cases} 0 & x < 1 \\ \frac{x^3}{7} - \frac{1}{7} & 1 \le x \le 2 \\ 1 & x > 2 \end{cases}$$

d) If $x < 0$, $F(x) = 0$ and if $x > 2$, $F(x) = 1$.

For $0 \le x \le 2$:
$$F(x) = \int_{-\infty}^{x} f(t)\,dt = \int_{-\infty}^{0} f(t)\,dt + \int_0^x f(t)\,dt$$
$$= \int_{-\infty}^{0} 0\,dt + \int_0^x \frac{1}{4}(6t^2 - 3t^3)\,dt$$
$$= 0 + \left[\frac{1}{4}\left(2t^3 - \frac{3t^4}{4}\right)\right]_0^x$$
$$= \frac{1}{4}\left(2x^3 - \frac{3x^4}{4}\right) = \frac{x^3}{2} - \frac{3x^4}{16}$$

So
$$F(x) = \begin{cases} 0 & x < 0 \\ \frac{x^3}{2} - \frac{3x^4}{16} & 0 \le x \le 2 \\ 1 & x > 2 \end{cases}$$

e) If $x < 0$, $F(x) = 0$ and if $x > 3$, $F(x) = 1$.

For $0 \le x \le 3$:
$$F(x) = \int_{-\infty}^{x} f(t)\,dt = \int_{-\infty}^{0} f(t)\,dt + \int_0^x f(t)\,dt$$
$$= \int_{-\infty}^{0} 0\,dt + \int_0^x \frac{2}{9}(3t - t^2)\,dt$$
$$= 0 + \left[\frac{2}{9}\left(\frac{3t^2}{2} - \frac{t^3}{3}\right)\right]_0^x$$
$$= \left[\frac{t^2}{3} - \frac{2t^3}{27}\right]_0^x = \frac{x^2}{3} - \frac{2x^3}{27}$$

So
$$F(x) = \begin{cases} 0 & x < 0 \\ \frac{x^2}{3} - \frac{2x^3}{27} & 0 \le x \le 3 \\ 1 & x > 3 \end{cases}$$

Q3 a) For $x < 0$, $F(x) = 0$.

For $0 \le x < 1$:

$$F(x) = \int_{-\infty}^{x} f(t)\,dt = \int_{-\infty}^{0} f(t)\,dt + \int_{0}^{x} f(t)\,dt$$
$$= F(0) + \int_{0}^{x} \frac{2}{5}\,dt = 0 + \left[\frac{2}{5}t\right]_0^x = \frac{2}{5}x$$

This tells you that $F(1) = \frac{2}{5}$

For $1 \le x \le 2$:

$$F(x) = \int_{-\infty}^{x} f(t)\,dt = \int_{-\infty}^{1} f(t)\,dt + \int_{1}^{x} f(t)\,dt$$
$$= F(1) + \int_{1}^{x} \frac{2}{5}t\,dt = \frac{2}{5} + \left[\frac{2t^2}{5 \times 2}\right]_1^x$$
$$= \frac{2}{5} + \left[\frac{t^2}{5}\right]_1^x = \frac{2}{5} + \left(\frac{x^2}{5} - \frac{1}{5}\right) = \frac{1}{5}(x^2 + 1)$$

$F(2) = \frac{1}{5}(4 + 1) = 1$, so the pieces join up.

So

$$F(x) = \begin{cases} 0 & x < 0 \\ \frac{2}{5}x & 0 \le x < 1 \\ \frac{1}{5}(x^2 + 1) & 1 \le x \le 2 \\ 1 & x > 2 \end{cases}$$

b) For $x \le 0$, $F(x) = 0$.

For $0 < x < 1$:

$$F(x) = \int_{-\infty}^{x} f(t)\,dt = \int_{-\infty}^{0} f(t)\,dt + \int_{0}^{x} f(t)\,dt$$
$$= F(0) + \int_{0}^{x} \frac{1}{3}\,dt = 0 + \left[\frac{1}{3}t\right]_0^x = \frac{1}{3}x$$

This tells you that $F(1) = \frac{1}{3}$

For $1 \le x < 2$:

$$F(x) = \int_{-\infty}^{x} f(t)\,dt = \int_{-\infty}^{1} f(t)\,dt + \int_{1}^{x} f(t)\,dt$$
$$= F(1) + \int_{1}^{x} \frac{1}{3}(2t - 1)\,dt = \frac{1}{3} + \left[\frac{1}{3}(t^2 - t)\right]_1^x$$
$$= \frac{1}{3} + \left[\left(\frac{1}{3}(x^2 - x)\right) - \left(\frac{1}{3}(1^2 - 1)\right)\right]$$
$$= \frac{1}{3} + \left[\left(\frac{1}{3}(x^2 - x)\right) - 0\right]$$
$$= \frac{1}{3}(x^2 - x + 1)$$

$F(2) = \frac{1}{3}(4 - 2 + 1) = \frac{3}{3} = 1$, so the pieces join up.

So

$$F(x) = \begin{cases} 0 & x \le 0 \\ \frac{1}{3}x & 0 < x < 1 \\ \frac{1}{3}(x^2 - x + 1) & 1 \le x < 2 \\ 1 & x \ge 2 \end{cases}$$

Q4 a) For $x < 0$, $F(x) = 0$.

For $0 \le x < 1$:

$$F(x) = \int_{-\infty}^{x} f(t)\,dt = \int_{-\infty}^{0} f(t)\,dt + \int_{0}^{x} f(t)\,dt$$
$$= F(0) + \int_{0}^{x} \frac{1}{3}\,dt = 0 + \left[\frac{1}{3}t\right]_0^x = \frac{1}{3}x$$

This tells you $F(1) = \frac{1}{3}$.

For $1 \le x \le 2$:

$$F(x) = \int_{-\infty}^{x} f(t)\,dt = \int_{-\infty}^{1} f(t)\,dt + \int_{1}^{x} f(t)\,dt$$
$$= F(1) + \int_{1}^{x} -\frac{1}{2}(1 - t^2)\,dt$$
$$= \frac{1}{3} + \left[-\frac{1}{2}\left(t - \frac{t^3}{3}\right)\right]_1^x$$
$$= \frac{1}{3} + \left[\frac{t^3}{6} - \frac{t}{2}\right]_1^x = \frac{1}{3} + \left[\left(\frac{x^3}{6} - \frac{x}{2}\right) - \left(\frac{1}{6} - \frac{1}{2}\right)\right]$$
$$= \frac{x^3}{6} - \frac{x}{2} + \frac{2}{3} = \frac{1}{6}(x^3 - 3x + 4)$$

$F(2) = \frac{1}{6}(8 - 6 + 4) = 1$, so the pieces join up.

So

$$F(x) = \begin{cases} 0 & x < 0 \\ \frac{1}{3}x & 0 \le x < 1 \\ \frac{1}{6}(x^3 - 3x + 4) & 1 \le x \le 2 \\ 1 & x > 2 \end{cases}$$

You could have done this using the constants of integration approach... but you should have ended up with the same final answer.

b) $x = \frac{3}{4}$ is in $0 \le x < 1$ so use $F(x) = \frac{1}{3}x$.

$$F\left(\frac{3}{4}\right) = \frac{1}{3} \times \frac{3}{4} = \frac{1}{4} = 0.25$$

Exercise 2.2 — Finding probability density functions by differentiating

Q1 a)
$$f(x) = \frac{d}{dx}(F(x)) = \begin{cases} 0 & x < 0 \\ 6x - 6x^2 & 0 \le x \le 1 \\ 0 & x > 1 \end{cases}$$
$$= \begin{cases} 6x - 6x^2 & 0 \le x \le 1 \\ 0 & \text{otherwise} \end{cases}$$

b)
$$f(x) = \frac{d}{dx}(F(x)) = \begin{cases} 0 & x < 0 \\ \frac{1}{4}(3x^2 + 6x) & 0 \le x \le 1 \\ 0 & x > 1 \end{cases}$$
$$= \begin{cases} \frac{3}{4}(x^2 + 2x) & 0 \le x \le 1 \\ 0 & \text{otherwise} \end{cases}$$

c)
$$f(x) = \frac{d}{dx}(F(x)) = \begin{cases} 0 & x < 0 \\ \frac{1}{4} & 0 \le x < 1 \\ \frac{1}{5}x^3 & 1 \le x \le 2 \\ 0 & x > 2 \end{cases}$$
$$= \begin{cases} \frac{1}{4} & 0 \le x < 1 \\ \frac{1}{5}x^3 & 1 \le x \le 2 \\ 0 & \text{otherwise} \end{cases}$$

Q2 a) $f(x) = \frac{d}{dx}(F(x)) = \begin{cases} 0 & x < 1 \\ \frac{2}{3}x & 1 \le x \le 2 \\ 0 & x > 2 \end{cases}$

$= \begin{cases} \frac{2}{3}x & 1 \le x \le 2 \\ 0 & \text{otherwise} \end{cases}$

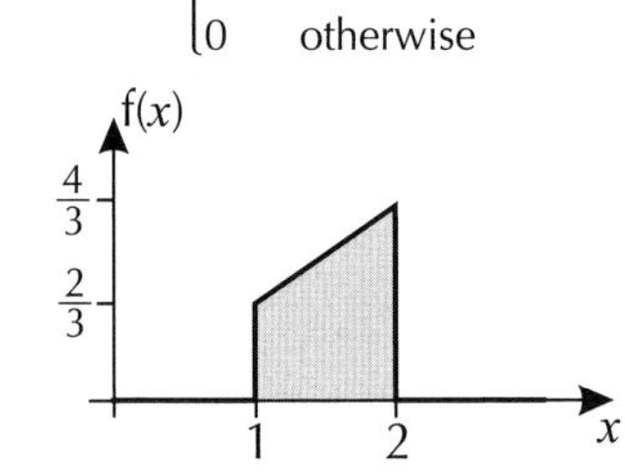

b) $f(x) = \frac{d}{dx}(F(x)) = \begin{cases} 0 & x < 0 \\ \frac{1}{3} & 0 \le x < 2 \\ \frac{2}{3} - \frac{1}{6}x & 2 \le x \le 4 \\ 0 & x > 4 \end{cases}$

$= \begin{cases} \frac{1}{3} & 0 \le x < 2 \\ \frac{2}{3} - \frac{1}{6}x & 2 \le x \le 4 \\ 0 & \text{otherwise} \end{cases}$

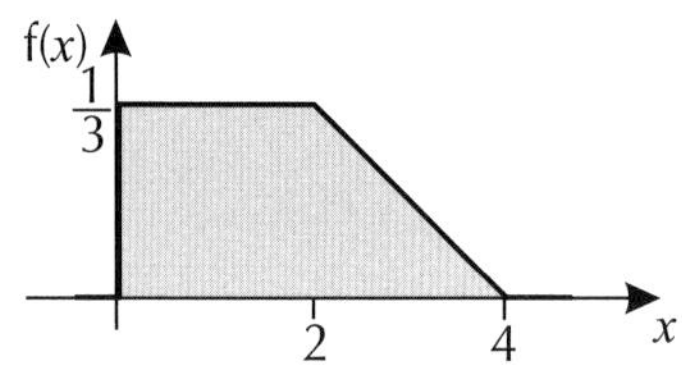

Exercise 2.3 — Finding probabilities using a cumulative distribution function

Q1 a) $P(X \le 0.2) = F(0.2)$

$= \frac{1}{4}((0.2)^3 + 3(0.2)^2) = 0.032$

b) $P(X < 0.5) = P(X \le 0.5) = F(0.5)$

$= \frac{1}{4}((0.5)^3 + 3(0.5)^2) = 0.219\,(3\text{ d.p.})$

c) $P(0.3 \le X \le 0.8) = P(X \le 0.8) - P(X < 0.3)$

$= P(X \le 0.8) - P(X \le 0.3)$

$= F(0.8) - F(0.3)$

$= \frac{1}{4}((0.8)^3 + 3(0.8)^2)$

$- \frac{1}{4}((0.3)^3 + 3(0.3)^2)$

$= 0.534$

Q2 a) $P(X \le 1) = F(1) = \frac{1}{3}(1) = \frac{1}{3}$

b) $P(X > 3) = 1 - P(X \le 3) = 1 - F(3)$

$= 1 - \left(\frac{2}{3}(3) - \frac{1}{12}(3)^2 - \frac{1}{3}\right)$

$= 1 - \left(2 - \frac{3}{4} - \frac{1}{3}\right) = \frac{1}{12}$

c) $P(1 \le X \le 2) = P(X \le 2) - P(X < 1)$

$= P(X \le 2) - P(X \le 1)$

$= F(2) - F(1)$

$= \left(\frac{2}{3}(2) - \frac{1}{12}(2)^2 - \frac{1}{3}\right) - \frac{1}{3}(1)$

$= \left(\frac{4}{3} - \frac{1}{3} - \frac{1}{3}\right) - \frac{1}{3}$

$= \frac{1}{3}$

Remember... the different 'pieces' of a c.d.f. must join smoothly, so you can check your value of F(2) using the definition of F(x) for 0 ≤ x < 2 (which is a slightly easier formula).

Q3 a) For $x < 0$, $F(x) = 0$ and for $x > 4$, $F(x) = 1$.

For $0 \le x \le 4$:

$F(x) = \int_{-\infty}^{x} f(t)\,dt = \int_{-\infty}^{0} f(t)\,dt + \int_{0}^{x} f(t)\,dt$

$= \int_{-\infty}^{0} 0\,dt + \int_{0}^{x} \frac{1}{8}t\,dt$

$= 0 + \left[\frac{t^2}{8 \times 2}\right]_0^x = \frac{x^2}{16}$

So $F(x) = \begin{cases} 0 & x < 0 \\ \frac{x^2}{16} & 0 \le x \le 4 \\ 1 & x > 4 \end{cases}$

b) (i) $P(X < 1) = P(X \le 1) = F(1) = \frac{1^2}{16} = 0.0625$

(ii) $P(2 < X < 3) = P(X < 3) - P(X \le 2)$

$= P(X \le 3) - P(X \le 2)$

$= F(3) - F(2)$

$= \frac{3^2}{16} - \frac{2^2}{16} = \frac{5}{16} = 0.3125$

Q4 a) $\int \frac{1}{12}\,dx = \frac{1}{12}x + C_1$

b) The above integral equals F(x) for $0 \le x \le 1$.
So if $F(0) = 0$, then $C_1 = 0$.

c) $\int -\frac{1}{3}(1 - x^3)\,dx = -\frac{1}{3}\left(x - \frac{x^4}{4}\right) + C_2$

$= -\frac{x}{3} + \frac{x^4}{12} + C_2$

d) The above integral equals F(x) for $1 < x \le 2$.
So if $F(2) = 1$, then

$-\frac{2}{3} + \frac{2^4}{12} + C_2 = 1 \Rightarrow \frac{2}{3} + C_2 = 1 \Rightarrow C_2 = \frac{1}{3}$

e) $F(x) = \begin{cases} 0 & x < 0 \\ \frac{1}{12}x & 0 \le x \le 1 \\ \frac{x^4}{12} - \frac{x}{3} + \frac{1}{3} & 1 < x \le 2 \\ 1 & x > 2 \end{cases}$

f) (i) $P(X < 0.5) = F(0.5) = 0.5 \div 12 = \frac{1}{24}$

(ii) $P(X > 1.5) = 1 - P(X \le 1.5) = 1 - F(1.5)$
$= 1 - 0.2552... = 0.745$ (to 3 d.p.).

Q5 a) For $x < 0$, $F(x) = 0$ and for $x > 5$, $F(x) = 1$.

For $0 \le x < 3$:

$$F(x) = \int_{-\infty}^{x} f(t)\,dt = \int_{-\infty}^{0} f(t)\,dt + \int_{0}^{x} f(t)\,dt$$
$$= F(0) + \int_{0}^{x} \frac{1}{4}\,dt = 0 + \left[\frac{1}{4}t\right]_0^x = \frac{1}{4}x$$

This tells you that $F(3) = \frac{3}{4}$.

For $3 \le x \le 5$:

$$F(x) = \int_{-\infty}^{x} f(t)\,dt = \int_{-\infty}^{3} f(t)\,dt + \int_{3}^{x} f(t)\,dt$$
$$= F(3) + \int_{3}^{x} \frac{1}{8}(5 - t)\,dt$$
$$= \frac{3}{4} + \left[\frac{1}{8}\left(5t - \frac{t^2}{2}\right)\right]_3^x$$
$$= \frac{3}{4} + \left[\frac{1}{8}\left(5x - \frac{x^2}{2}\right) - \frac{1}{8}\left(15 - \frac{9}{2}\right)\right]$$
$$= \frac{5x}{8} - \frac{x^2}{16} - \frac{9}{16}$$

When $x = 5$, $F(x) = \frac{25}{8} - \frac{25}{16} - \frac{9}{16} = 1$, so the pieces match up.

So
$$F(x) = \begin{cases} 0 & x < 0 \\ \frac{1}{4}x & 0 \le x < 3 \\ \frac{5x}{8} - \frac{x^2}{16} - \frac{9}{16} & 3 \le x \le 5 \\ 1 & x > 5 \end{cases}$$

b) (i) $P(X < 2) = P(X \le 2) = F(2) = \frac{1}{4}(2) = 0.5$

(ii) $P(X > 4) = 1 - P(X \le 4) = 1 - F(4)$
$$= 1 - \left(\frac{5(4)}{8} - \frac{(4)^2}{16} - \frac{9}{16}\right) = \frac{1}{16} = 0.0625$$

(iii) $P(1 \le X \le 3) = P(X \le 3) - P(X \le 1)$
$$= F(3) - F(1) = \frac{1}{4}(3) - \frac{1}{4}(1) = 0.5$$

(iv) $P(X = 4.5) = 0$

The probability of a continuous random variable taking any single value is 0.

3. Mean and Variance

Exercise 3.1 — Mean of a continuous random variable

Q1 a) $E(X) = \int_{-\infty}^{\infty} xf(x)\,dx = \int_{0}^{2} x\left(1 - \frac{1}{2}x\right)dx$
$$= \int_{0}^{2}\left(x - \frac{1}{2}x^2\right)dx = \left[\frac{x^2}{2} - \frac{x^3}{6}\right]_0^2$$
$$= \left(\frac{2^2}{2} - \frac{2^3}{6}\right) - \left(\frac{0^2}{2} - \frac{0^3}{6}\right) = \frac{2}{3}$$

b) $E(X) = \int_{-\infty}^{\infty} xf(x)\,dx = \int_{0}^{2} x\left(\frac{1}{4}x^3\right)dx$
$$= \int_{0}^{2}\frac{1}{4}x^4\,dx = \left[\frac{x^5}{20}\right]_0^2 = \frac{32}{20} = \frac{8}{5}$$

c) $E(X) = \int_{-\infty}^{\infty} xf(x)\,dx = \int_{0}^{3} x\left(\frac{2}{9}(3x - x^2)\right)dx$
$$= \int_{0}^{3}\left(\frac{2}{9}(3x^2 - x^3)\right)dx = \left[\frac{2}{9}\left(x^3 - \frac{x^4}{4}\right)\right]_0^3$$
$$= \left(\frac{2}{9}\left(3^3 - \frac{3^4}{4}\right)\right) - \left(\frac{2}{9}\left(0^3 - \frac{0^4}{4}\right)\right) = \frac{3}{2}$$

Q2 a) $\mu = E(X) = \int_{-\infty}^{\infty} xf(x)\,dx = \int_{1}^{2} x\left(\frac{3}{7}x^2\right)dx$
$$= \int_{1}^{2}\frac{3}{7}x^3\,dx = \left[\frac{3x^4}{28}\right]_1^2 = \frac{48}{28} - \frac{3}{28} = \frac{45}{28}$$
$$= 1.607 \text{ (3 d.p.)}$$

b) $E(g(x)) = \int_{-\infty}^{\infty} g(x)f(x)\,dx$.

Here $g(X) = \frac{1}{3X}$. So...
$$E\left(\frac{1}{3X}\right) = \int_{-\infty}^{\infty}\frac{1}{3x}f(x)\,dx = \int_{1}^{2}\frac{1}{3x}\left(\frac{3}{7}x^2\right)dx$$
$$= \int_{1}^{2}\frac{1}{7}x\,dx = \left[\frac{1}{14}x^2\right]_1^2 = \frac{4}{14} - \frac{1}{14} = \frac{3}{14}$$
$$= 0.214 \text{ (3 d.p.)}$$

c) $E(2X - 1) = 2E(X) - 1 = 2\left(\frac{45}{28}\right) - 1$
$$= \frac{31}{14} = 2.214 \text{ (3 d.p.)}$$

d) $P(X < \mu) = P\left(X < \frac{45}{28}\right) = \int_{1}^{\frac{45}{28}}\frac{3}{7}x^2\,dx = \left[\frac{3x^3}{7 \times 3}\right]_1^{\frac{45}{28}}$
$$= \left[\frac{x^3}{7}\right]_1^{\frac{45}{28}} = \left(\frac{\left(\frac{45}{28}\right)^3}{7}\right) - \left(\frac{1^3}{7}\right) = 0.450 \text{ (3 d.p.)}$$

Q3 a) $\mu = E(X) = \int_{-\infty}^{\infty} xf(x)\,dx$
$$= \int_{0}^{1} x\left(\frac{2}{5}\right)dx + \int_{1}^{2} x\left(\frac{2}{5}x\right)dx$$
$$= \int_{0}^{1}\frac{2}{5}x\,dx + \int_{1}^{2}\frac{2}{5}x^2\,dx = \left[\frac{x^2}{5}\right]_0^1 + \left[\frac{2x^3}{15}\right]_1^2$$
$$= \left[\left(\frac{1^2}{5}\right) - \left(\frac{0^2}{5}\right)\right] + \left[\left(\frac{2(2)^3}{15}\right) - \left(\frac{2(1)^3}{15}\right)\right]$$
$$= \frac{1}{5} + \left[\frac{16}{15} - \frac{2}{15}\right] = \frac{1}{5} + \frac{14}{15} = \frac{17}{15} = 1.133 \text{ (3 d.p.)}$$

b) $E(g(x)) = \int_{-\infty}^{\infty} g(x)f(x)\,dx$.

Here $g(X) = 5X^2$. So...
$$E(5X^2) = \int_{-\infty}^{\infty} 5x^2 f(x)\,dx$$
$$= \int_{0}^{1} 5x^2\left(\frac{2}{5}\right)dx + \int_{1}^{2} 5x^2\left(\frac{2}{5}x\right)dx$$
$$= \int_{0}^{1} 2x^2\,dx + \int_{1}^{2} 2x^3\,dx = \left[\frac{2}{3}x^3\right]_0^1 + \left[\frac{1}{2}x^4\right]_1^2$$
$$= \left[\left(\frac{2}{3}\right) - (0)\right] + \left[\left(\frac{1}{2} \times 2^4\right) - \left(\frac{1}{2} \times 1^4\right)\right]$$
$$= \frac{2}{3} + \frac{15}{2} = \frac{49}{6} = 8.167 \text{ (3 d.p.)}$$

c) $E(4X + 2) = 4E(X) + 2 = 4\left(\frac{17}{15}\right) + 2$
$$= \frac{98}{15} = 6.533 \text{ (3 d.p.)}$$

Q4 a) $\mu = E(X) = \int_{-\infty}^{\infty} xf(x)\,dx$
$$= \int_{0}^{1} x\left(\frac{1}{3}\right)dx + \int_{1}^{2} x\left(-\frac{1}{2}(1 - x^2)\right)dx$$
$$= \int_{0}^{1}\frac{x}{3}\,dx + \int_{1}^{2}\left(-\frac{1}{2}x + \frac{1}{2}x^3\right)dx$$
$$= \left[\frac{x^2}{6}\right]_0^1 + \left[-\frac{x^2}{4} + \frac{x^4}{8}\right]_1^2$$
$$= \left[\left(\frac{1^2}{6}\right) - \left(\frac{0^2}{6}\right)\right] + \left[\left(-\frac{2^2}{4} + \frac{2^4}{8}\right) - \left(-\frac{1^2}{4} + \frac{1^4}{8}\right)\right]$$
$$= \frac{1}{6} + \left[1 + \frac{1}{8}\right]$$
$$= \frac{31}{24} = 1.292 \text{ (3 d.p.)}$$

b) $E(X^2+1) = \int_{-\infty}^{\infty}(x^2+1)f(x)\,dx$

$= \int_0^1 (x^2+1)\left(\frac{1}{3}\right)dx + \int_1^2 (x^2+1)\left(-\frac{1}{2}(1-x^2)\right)dx$

$= \int_0^1 \left(\frac{x^2}{3}+\frac{1}{3}\right)dx + \int_1^2 \left(\frac{1}{2}x^4 - \frac{1}{2}\right)dx$

$= \left[\frac{1}{9}x^3 + \frac{1}{3}x\right]_0^1 + \left[\frac{1}{10}x^5 - \frac{1}{2}x\right]_1^2$

$= \left[\left(\frac{1}{9}+\frac{1}{3}\right) - (0)\right] + \left[\left(\frac{32}{10} - 1\right) - \left(\frac{1}{10} - \frac{1}{2}\right)\right]$

$= \frac{4}{9} + \frac{13}{5} = \frac{137}{45} = 3.044$ (3 d.p.)

c) $E(3X-2) = 3E(X) - 2 = 3\left(\frac{31}{24}\right) - 2$

$= \frac{15}{8} = 1.875$

Q5 a) $\int_0^4 \frac{1}{4}x^2\,dx = \left[\frac{x^3}{12}\right]_0^4 = \left(\frac{4^3}{12}\right) - \left(\frac{0^3}{12}\right) = \frac{16}{3}$

b) $E(X) = \int_{-\infty}^{\infty} xf(x)\,dx = \int_0^4 x\left(\frac{1}{8}x\right)dx = \int_0^4 \frac{1}{8}x^2\,dx$

$= \frac{1}{2}\int_0^4 \frac{1}{4}x^2\,dx = \frac{1}{2}\left(\frac{16}{3}\right) = \frac{16}{6} = \frac{8}{3}$

Exercise 3.2 — Variance of a continuous random variable

Q1 a) Work out $E(X^2)$ first, as you've already worked out $E(X)$ in Exercise 3.1, Q1 part a): $E(X) = \frac{2}{3}$

$E(X^2) = \int_{-\infty}^{\infty} x^2 f(x)\,dx = \int_0^2 x^2\left(1 - \frac{1}{2}x\right)dx$

$= \int_0^2 \left(x^2 - \frac{1}{2}x^3\right)dx = \left[\frac{x^3}{3} - \frac{x^4}{8}\right]_0^2$

$= \left(\frac{2^3}{3} - \frac{2^4}{8}\right) - \left(\frac{0^3}{3} - \frac{0^4}{8}\right) = \frac{2}{3}$

$Var(X) = E(X^2) - [E(X)]^2 = \frac{2}{3} - \left(\frac{2}{3}\right)^2 = \frac{2}{9}$

b) Work out $E(X^2)$ first, as you've already worked out $E(X)$ in Exercise 3.1, Q1 part b): $E(X) = \frac{8}{5}$

$E(X^2) = \int_{-\infty}^{\infty} x^2 f(x)\,dx = \int_0^2 x^2\left(\frac{1}{4}x^3\right)dx$

$= \int_0^2 \frac{1}{4}x^5\,dx = \left[\frac{x^6}{24}\right]_0^2 = \frac{8}{3}$

$Var(X) = E(X^2) - [E(X)]^2 = \frac{8}{3} - \left(\frac{8}{5}\right)^2 = \frac{8}{75}$

c) Work out $E(X^2)$ first, as you've already worked out $E(X)$ in Exercise 3.1, Q1 part c): $E(X) = \frac{3}{2}$

$E(X^2) = \int_{-\infty}^{\infty} x^2 f(x)\,dx = \int_0^3 x^2\left(\frac{2}{9}(3x - x^2)\right)dx$

$= \int_0^3 \left(\frac{2}{9}(3x^3 - x^4)\right)dx = \left[\frac{2}{9}\left(\frac{3x^4}{4} - \frac{x^5}{5}\right)\right]_0^3$

$= \left(\frac{2}{9}\left(\frac{3(3)^4}{4} - \frac{(3)^5}{5}\right)\right) - \left(\frac{2}{9}\left(\frac{3(0)^4}{4} - \frac{(0)^5}{5}\right)\right)$

$= \left(\frac{2}{9}\left(\frac{243}{4} - \frac{243}{5}\right)\right) - 0 = \frac{27}{10}$

$Var(X) = E(X^2) - [E(X)]^2 = \frac{27}{10} - \left(\frac{3}{2}\right)^2 = \frac{9}{20}$

Q2 a) In Exercise 3.1, Q2 a) you showed that $E(X) = \frac{45}{28}$.

$E(X^2) = \int_{-\infty}^{\infty} x^2 f(x)\,dx = \int_1^2 x^2\left(\frac{3}{7}x^2\right)dx$

$= \int_1^2 \frac{3}{7}x^4\,dx = \left[\frac{3x^5}{35}\right]_1^2 = \frac{96}{35} - \frac{3}{35} = \frac{93}{35}$

$\sigma^2 = Var(X) = \frac{93}{35} - \left(\frac{45}{28}\right)^2 = \frac{291}{3920} = 0.074$ (3 d.p.)

b) $Var(2X) = 2^2 Var(X) = 4 \times \frac{291}{3920} = \frac{291}{980}$
$= 0.297$ (3 d.p.)

c) $Var(2X+1) = 2^2 Var(X) = \frac{291}{980} = 0.297$ (3 d.p.)

d) $\sigma = \sqrt{Var(X)} = \sqrt{\frac{291}{3920}} = 0.272$ (3 d.p.)

Q3 a) In Exercise 3.1, Q3 a) you showed that $E(X) = \frac{17}{15}$.

$E(X^2) = \int_{-\infty}^{\infty} x^2 f(x)\,dx$

$= \int_0^1 x^2\left(\frac{2}{5}\right)dx + \int_1^2 x^2\left(\frac{2}{5}x\right)dx$

$= \int_0^1 \frac{2}{5}x^2\,dx + \int_1^2 \frac{2}{5}x^3\,dx = \left[\frac{2x^3}{15}\right]_0^1 + \left[\frac{x^4}{10}\right]_1^2$

$= \frac{2}{15} + \left[\left(\frac{2^4}{10}\right) - \left(\frac{1^4}{10}\right)\right] = \frac{2}{15} + \frac{15}{10} = \frac{49}{30}$

So $Var(X) = \frac{49}{30} - \left(\frac{17}{15}\right)^2 = \frac{157}{450} = 0.349$ (3 d.p.)

b) $Var(4X+2) = 4^2 Var(X) = 16 \times \frac{157}{450} = \frac{1256}{225}$
$= 5.582$ (3 d.p.)

Q4 a) In Exercise 3.1, Q4 a) you showed that $E(X) = \frac{31}{24}$.

$E(X^2) = \int_{-\infty}^{\infty} x^2 f(x)\,dx$

$= \int_0^1 x^2\left(\frac{1}{3}\right)dx + \int_1^2 x^2\left(-\frac{1}{2}(1-x^2)\right)dx$

$= \int_0^1 \frac{x^2}{3}\,dx + \int_1^2 \left(-\frac{1}{2}x^2 + \frac{1}{2}x^4\right)dx$

$= \left[\frac{x^3}{9}\right]_0^1 + \left[-\frac{x^3}{6} + \frac{x^5}{10}\right]_1^2$

$= \frac{1}{9} + \left[\left(-\frac{2^3}{6} + \frac{2^5}{10}\right) - \left(-\frac{1^3}{6} + \frac{1^5}{10}\right)\right]$

$= \frac{1}{9} + \left[\left(-\frac{8}{6} + \frac{32}{10}\right) - \left(-\frac{1}{6} + \frac{1}{10}\right)\right]$

$= \frac{1}{9} + \left[\frac{28}{15} + \frac{1}{15}\right] = \frac{92}{45}$

So $Var(X) = \frac{92}{45} - \left(\frac{31}{24}\right)^2 = \frac{361}{960} = 0.376$ (3 d.p.).

b) $Var(-X) = (-1)^2 Var(X) = Var(X) = \frac{361}{960}$
$= 0.376$ (3 d.p.).

c) $Var(3X+2) = 3^2 Var(X) = 9 \times \frac{361}{960} = \frac{1083}{320}$
$= 3.384$ (3 d.p.).

d) $\sigma = \sqrt{Var(X)} = \sqrt{\frac{361}{960}} = 0.613$ (3 d.p.).

Q5 a) $E(X^3) = \int_{-\infty}^{\infty} x^3 f(x)\,dx = \int_0^4 x^3 \times \frac{4-x}{8}\,dx$

$= \int_0^4 \left(\frac{4x^3 - x^4}{8}\right)dx = \int_0^4 \left(\frac{x^3}{2} - \frac{x^4}{8}\right)dx$

$= \left[\frac{1}{8}x^4 - \frac{1}{40}x^5\right]_0^4 = \left[\frac{256}{8} - \frac{1024}{40}\right] - 0$

$= \frac{32}{5} = 6.4$

b) $E(X^6) = \int_{-\infty}^{\infty} x^6 f(x)\,dx = \int_0^4 x^6 \times \frac{4-x}{8}\,dx$

$= \int_0^4 \left(\frac{4x^6 - x^7}{8}\right) dx = \int_0^4 \left(\frac{x^6}{2} - \frac{x^7}{8}\right) dx$

$= \left[\frac{1}{14}x^7 - \frac{1}{64}x^8\right]_0^4 = \left[\frac{16384}{14} - \frac{65536}{64}\right] - 0$

$= \frac{1024}{7} = 146\text{ (3 s.f.)}$

c) $\text{Var}(X^3) = E((X^3)^2) - [E(X^3)]^2$

$= E(X^6) - [E(X^3)]^2 = \frac{1024}{7} - \left(\frac{32}{5}\right)^2$

$= \frac{18432}{175} = 105\text{ (3 s.f.)}$

4. Quartiles and Percentiles

Exercise 4.1 — Finding the quartiles and percentiles

Q1 To find the median, let $\int_{-\infty}^{Q_2} f(x)\,dx = 0.5 \Rightarrow$

$\int_0^{Q_2} 2x\,dx = 0.5 \Rightarrow [x^2]_0^{Q_2} = 0.5 \Rightarrow Q_2^2 = 0.5$

$\Rightarrow Q_2 = \sqrt{0.5} \Rightarrow Q_2 = 0.7071\text{ (4 d.p.)}$

Q_2 cannot be negative as $0 \le Q_2 \le 1$.

Q2 **a)** The median is Q_2 where $F(Q_2) = 0.5$

$\Rightarrow 1 + 3Q_2 = 0.5 \Rightarrow 3Q_2 = -0.5 \Rightarrow Q_2 = -\frac{1}{6}$.

b) The lower quartile is Q_1 where $F(Q_1) = 0.25$.

$\Rightarrow 1 + 3Q_1 = 0.25 \Rightarrow 3Q_1 = -0.75 \Rightarrow Q_1 = -\frac{1}{4}$.

c) The upper quartile is Q_3 where $F(Q_3) = 0.75$.

$\Rightarrow 1 + 3Q_3 = 0.75 \Rightarrow 3Q_3 = -0.25 \Rightarrow Q_3 = -\frac{1}{12}$.

Q3 Before you start working out the quartiles and median, work out the value of F(x) at the end of each 'piece' to see which interval each quartile lies in.

$F(1) = \frac{2}{5} = 0.4$, so the lower quartile lies in $0 \le x < 1$ and the median and upper quartile lie in $1 \le x \le 2$.

a) To find the median, Q_2, let $F(Q_2) = 0.5$.

$1 \le Q_2 \le 2$ so $\frac{1}{5}(Q_2^2 + 1) = 0.5 \Rightarrow Q_2^2 + 1 = 2.5$

$\Rightarrow Q_2^2 = 1.5 \Rightarrow Q_2 = \sqrt{1.5} = 1.225\text{ (3 d.p.)}$.

b) The upper quartile, Q_3, is such that $F(Q_3) = 0.75$

$1 \le Q_3 \le 2$ so $\frac{1}{5}(Q_3^2 + 1) = 0.75 \Rightarrow Q_3^2 + 1 = 3.75$

$\Rightarrow Q_3^2 = 2.75 \Rightarrow Q_3 = \sqrt{2.75} = 1.658\text{ (3 d.p.)}$.

c) $0.14 < 0.4$ so this percentile lies in $0 \le x < 1$

$F(P_{14}) = 0.14$ and $0 \le P_{14} < 1$, so $\frac{2}{5}P_{14} = 0.14$

$\Rightarrow P_{14} = 0.35$.

Q4 $F(1.56) = \frac{1}{20} \times 1.56^4 + \frac{1}{5} = 0.496\text{ (3 d.p.)}$

$F(1.57) = \frac{1}{20} \times 1.57^4 + \frac{1}{5} = 0.504\text{ (3 d.p.)}$

These are either side of 0.5, so the median lies between these two points.

Q5 **a)** For $x < 1$, $F(x) = 0$.

For $1 \le x \le 3$:

$F(x) = \int_{-\infty}^{x} f(t)\,dt = \int_{-\infty}^{1} f(t)\,dt + \int_1^x f(t)\,dt$

$= F(1) + \int_1^x \frac{3}{34}(t^3 - t^2)\,dt = 0 + \left[\frac{3}{34}\left(\frac{t^4}{4} - \frac{t^3}{3}\right)\right]_1^x$

$= \left[\frac{3}{34}\left(\frac{x^4}{4} - \frac{x^3}{3}\right) - \frac{3}{34}\left(\frac{1}{4} - \frac{1}{3}\right)\right] = \frac{3}{34}\left(\frac{x^4}{4} - \frac{x^3}{3} + \frac{1}{12}\right)$

When $x = 3$:

$F(x) = \frac{3}{34}\left(\frac{81}{4} - \frac{27}{3} + \frac{1}{12}\right) = \frac{3}{34}\left(\frac{34}{3}\right) = 1$,

so the pieces match up.

So

$$F(x) = \begin{cases} 0 & x < 1 \\ \frac{3}{34}\left(\frac{x^4}{4} - \frac{x^3}{3} + \frac{1}{12}\right) & 1 \le x \le 3 \\ 1 & x > 3 \end{cases}$$

b) $F(2.6) = \frac{3}{34}\left(\frac{2.6^4}{4} - \frac{2.6^3}{3} + \frac{1}{12}\right) = 0.498\text{ (3 d.p.)}$

$F(2.7) = \frac{3}{34}\left(\frac{2.7^4}{4} - \frac{2.7^3}{3} + \frac{1}{12}\right) = 0.601\text{ (3 d.p.)}$

These are either side of 0.5, so the median lies between these two points.

c) To find the median to one d.p., calculate $F(2.65) = 0.548$ (3 d.p.).

This means the median must be less than 2.65, and so $Q_2 = 2.6$ (to 1 d.p.)

Q6 **a)** For $x < 1$, $F(x) = 0$

For $1 \le x \le 3$:

$F(x) = \int_{-\infty}^{x} f(t)\,dt = \int_{-\infty}^{1} f(t)\,dt + \int_1^x f(t)\,dt$

$= F(1) + \int_1^x \frac{1}{2}(3 - t)\,dt = 0 + \left[\frac{1}{2}\left(3t - \frac{t^2}{2}\right)\right]_1^x$

$= \frac{1}{2}\left(3x - \frac{x^2}{2}\right) - \frac{1}{2}\left(3 - \frac{1}{2}\right) = \frac{3x}{2} - \frac{x^2}{4} - \frac{5}{4}$

$= \frac{1}{4}(6x - x^2 - 5)$

For $x = 3$, $F(3) = \frac{1}{4}(6(3) - (3)^2 - 5) = 1$

So the pieces match up and:

$$F(x) = \begin{cases} 0 & x < 1 \\ \frac{1}{4}(6x - x^2 - 5) & 1 \le x \le 3 \\ 1 & x > 3 \end{cases}$$

b) To find the median let $F(Q_2) = 0.5$

$\Rightarrow \frac{1}{4}(6Q_2 - Q_2^2 - 5) = 0.5$

$\Rightarrow 6Q_2 - Q_2^2 - 5 = 2$

$\Rightarrow 6Q_2 - Q_2^2 - 7 = 0$

$\Rightarrow Q_2 = \frac{-6 \pm \sqrt{36 - (4 \times -1 \times -7)}}{-2}$

$= 3 \pm \sqrt{2} = 4.414 \text{ or } 1.586\text{ (3 d.p.)}$

The median must be 1.586 as $1 \le Q_2 \le 3$.

c) To find the lower quartile, let $F(Q_1) = 0.25$

$\Rightarrow \frac{1}{4}(6Q_1 - Q_1^2 - 5) = 0.25$
$\Rightarrow 6Q_1 - Q_1^2 - 5 = 1$
$\Rightarrow 6Q_1 - Q_1^2 - 6 = 0$

$$\Rightarrow Q_1 = \frac{-6 \pm \sqrt{36 - (4 \times -1 \times -6)}}{-2}$$
$$= 3 \pm \sqrt{3} = 4.7320... \text{ or } 1.2679...$$
$$= 4.732 \text{ or } 1.268 \text{ (3 d.p.)}$$

So the lower quartile is 1.268 since $1 \leq Q_1 \leq 3$.

d) To find the 40th percentile, let $F(P_{40}) = 0.40$

$\Rightarrow \frac{1}{4}(6P_{40} - P_{40}^2 - 5) = 0.40 = \frac{2}{5}$
$\Rightarrow \frac{5}{8}(6P_{40} - P_{40}^2 - 5) = 1$
$\Rightarrow \frac{15}{4}P_{40} - \frac{5}{8}P_{40}^2 - \frac{33}{8} = 0$
$\Rightarrow 30P_{40} - 5P_{40}^2 - 33 = 0$
$\Rightarrow 5P_{40}^2 - 30P_{40} + 33 = 0$

$$\Rightarrow P_{40} = \frac{-(-30) \pm \sqrt{900 - (4 \times 5 \times 33)}}{10}$$
$$= \frac{30 \pm \sqrt{240}}{10} = 3 \pm \frac{\sqrt{240}}{10}$$
$$= 4.5492 \text{ or } 1.4508 \text{ (4 d.p.)}$$

So $P_{40} = 1.4508$
The other solution is not in the range $1 \leq x \leq 3$.

e) The mean is:

$$E(X) = \int_{-\infty}^{\infty} x f(x)\,dx = \int_1^3 x\left(\tfrac{1}{2}(3 - x)\right)dx$$
$$= \int_1^3 \left(\frac{3x}{2} - \frac{x^2}{2}\right)dx = \left[\frac{3x^2}{4} - \frac{x^3}{6}\right]_1^3$$
$$= \left(\frac{27}{4} - \frac{27}{6}\right) - \left(\frac{3}{4} - \frac{1}{6}\right) = \frac{5}{3}$$

Find $E(X^2)$ before finding the variance:

$$E(X^2) = \int_{-\infty}^{\infty} x^2 f(x)\,dx = \int_1^3 x^2\left(\tfrac{1}{2}(3 - x)\right)dx$$
$$= \int_1^3 \left(\frac{3x^2}{2} - \frac{x^3}{2}\right)dx = \left[\frac{x^3}{2} - \frac{x^4}{8}\right]_1^3$$
$$= \left(\frac{3^3}{2} - \frac{3^4}{8}\right) - \left(\frac{1^3}{2} - \frac{1^4}{8}\right) = 3$$

So the variance is $E(X^2) - [E(X)]^2 = 3 - \left(\frac{5}{3}\right)^2 = \frac{2}{9}$

f) $E(3X - 2) = 3E(X) - 2 = 3\left(\frac{5}{3}\right) - 2 = 3$

$Var(3X - 2) = 3^2 Var(X) = 9 \times \frac{2}{9} = 2$

5. The Rectangular Distribution

Exercise 5.1 — Rectangular distributions

Q1 a) $a = 2$ and $b = 7$, so $\frac{1}{b - a} = \frac{1}{5} = 0.2$

$$\Rightarrow f(x) = \begin{cases} 0.2 & \text{for } 2 \leq x \leq 7 \\ 0 & \text{otherwise} \end{cases}$$

A sketch of the p.d.f. looks like this:

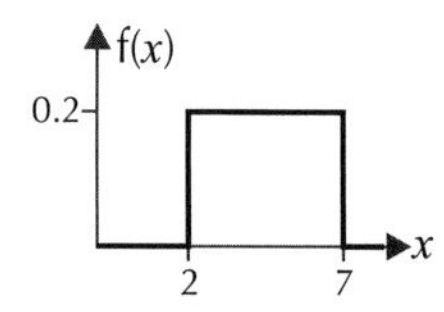

b) $a = -0.5$ and $b = 1.5$, so $\frac{1}{b - a} = \frac{1}{2} = 0.5$

$$\Rightarrow f(x) = \begin{cases} 0.5 & \text{for } -0.5 \leq x \leq 1.5 \\ 0 & \text{otherwise} \end{cases}$$

A sketch of the p.d.f. looks like this:

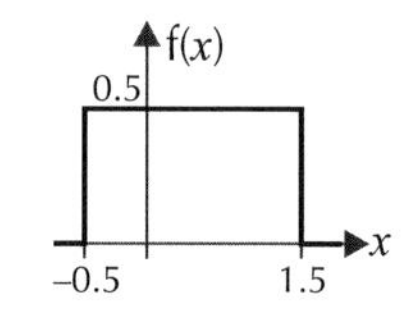

c) $a = \frac{1}{3}$ and $b = 1$, so $\frac{1}{b - a} = \frac{3}{2} = 1.5$

$$\Rightarrow f(x) = \begin{cases} 1.5 & \text{for } \frac{1}{3} \leq x \leq 1 \\ 0 & \text{otherwise} \end{cases}$$

A sketch of the p.d.f. looks like this:

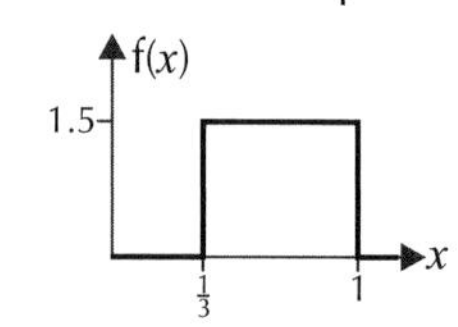

Q2 a) Using the definition of $f(x)$:

$$\frac{1}{b - a} = 0.25 \Rightarrow \frac{1}{k - (-3)} = 0.25$$
$$\Rightarrow \frac{1}{k + 3} = 0.25 \Rightarrow k + 3 = 4 \Rightarrow k = 1$$

b) Using the definition of $f(x)$:

$$\frac{1}{b - a} = \frac{5}{8} \Rightarrow \frac{1}{7 - k} = \frac{5}{8}$$
$$\Rightarrow 7 - k = 1.6 \Rightarrow k = 5.4$$

Do these by drawing a sketch if you find it's easier.

Q3 a) Area under $f(x) = 1 \Rightarrow (k - 3) \times 1 = 1$
$\Rightarrow k - 3 = 1 \Rightarrow k = 4$

$$\text{So, } f(x) = \begin{cases} 1 & \text{for } 3 \leq x \leq 4 \\ 0 & \text{otherwise} \end{cases}$$

b) Area under $f(x) = 1 \Rightarrow (1 - k) \times 0.2 = 1$
$\Rightarrow 1 - k = 5 \Rightarrow k = -4$

$$\text{So, } f(x) = \begin{cases} 0.2 & \text{for } -4 \leq x \leq 1 \\ 0 & \text{otherwise} \end{cases}$$

Q4 Y represents the weight of the heavier piece, so it takes values between 400 g and 800 g.
If it weighed less than 400 g, it'd be the lighter piece.

The weight is equally likely to be anywhere within this interval, so Y follows a rectangular distribution over the interval [400, 800].

Q5 Since Fred leaves his house at a random time, the time he has to wait for his train is equally likely to be anywhere between 0 minutes and 15 minutes, so T follows a rectangular distribution over the interval [0, 15].

Q6 **a)** The diameter is equally likely to be anywhere between 5.9 cm and 6.3 cm, so D follows a rectangular distribution over the interval [5.9, 6.3].

b) $f(x) = \begin{cases} 2.5 & \text{for } 5.9 \leq x \leq 6.3 \\ 0 & \text{otherwise} \end{cases}$

A sketch of the p.d.f. looks like this:

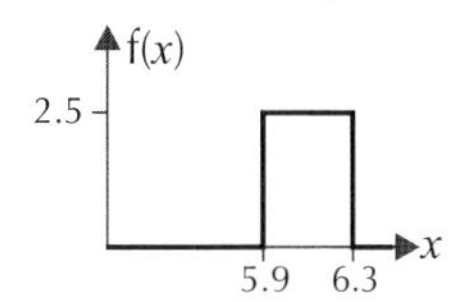

Exercise 5.2 — Finding probabilities

Q1 It's a good idea to sketch the p.d.f.

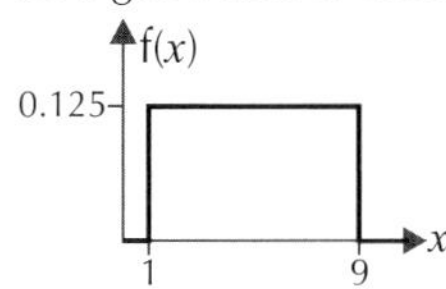

a) $P(X > 5) = (9 - 5) \times 0.125 = 0.5$

b) $P(2 < X < 7) = (7 - 2) \times 0.125 = 0.625$

c) $P(X \leq 2.4) = (2.4 - 1) \times 0.125 = 0.175$

Q2 Sketch the p.d.f.

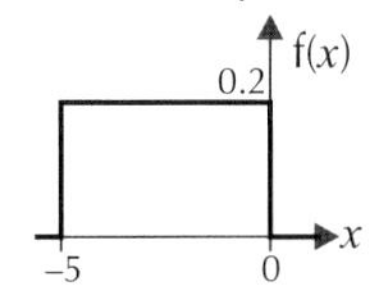

a) $P(X \geq -3) = (0 - (-3)) \times 0.2 = 0.6$

b) $P(-2.4 \leq X \leq -1.2) = (-1.2 - (-2.4)) \times 0.2 = 0.24$

c) $P(X > -6) = 1$
X can only take values in the range -5 to 0, so it's certain to take a value greater than -6.

Q3 Sketch the p.d.f.

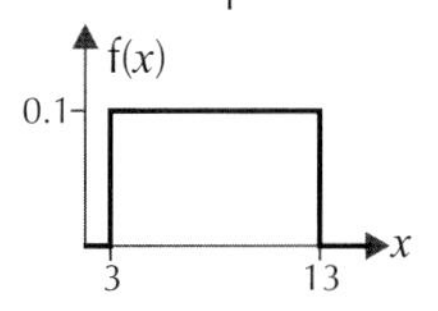

a) $P(X > 7) = (13 - 7) \times 0.1 = 0.6$

b) $P(4 < X < 11) = (11 - 4) \times 0.1 = 0.7$

c) $P(X \geq 10.1) = (13 - 10.1) \times 0.1 = 0.29$

Q4 Sketching what you know will really help here:

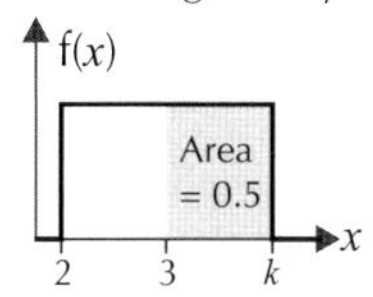

Since the area above $x = 3$ is 0.5, the area below $x = 3$ must also be 0.5. So the distribution is symmetrical about $x = 3$.
This means that $k = 3 + 1 = 4$.
Or you could use the fact that the area between $x = 2$ and $x = 3$ is 0.5 to find the height of the rectangle. Then use height × $(k - 3) = 0.5$ to find k.

Q5 **a)** Again, start by sketching what you know.

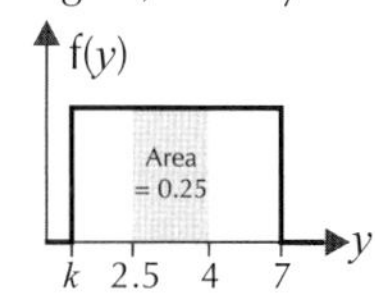

So height of rectangle $= 0.25 \div (4 - 2.5)$
$= 0.25 \div 1.5$
$= \frac{1}{4} \div \frac{3}{2} = \frac{1}{4} \times \frac{2}{3} = \frac{1}{6}$

Which means:

$(7 - k) \times \frac{1}{6} = 1$

$\Rightarrow 7 - k = 6$

$\Rightarrow k = 1$

b) Y follows a rectangular distribution over the interval [1, 7], so Z follows a rectangular distribution over the interval $[(2 \times 1 + 1), (2 \times 7 + 1)] = [3, 15]$

The p.d.f. of Z is a rectangle with a width of 12 and a height of $\frac{1}{12}$.

So $P(Z < 6) = (6 - 3) \times \frac{1}{12} = \frac{3}{12} = \frac{1}{4} = 0.25$

Q6 A sketch of both p.d.f.s looks like this:

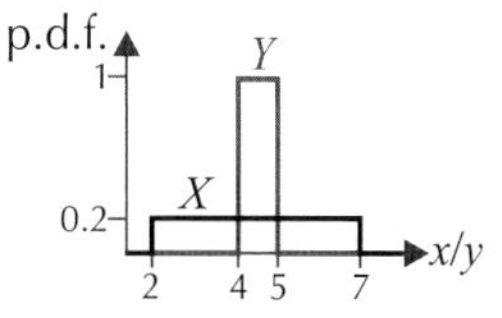

X and Y are independent, so: $P(X > 4.5 \text{ and } Y > 4.5)$
$= P(X > 4.5) \times P(Y > 4.5)$
$= [0.2 \times (7 - 4.5)] \times [1 \times (5 - 4.5)]$
$= 0.5 \times 0.5$
$= 0.25$

Q7 **a)** The heights are correct to the nearest cm, so the error could be anywhere between –0.5 cm and 0.5 cm. It's equally likely to be anywhere within this interval, so X follows a rectangular distribution over the interval [–0.5, 0.5].

b) The p.d.f. of X is a rectangle with a width of $(0.5 - (-0.5)) = 1$ and therefore a height of $1 \div 1 = 1$.
So $P(X > 0.1) = (0.5 - 0.1) \times 1 = 0.4$.
If you need to, draw a sketch of the p.d.f. here.

Q8 **a)** The weights are correct to the nearest 0.25 g, so the error could be anywhere between –0.125 g and 0.125 g. It's equally likely to be anywhere within this interval, so X follows a rectangular distribution over the interval [–0.125, 0.125].

b) The probability that the recorded weight is inaccurate by at least 0.1 g is given by:
$P(X < -0.1 \text{ or } X > 0.1)$.
The p.d.f. of X is a rectangle with a width of $(0.125 - (-0.125)) = 0.25$ and therefore a height of $1 \div 0.25 = 4$.
So $P(X > 0.1) = (0.125 - 0.1) \times 4 = 0.1$ and, by symmetry, $P(X < -0.1)$ is also 0.1.
So, $P(X < -0.1 \text{ or } X > 0.1) = 0.1 + 0.1 = 0.2$
'X > 0.1' and 'X < –0.1' are mutually exclusive events, so to find the probability of one or the other happening, you add the individual probabilities.

c) Assuming that the errors in the recorded weights of the two chocolate bars are independent of each other, this probability = $0.2 \times 0.2 = 0.04$.

Exercise 5.3 — The mean and variance

Q1 **a)** $E(X) = \frac{1+7}{2} = \frac{8}{2} = 4.$

b) $E(X) = \frac{0+\frac{1}{3}}{2} = \frac{\left(\frac{1}{3}\right)}{2} = \frac{1}{6}.$

c) $E(X) = \frac{-24+(-6)}{2} = \frac{-30}{2} = -15.$

Q2 **a)** $\text{Var}(X) = \frac{(5-2)^2}{12} = \frac{9}{12} = \frac{3}{4}$

b) $\text{Var}(X) = \frac{(0.75-(-0.25))^2}{12} = \frac{1}{12}$

c) $\text{Var}(X) = \frac{(-18-(-30))^2}{12} = \frac{144}{12} = 12$

Q3 The continuous random variable X follows a rectangular distribution over the interval [3.9, 6.4].
$E(X) = \frac{3.9+6.4}{2} = 5.15$
$\text{Var}(X) = \frac{(6.4-3.9)^2}{12} = \frac{25}{48} = 0.521$ (3 d.p.)

Q4 The continuous random variable X follows a rectangular distribution over the interval [1.7, 4.1].
$E(X) = \frac{1.7+4.1}{2} = 2.9$
$\text{Var}(X) = \frac{(4.1-1.7)^2}{12} = 0.48$

Q5 **a)** $E(X) = \frac{13+17}{2} = 15$
$\text{Var}(X) = \frac{(17-13)^2}{12} = \frac{4}{3} = 1.333$ (3 d.p.)

b) Y follows a rectangular distribution over the interval $[(2 \times 13) - 9, (2 \times 17) - 9] = [17, 25]$
$E(Y) = \frac{17+25}{2} = 21$
$\text{Var}(Y) = \frac{(25-17)^2}{12} = \frac{16}{3} = 5.333$ (3 d.p.)
Or you could say E(Y) = 2E(X) – 9, and Var(Y) = 2^2Var(X).

Q6 $E(X) = \frac{3+k}{2} = 4.5 \Rightarrow 3 + k = 9 \Rightarrow k = 6.$

Q7 **a)** X represents the error in a measurement to the nearest 10 g. The error in the measurement could be anywhere from –5 g to 5 g. So X follows a rectangular distribution over the interval [–5, 5].

b) $E(X) = \frac{-5+5}{2} = 0$
$\text{Var}(X) = \frac{(5-(-5))^2}{12} = \frac{25}{3} = 8.333$ (3 d.p.)

Review Exercise — Chapter 3

Q1 **a)** Sketch the p.d.f.:

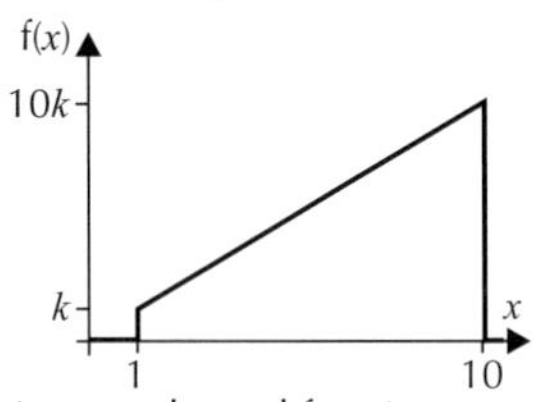

Area under p.d.f. = 1
So $\frac{10k+k}{2} \times (10-1) = \frac{99k}{2} = 1.$
$\Rightarrow k = \frac{2}{99}.$

b) Sketch the p.d.f.:

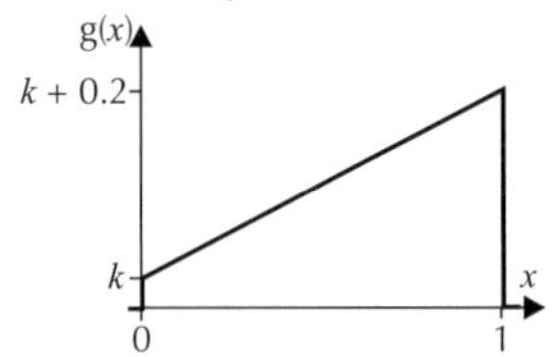

Area under p.d.f. = 1
So $\frac{2k+0.2}{2} \times 1 = k + 0.1 = 1.$
$\Rightarrow k = 0.9.$

Q2 **a)** Sketch the p.d.f.:

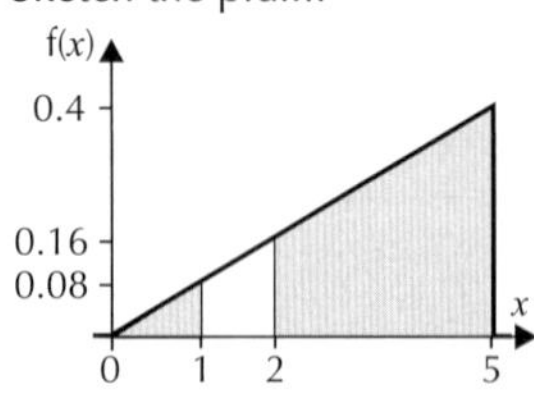

(i) Area under p.d.f. between $x = 0$ and $x = 1$ is: $1 \times 0.08 \div 2 = 0.04$, so $P(X < 1) = 0.04$.

(ii) Area under p.d.f. between $x = 2$ and $x = 5$ is: $\frac{0.16+0.4}{2} \times 3 = 0.84$
so $P(2 \leq X \leq 5) = 0.84$.

(iii) Area under p.d.f. at the point $x = 4$ is 0. So $P(X = 4) = 0$.

b) Sketch the p.d.f.:

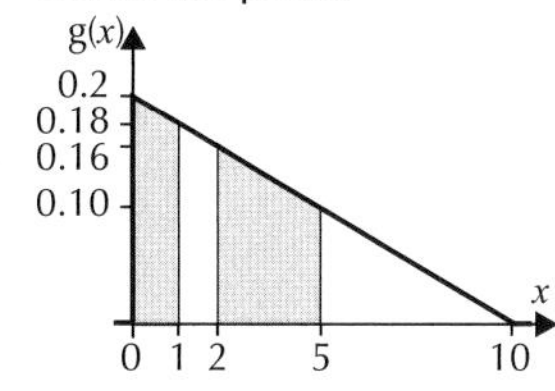

(i) Area under p.d.f. between $x = 0$ and $x = 1$ is: $\frac{0.2 + 0.18}{2} \times 1 = 0.19$, so $P(X < 1) = 0.19$.

(ii) Area under p.d.f. between $x = 2$ and $x = 5$ is: $\frac{0.16 + 0.1}{2} \times 3 = 0.39$ so $P(2 \le X \le 5) = 0.39$.

(iii) Area under p.d.f. at the point $x = 4$ is 0. So $P(X = 4) = 0$.

Q3 a) $\int_{-\infty}^{\infty} f(x)dx = k\int_0^5 x^2 dx = k\left[\frac{x^3}{3}\right]_0^5 = \frac{125k}{3} = 1,$

so $k = \frac{3}{125}$.

$P(X < 1) = \int_0^1 \frac{3}{125}x^2 dx = \frac{3}{125}\left[\frac{x^3}{3}\right]_0^1 = \frac{1}{125}$.

b) $\int_{-\infty}^{\infty} g(x)dx = \int_0^2 (0.1x^2 + kx)dx$

$= \left[\frac{0.1x^3}{3} + \frac{kx^2}{2}\right]_0^2 = \frac{0.8}{3} + 2k = 1.$

So $k = \frac{1}{2} - \frac{0.4}{3} = \frac{15 - 4}{30} = \frac{11}{30}$

$P(X < 1) = \int_0^1 \left(0.1x^2 + \frac{11}{30}x\right)dx$

$= \left[\frac{0.1x^3}{3} + \frac{11x^2}{60}\right]_0^1$

$= \frac{0.1}{3} + \frac{11}{60} = \frac{13}{60}$

Q4 a) $\int_{-\infty}^{\infty} f(x)dx = \int_0^2 (0.1x^2 + 0.2)dx$

$= \left[\frac{0.1x^3}{3} + 0.2x\right]_0^2 = \frac{0.8}{3} + 0.4 \ne 1$

So f(x) is not a p.d.f.

b) $g(x) < 0$ for $-1 \le x < 0$, so g(x) is not a p.d.f.

Q5 *We'll use the constant of integration method for a change here — see p51 for a reminder.*

a) Integrate the pieces of the p.d.f., and then make sure the 'joins' are smooth using a suitable constant of integration (k).

$$F(x) = \begin{cases} 0 \text{ for } x < 0 \\ 0.04x^2 + k \text{ for } 0 \le x \le 5 \\ 1 \text{ for } x > 5 \end{cases}$$

Since $F(0) = 0$ and $F(5) = 1$, the pieces of this function join smoothly with $k = 0$.
So

$$F(x) = \begin{cases} 0 \text{ for } x < 0 \\ 0.04x^2 \text{ for } 0 \le x \le 5 \\ 1 \text{ for } x > 5 \end{cases}$$

b) Integrate the pieces of the p.d.f., and then make sure the 'joins' are smooth using a suitable constant of integration (k).

$$G(x) = \begin{cases} 0 \text{ for } x < 0 \\ 0.2x - 0.01x^2 + k \text{ for } 0 \le x \le 10 \\ 1 \text{ for } x > 10 \end{cases}$$

Since $G(0) = 0$ and $G(10) = 1$, the pieces of this function join smoothly with $k = 0$.
So

$$G(x) = \begin{cases} 0 \text{ for } x < 0 \\ 0.2x - 0.01x^2 \text{ for } 0 \le x \le 10 \\ 1 \text{ for } x > 10 \end{cases}$$

c) Integrate the pieces of the p.d.f., and then make sure the 'joins' are smooth using suitable constants of integration (k_1 - k_3).

$$H(x) = \begin{cases} 0 \text{ for } x < 0 \\ x^2 + k_1 \text{ for } 0 \le x \le 0.5 \\ x + k_2 \text{ for } 0.5 \le x \le 1 \\ 3x - x^2 + k_3 \text{ for } 1 \le x \le 1.5 \\ 1 \text{ for } x > 1.5 \end{cases}$$

$H(0) = 0$ means that $k_1 = 0$, which then gives $H(0.5) = 0.25$.
$H(0.5) = 0.25$ means that $k_2 = -0.25$, giving $H(1) = 0.75$.
$H(1) = 0.75$ means that $k_3 = -1.25$, giving $H(1.5) = 1$.
This means all the joins are now 'smooth'.
So

$$H(x) = \begin{cases} 0 \text{ for } x < 0 \\ x^2 \text{ for } 0 \le x \le 0.5 \\ x - 0.25 \text{ for } 0.5 \le x \le 1 \\ 3x - x^2 - 1.25 \text{ for } 1 \le x \le 1.5 \\ 1 \text{ for } x > 1.5 \end{cases}$$

d) Integrate the pieces of the p.d.f., and then make sure the 'joins' are smooth using suitable constants of integration (k_1 and k_2).

$$M(x) = \begin{cases} 0 \text{ for } x < 2 \\ 0.5x - 0.05x^2 + k_1 \text{ for } 2 \le x \le 4 \\ 0.1x + k_2 \text{ for } 4 \le x \le 10 \\ 1 \text{ for } x > 10 \end{cases}$$

$M(2) = 0$ means that $k_1 = -0.8$, which gives $M(4) = 0.4$.
$M(4) = 0.4$ means that $k_2 = 0$, which gives $M(10) = 1$.
This means all the joins are now 'smooth'.
So

$$M(x) = \begin{cases} 0 \text{ for } x < 2 \\ 0.5x - 0.05x^2 - 0.8 \text{ for } 2 \le x \le 4 \\ 0.1x \text{ for } 4 \le x \le 10 \\ 1 \text{ for } x > 10 \end{cases}$$

Q6 a) Differentiate the different parts of the c.d.f.:

$$f(x) = \begin{cases} 4x^3 & \text{for } 0 \leq x \leq 1 \\ 0 & \text{otherwise} \end{cases}$$

b)

$$g(x) = \begin{cases} \frac{1}{50}(x-1) & \text{for } 1 \leq x < 6 \\ \frac{3}{8} & \text{for } 6 \leq x \leq 8 \\ 0 & \text{otherwise} \end{cases}$$

Q7

$$E(X) = \int_{-\infty}^{\infty} x f(x)\,dx$$
$$= \int_1^2 x\left(\tfrac{2}{3}(x-1)\right)dx + \int_2^3 x\left(\tfrac{2}{3}\right)dx$$
$$= \int_1^2 \tfrac{2}{3}(x^2 - x)\,dx + \int_2^3 \tfrac{2}{3}x\,dx$$
$$= \left[\frac{2x^3}{9} - \frac{x^2}{3}\right]_1^2 + \left[\frac{1}{3}x^2\right]_2^3$$
$$= \left(\frac{2(2)^3}{9} - \frac{(2)^2}{3}\right) - \left(\frac{2(1)^3}{9} - \frac{(1)^2}{3}\right) + \left(\tfrac{1}{3}(3^2)\right) - \left(\tfrac{1}{3}(2^2)\right)$$
$$= \tfrac{4}{9} - \left(-\tfrac{1}{9}\right) + 3 - \tfrac{4}{3} = \tfrac{20}{9}$$

Q8 a)

$$E(X) = \int_{-\infty}^{\infty} x f(x)dx = \int_0^5 0.08x^2 dx = 0.08\left[\frac{x^3}{3}\right]_0^5$$
$$= \frac{125 \times 0.08}{3} = \frac{10}{3}$$
$$\text{Var}(X) = \int_{-\infty}^{\infty} x^2 f(x)dx - \mu^2$$
$$= \int_0^5 0.08x^3 dx - \left(\tfrac{10}{3}\right)^2$$
$$= 0.08\left[\frac{x^4}{4}\right]_0^5 - \left(\frac{10}{3}\right)^2 = \frac{625 \times 0.08}{4} - \left(\frac{10}{3}\right)^2$$
$$= \frac{25}{2} - \left(\frac{10}{3}\right)^2 = \frac{25}{18} = 1.39 \text{ (to 2 d.p.)}.$$

$$E(Y) = \int_{-\infty}^{\infty} y g(y)dy = \int_0^{10} 0.02y(10-y)dy$$
$$= 0.02\left[5y^2 - \frac{y^3}{3}\right]_0^{10}$$
$$= 0.02\left(500 - \frac{1000}{3}\right) = 10 - \frac{20}{3} = \frac{10}{3}$$

$$\text{Var}(Y) = \int_{-\infty}^{\infty} y^2 g(y)dy - \mu^2$$
$$= \int_0^{10} 0.02y^2(10-y)dy - \left(\tfrac{10}{3}\right)^2$$
$$= 0.02\left[\frac{10y^3}{3} - \frac{y^4}{4}\right]_0^{10} - \left(\tfrac{10}{3}\right)^2$$
$$= 0.02 \times \left(\frac{10\,000}{3} - \frac{10\,000}{4}\right) - \left(\tfrac{10}{3}\right)^2$$
$$= \frac{50}{3} - \left(\frac{10}{3}\right)^2 = \frac{50}{9} = 5.56 \text{ (to 2 d.p.)}.$$

b)

$$E(X^2) = \int_{-\infty}^{\infty} x^2 f(x)\,dx = \int_0^5 x^2(0.08x)\,dx$$
$$= \int_0^5 0.08x^3\,dx = [0.02x^4]_0^5$$
$$= 0.02(5^4) - 0 = 12.5$$
$$\text{Var}(X^2) = E((X^2)^2) - [E(X^2)]^2$$
$$= \int_{-\infty}^{\infty} x^4 f(x)\,dx - 12.5^2$$
$$= \int_0^5 0.08x^5\,dx - 12.5^2$$
$$= \left[\frac{0.08}{6}x^6\right]_0^5 - 12.5^2$$
$$= \left(\frac{0.08}{6} \times 5^6\right) - 12.5^2$$
$$= 52.083 \text{ (3 d.p.)}$$

c) $E(4X + 2) = 4E(X) + 2 = 4 \times \frac{10}{3} + 2 = \frac{46}{3}$
$= 15.33$ (to 2 d.p.)

$E(3Y - 4) = 3E(Y) - 4 = 3 \times \frac{10}{3} - 4 = 6$

$\text{Var}(4X + 2) = 4^2 \times \text{Var}(X)$
$= 16 \times \frac{25}{18} = \frac{200}{9} = 22.22$ (to 2 d.p.).

$\text{Var}(3Y - 4) = 3^2 \times \text{Var}(Y) = 9 \times \frac{50}{9} = 50$

d) The median is Q_2, where:

$$\int_0^{Q_2} 0.08x\,dx = 0.08\left[\frac{x^2}{2}\right]_0^{Q_2} = 0.04Q_2^2 = 0.5$$

So the median $= \sqrt{12.5} = 3.54$ (to 2 d.p.).

You usually work out the median by finding F(x), and then solving $F(Q_2) = 0.5$.
But you haven't been asked to find F(x) here, so just use the definition $F(Q_2) = \int_{-\infty}^{Q_2} f(x)\,dx$.

e) The lower quartile is Q_1, where:

$$\int_0^{Q_1} 0.08x\,dx = 0.08\left[\frac{x^2}{2}\right]_0^{Q_1} = 0.04Q_1^2 = 0.25$$

So $Q_1 = \sqrt{6.25} = 2.5$.

The upper quartile is Q_3, where:

$$\int_0^{Q_3} 0.08x\,dx = 0.08\left[\frac{x^2}{2}\right]_0^{Q_3} = 0.04Q_3^2 = 0.75$$

So $Q_3 = \sqrt{18.75} = 4.33$ (to 2 d.p.).

Q9 a) You need the total area to be 1, so integrate:

$$\int_{-\infty}^{\infty} f(x)\,dx = \int_1^2 k(x^2 - 3x)\,dx = \left[k\left(\frac{x^3}{3} - \frac{3x^2}{2}\right)\right]_1^2$$
$$= k\left(\frac{2^3}{3} - \frac{3(2)^2}{2}\right) - k\left(\frac{1^3}{3} - \frac{3(1)^2}{2}\right)$$
$$= k\left(\frac{8}{3} - \frac{12}{2} - \frac{1}{3} + \frac{3}{2}\right) = -\frac{13}{6}k$$

So $-\frac{13}{6}k = 1 \Rightarrow k = -\frac{6}{13}$.

This p.d.f. is non-negative between 1 and 2, so it is valid.

b) For $x < 1$, $F(x) = 0$.
For $1 \le x \le 2$:

$$F(x) = \int_{-\infty}^{x} f(t)\,dt = \int_{-\infty}^{1} f(t)\,dt + \int_{1}^{x} f(t)\,dt$$
$$= F(1) + \int_{1}^{x} -\frac{6}{13}(t^2 - 3t)\,dt$$
$$= 0 + \left[-\frac{6}{13}\left(\frac{t^3}{3} - \frac{3t^2}{2}\right)\right]_1^x$$
$$= -\frac{6}{13}\left(\frac{x^3}{3} - \frac{3x^2}{2}\right) - \left(-\frac{6}{13}\left(\frac{1}{3} - \frac{3}{2}\right)\right)$$
$$= -\frac{1}{13}\left(\frac{6x^3}{3} - \frac{18x^2}{2}\right) - \frac{7}{13}$$
$$= -\frac{1}{13}(2x^3 - 9x^2 + 7)$$

So, $F(2) = -\frac{1}{13}(2(2)^3 - 9(2)^2 + 7) = 1$.

So the pieces join up and

$$F(x) = \begin{cases} 0 & x < 1 \\ -\frac{1}{13}(2x^3 - 9x^2 + 7) & 1 \le x \le 2 \\ 1 & x > 2 \end{cases}$$

c) $F(1.5) = -\frac{1}{13}(2(1.5)^3 - 9(1.5)^2 + 7) = 0.5$
So the median is 1.5.

d) $F(1.2) = 0.193$ (3 d.p.), $F(1.3) = 0.294$ (3 d.p.)
So Q_1, where $F(Q_1) = 0.25$, lies between 1.2 and 1.3.

$F(1.7) = 0.706$ (3 d.p.), $F(1.8) = 0.807$ (3 d.p.)
So Q_3, where $F(Q_3) = 0.75$, lies between 1.7 and 1.8.

e) $F(1.25) = 0.243$ (3 d.p.) so $Q_1 = 1.3$ to 1 d.p.
$F(1.75) = 0.757$ (3 d.p.) so $Q_3 = 1.7$ to 1 d.p.

Q10 a) $f(x) = \begin{cases} 0.1 & 0 \le x \le 10 \\ 0 & \text{otherwise} \end{cases}$

Sketch the p.d.f:

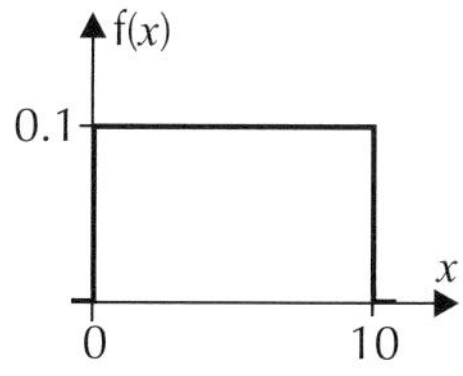

b) (i) On the sketch of the p.d.f.:

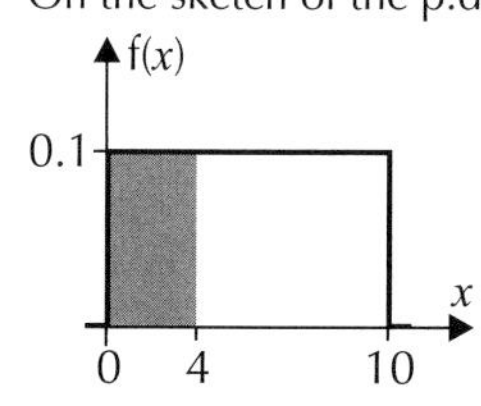

The shaded area represents $P(X < 4)$.
This is $4 \times 0.1 = 0.4$.

(ii) Similarly, $P(X \ge 8) = 2 \times 0.1 = 0.2$.

(iii) $P(X = 5) = 0$ [$P(X = k) = 0$ for any k and any continuous random variable X.]

(iv) $P(3 < X \le 7) = 4 \times 0.1 = 0.4$.

Q11 Y follows a rectangular distribution over the interval $[5 \times 1 + 2, 5 \times 4 + 2] = [7, 22]$.

So the p.d.f. is $f(y) = \begin{cases} \frac{1}{15} & 7 \le y \le 22 \\ 0 & \text{otherwise} \end{cases}$

and it looks like this:

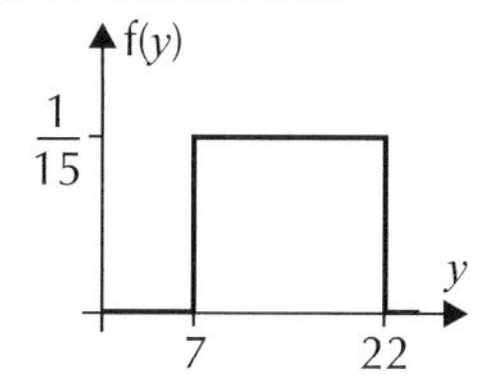

Q12 The error could be anything from –0.5 to 0.5 with equal probability. So X follows a rectangular distribution over the interval [–0.5, 0.5].

Q13 a) The p.d.f. of X is a rectangle of height $1 \div 4 = 0.25$, while the p.d.f. of Y is a rectangle of height $1 \div 20 = 0.05$.
$P(X < 6) = (6 - 4) \times 0.25 = 0.5$.
$P(Y > 0) = (12 - 0) \times 0.05 = 0.6$.
So $P(X < 6 \text{ and } Y > 0) = 0.5 \times 0.6 = 0.3$.
You can multiply these probabilities because X and Y are independent random variables.

b) $P(X < 6 \text{ or } Y > 0)$
$= P(X < 6) + P(Y > 0) - P(X < 6 \text{ and } Y > 0)$
$= 0.5 + 0.6 - 0.3 = 0.8$
Remember, for events A and B,
P(A or B) = P(A) + P(B) – P(A and B).

Q14 Let X be the number of minutes the train is delayed. Then X follows a rectangular distribution over the interval [0, 12], and its p.d.f. would be a rectangle of height $\frac{1}{12}$.

a) P(late for work) $= P(X > 8) = 4 \times \frac{1}{12} = \frac{1}{3}$

b) P(on time for work) $= P(X \le 8) = 1 - \frac{1}{3} = \frac{2}{3}$
Since the delays are random, the individual delays are independent and the probabilities can be multiplied.
So P(on time every day)
$= \left(\frac{2}{3}\right)^5 = \frac{32}{243} = 0.132$ (to 3 d.p.).

Exam-Style Questions — Chapter 3

1 a)

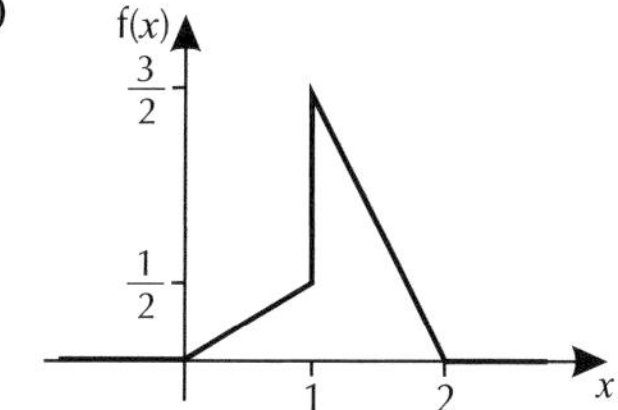

[1 mark]

b) Integrate the pieces of the p.d.f., and then make sure the 'joins' are smooth using constants of integration (k_1 and k_2).
[1 mark].

$$F(x) = \begin{cases} 0 & x < 0 \\ \frac{x^2}{4} + k_1 & 0 \le x < 1 \\ -\frac{3x^2}{4} + 3x + k_2 & 1 \le x \le 2 \\ 1 & x > 2 \end{cases}$$

[1 mark for each part correctly found]

All the joins are 'smooth' if $k_1 = 0$ and $k_2 = -2$, so the c.d.f. is:

$$F(x) = \begin{cases} 0 & x < 0 \\ \frac{x^2}{4} & 0 \le x < 1 \\ -\frac{3x^2}{4} + 3x - 2 & 1 \le x \le 2 \\ 1 & x > 2 \end{cases}$$

[1 mark for final answer]

c) $F(1) = \frac{1}{4} = 0.25$, so the lower quartile is $Q_1 = 1$ ***[1 mark]***.

$F(Q_2) = 0.5$ ***[1 mark]*** where $1 < Q_2 \le 2$

$$\Rightarrow -\frac{3Q_2^2}{4} + 3Q_2 - 2 = 0.5$$

$$\Rightarrow -\frac{3Q_2^2}{4} + 3Q_2 - \frac{5}{2} = 0$$

$$\Rightarrow -3Q_2^2 + 12Q_2 - 10 = 0$$

$$\Rightarrow Q_2 = \frac{-12 \pm \sqrt{144 - (4 \times -3 \times -10)}}{-6}$$

$$= \frac{-12 \pm 2\sqrt{6}}{-6} = 2 \pm \frac{\sqrt{6}}{3}$$

$= 2.816$ or 1.184 (3 d.p.) ***[1 mark]***

So the median is 1.184 to 3 d.p. (since 2.816 is not in the range $1 \le x \le 2$). ***[1 mark]***

$F(Q_3) = 0.75$ ***[1 mark]*** where $1 < Q_3 \le 2$

$$\Rightarrow -\frac{3Q_3^2}{4} + 3Q_3 - 2 = 0.75$$

$$\Rightarrow -\frac{3Q_3^2}{4} + 3Q_3 - \frac{11}{4} = 0$$

$$\Rightarrow -3Q_3^2 + 12Q_3 - 11 = 0$$

$$\Rightarrow Q_3 = \frac{-12 \pm \sqrt{144 - (4 \times -3 \times -11)}}{-6}$$

$$= \frac{-12 \pm \sqrt{12}}{-6} = 2 \pm \frac{\sqrt{3}}{3}$$

$= 1.423$ or 2.577 (3 d.p.) ***[1 mark]***

So the upper quartile is $Q_3 = 1.423$ (3 d.p.) (2.577 is too big) ***[1 mark]***.

2 a) $P(0.25 \le X \le 0.75)$

$= P(X \le 0.75) - P(X \le 0.25)$ ***[1 mark]***

$= F(0.75) - F(0.25) = \frac{27}{32} - \frac{5}{32}$

$= \frac{11}{16} = 0.6875$ ***[1 mark]***

b) $F(0.67) = 0.745$ (3 d.p.) ***[1 mark]*** and $F(0.68) = 0.758$ (3 d.p.) ***[1 mark]***, so the upper quartile Q_3, where $F(Q_3) = 0.75$, is between 0.67 and 0.68 ***[1 mark]***.

c) $F(0.5) = 3(0.5)^2 - 2(0.5)^3$ ***[1 mark]***
$= 0.75 - 0.25 = 0.5$ ***[1 mark]***.

d) (i) Differentiate each bit to find the p.d.f. ***[1 mark]***

$$f(x) = \begin{cases} 6x - 6x^2 & 0 \le x \le 1 \\ 0 & \text{otherwise} \end{cases}$$

[1 mark for correct p.d.f.]

(ii)

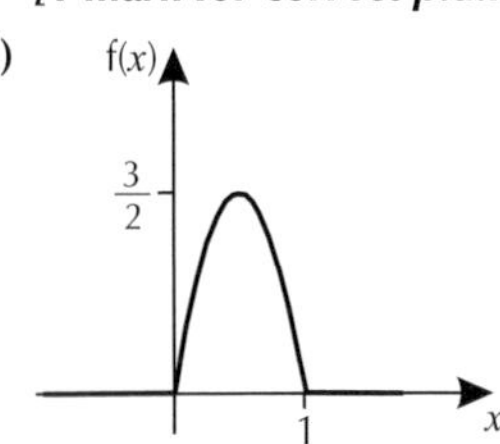

[1 mark]

e) $\mu = E(X) = \int_{-\infty}^{\infty} xf(x)\,dx$

$= \int_0^1 x(6x - 6x^2)\,dx$ ***[1 mark]***

$= \int_0^1 (6x^2 - 6x^3)\,dx = \left[2x^3 - \frac{3}{2}x^4\right]_0^1$ ***[1 mark]***

$= 2 - \frac{3}{2} = \frac{1}{2}$ ***[1 mark]***

3 a) X is equally likely to take any value between 0 and 20, so X follows a rectangular distribution over the interval [0, 20]
[1 mark for using a rectangular distribution, 1 mark for the correct limits].

b)

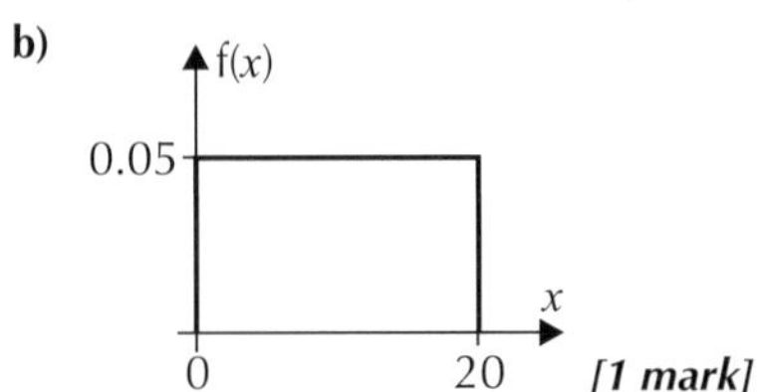

[1 mark]

c) $E(X) = \frac{0 + 20}{2} = 10$ ***[1 mark]***

$\text{Var}(X) = \frac{(20 - 0)^2}{12}$ ***[1 mark]***

$= \frac{400}{12} = 33.3$ (to 3 sig. fig.) ***[1 mark]***.

d) (i) $P(X > 5) = (20 - 5) \times 0.05 = 0.75$ ***[1 mark]***

(ii) $P(X = 2) = 0$ ***[1 mark]***

Remember... $P(X = k) = 0$ for any value of k if X is a continuous random variable.

4 a) $\int_{-\infty}^{\infty} f(x)dx = \frac{1}{k}\int_0^2 (x+4)dx$

$= \frac{1}{k}\left[\frac{x^2}{2} + 4x\right]_0^2 = \frac{10}{k}$ ***[1 mark]***

This must be equal to 1 ***[1 mark]***.

So $k = 10$ ***[1 mark]***.

b) Integrate the pieces of the p.d.f., and then make sure the 'joins' are smooth using a constant of integration (k).
[1 mark].

$$F(x) = \begin{cases} 0 \text{ for } x < 0 \\ 0.05x^2 + 0.4x + k \text{ for } 0 \le x \le 2 \\ 1 \text{ for } x > 2 \end{cases}$$

[1 mark for each part correctly found]

All the joins are 'smooth' if $k = 0$, so the c.d.f. is:

$$F(x) = \begin{cases} 0 \text{ for } x < 0 \\ 0.05x^2 + 0.4x \text{ for } 0 \le x \le 2 \\ 1 \text{ for } x > 2 \end{cases}$$

[1 mark for final answer]

You must define a c.d.f. for all values of x. Don't just do the tricky bits in the middle and assume you're finished.

c) $E(X) = \int_{-\infty}^{\infty} xf(x)dx$

$= \int_0^2 0.1(x^2 + 4x)dx$ ***[1 mark]***

$= 0.1\left[\frac{x^3}{3} + 2x^2\right]_0^2$ ***[1 mark]***

$= 0.1\left(\frac{8}{3} + 8\right) = \frac{32}{30} = \frac{16}{15}$

$= 1.067$ (to 3 d.p.) ***[1 mark]***

d) (i) $Var(X) = \int_{-\infty}^{\infty} x^2 f(x)dx - \mu^2$

$= 0.1\int_0^2 (x^3 + 4x^2)dx - \left(\frac{16}{15}\right)^2$ ***[1 mark]***

$= 0.1\left[\frac{x^4}{4} + \frac{4x^3}{3}\right]_0^2 - \left(\frac{16}{15}\right)^2$ ***[1 mark]***

$= 0.1\left(4 + \frac{32}{3}\right) - \left(\frac{16}{15}\right)^2$

$= \frac{22}{15} - \left(\frac{16}{15}\right)^2 = \frac{74}{225}$

$= 0.329$ (to 3 d.p.). ***[1 mark]***

(ii) $Var(4X - 2) = 4^2 \times Var(X)$ ***[1 mark]***

$= 16 \times \frac{74}{225} = \frac{1184}{225} = 5.262$ (to 3 d.p.).

[1 mark]

e) Use the c.d.f. from part b) to find the median.
The median is Q_2,
where $0.05Q_2^2 + 0.4Q_2 = 0.5$ ***[1 mark]***.
This simplifies to: $Q_2^2 + 8Q_2 - 10 = 0$ ***[1 mark]***.
Using the quadratic formula (and choosing the positive answer ***[1 mark]***) gives

$Q_2 = \frac{-8 + \sqrt{104}}{2} = 1.099$ (to 3 d.p.) ***[1 mark]***.

5 a) Using the third part of the c.d.f.,
$F(3) = 0.5$ ***[1 mark]***.
So F(3) must also equal 0.5 using the second part of the c.d.f., which means that $2k = 0.5$, or $k = 0.25$ ***[1 mark]***.

b) (i) Differentiate to find the p.d.f.:

$$f(x) = \begin{cases} 0.25 \text{ for } 1 \le x < 3 \textbf{ [1 mark]} \\ 0.5 \text{ for } 3 \le x \le 4 \textbf{ [1 mark]} \\ 0 \text{ otherwise } \textbf{[1 mark]} \end{cases}$$

(ii)

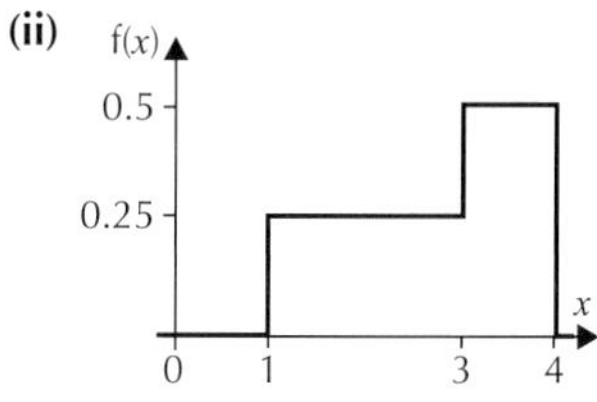

[1 mark]

c) $\mu = \int_{-\infty}^{\infty} xf(x)dx$

$= \int_1^3 0.25xdx + \int_3^4 0.5xdx$ ***[1 mark]***

$= [0.125x^2]_1^3 + [0.25x^2]_3^4$ ***[1 mark]***

$= 1 + \frac{7}{4} = \frac{11}{4} = 2.75$ ***[1 mark]***

$Var(X) = \sigma^2 = \int_{-\infty}^{\infty} x^2 f(x)dx - \mu^2$

$= \int_1^3 0.25x^2dx + \int_3^4 0.5x^2dx - 2.75^2$ ***[1 mark]***

$= \left[\frac{0.25x^3}{3}\right]_1^3 + \left[\frac{0.5x^3}{3}\right]_3^4 - 2.75^2$ ***[1 mark]***

$= \frac{13}{6} + \frac{37}{6} - \left(\frac{11}{4}\right)^2 = \frac{25}{3} - \frac{121}{16}$

$= \frac{37}{48} = 0.771$ (to 3 d.p.) ***[1 mark]***.

6 a) $a = -2$ and $b = 7$, so the p.d.f. is defined as:

$$f(x) = \begin{cases} \frac{1}{9} & -2 \le x \le 7 \\ 0 & \text{otherwise} \end{cases}$$

[1 mark for each part of the p.d.f. correct]

b)

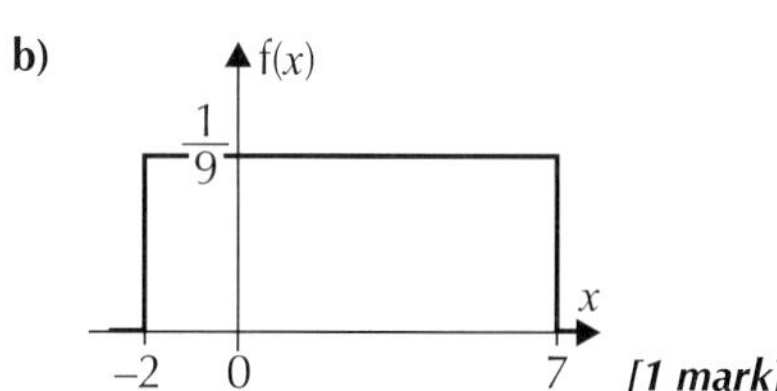

[1 mark]

c) Y follows a rectangular distribution over the interval $[3 \times (-2) + 6, 3 \times 7 + 6] = [0, 27]$
[1 mark]

So $E(Y) = \frac{0 + 27}{2} = 13.5$ ***[1 mark]***

$Var(Y) = \frac{(27 - 0)^2}{12}$ ***[1 mark]***

$= \frac{243}{4} = 60.75$ ***[1 mark]***

d) (i) $P(Y < 20) = (20 - 0) \times \frac{1}{27} = \frac{20}{27}$
$= 0.741$ (3 d.p.) *[1 mark]*

(ii) $P(10 < Y < 20) = (20 - 10) \times \frac{1}{27} = \frac{10}{27}$
$= 0.370$ (3 d.p.) *[1 mark]*

(iii) $P(10 < Y < 20 | Y < 20)$

$= \frac{P(10 < Y < 20 \text{ and } Y < 20)}{P(Y < 20)}$ *[1 mark]*

$= \frac{P(10 < Y < 20)}{P(Y < 20)}$ *[1 mark]*

$= \frac{10/27}{20/27} = \frac{1}{2}$ *[1 mark]*

Chapter 4: Estimation and Hypothesis Testing

1. Confidence Intervals

Exercise 1.1 — The 'family' of *t*-distributions

Q1 **a)** $x = 1.397$
b) $x = 1.812$
c) $x = -2.131$
d) $x = 1.725$

Q2 **a)** $p = 0.95$
b) $p = 0.95$
c) $p = 0.025$
d) $p = 0.1$

Exercise 1.2 — Confidence intervals for μ — normal population / unknown σ^2 / small n

Q1 **a)** $\sum x = 331$ so the sample mean $\bar{x} = \frac{331}{8}$
$= 41.375$

$\sum x^2 = 13785$ so

$$s = \sqrt{\frac{n}{n-1}\left[\frac{\sum x^2}{n} - \left(\frac{\sum x}{n}\right)^2\right]}$$

$$= \sqrt{\frac{8}{7}\left[\frac{13785}{8} - \left(\frac{331}{8}\right)^2\right]}$$

$$= \sqrt{\frac{719}{56}} = 3.583 \text{ (3 d.p.)}$$

b) $n = 8$, so you need to look up $t_{(7)}$ in the *t*-distribution tables.
It's a 95% confidence interval, so $p = 0.975$ — this gives $t_{(7)} = 2.365$.
So your confidence interval is:

$$\left(\bar{x} - \frac{s}{\sqrt{n}}t_{(n-1)},\ \bar{x} + \frac{s}{\sqrt{n}}t_{(n-1)}\right)$$

$$= \left(41.375 - \frac{\sqrt{719/56}}{\sqrt{10}} \times 2.365,\ 41.375 + \frac{\sqrt{719/56}}{\sqrt{10}} \times 2.365\right)$$

$= (38.7, 44.1)$ (to 3 sig. fig.)

Q2 **a)** The sample mean is $\bar{w} = \frac{\sum w}{n} = \frac{1162}{9}$
An estimate of the population variance is

$$s^2 = \frac{n}{n-1}\left[\frac{\sum w^2}{n} - \left(\frac{\sum w}{n}\right)^2\right]$$

$$= \frac{9}{8}\left[\frac{151200}{9} - \left(\frac{1162}{9}\right)^2\right] = \frac{2639}{18}$$

You need to assume now that the population follows a normal distribution — then you can use a *t*-distribution to find the confidence interval.

$n = 9$, so you need to look up $t_{(8)}$ in the *t*-distribution tables.
It's a 98% confidence interval, so look up $p = 0.99$ — this gives $t_{(8)} = 2.896$.
So your confidence interval is:

$$\left(\bar{w} - \frac{s}{\sqrt{n}}t_{(n-1)},\ \bar{w} + \frac{s}{\sqrt{n}}t_{(n-1)}\right)$$

$$= \left(\frac{1162}{9} - \frac{\sqrt{2639/18}}{\sqrt{9}} \times 2.896,\ \frac{1162}{9} + \frac{\sqrt{2639/18}}{\sqrt{9}} \times 2.896\right)$$

$= (117.4, 140.8)$ (1 d.p.)

b) This claimed value lies inside the 98% confidence interval, so it is a reasonable claim (assuming that the population follows a normal distribution).

Q3 **a)** The confidence interval is (12.7, 19.5), so the sample mean will be the mid-point of this interval. So the sample mean is $\bar{x} = 16.1$.

b) You're looking for an estimate of the standard error of the mean, i.e. $\frac{s}{\sqrt{n}}$.
You know that the upper limit of a confidence interval is given by $\bar{x} + \frac{s}{\sqrt{n}}t_{(n-1)}$,
so $\bar{x} + \frac{s}{\sqrt{n}}t_{(n-1)} = 19.5$.
The sample mean is 16.1 and it is a 99% confidence interval with $n = 15$, so you're looking for $t_{(14)}$ for $p = 0.995$ — this gives $t_{(14)} = 2.977$.
So $16.1 + \frac{s}{\sqrt{n}}(2.977) = 19.5$

$$\Rightarrow \frac{s}{\sqrt{n}} = \left(\frac{19.5 - 16.1}{2.977}\right) = 1.142 \text{ (3 d.p.)}$$

Q4 a) You must assume that the times are normally distributed in order to use the t-distribution.

$$\bar{t} = \frac{\sum t}{n} = \frac{156}{12} = 13 \text{ and}$$

$$s = \sqrt{\frac{\sum(t - \bar{t})^2}{n - 1}} = \sqrt{\frac{33}{11}} = \sqrt{3}$$

$n = 12$ and it is a 99% confidence interval, so you're looking for $t_{(11)}$ for $p = 0.995$.
This gives $t_{(11)} = 3.106$.

So the confidence interval is

$$\left(\bar{t} - \frac{s}{\sqrt{n}}t_{(n-1)},\ \bar{t} + \frac{s}{\sqrt{n}}t_{(n-1)}\right)$$

$$= (13 - \frac{\sqrt{3}}{\sqrt{12}} \times 3.106,\ 13 + \frac{\sqrt{3}}{\sqrt{12}} \times 3.106)$$

$$= (11.4, 14.6)\ (1\text{ d.p.})$$

b) 15 minutes lies outside of the confidence interval, so there is evidence to doubt this claim (assuming that the population follows a normal distribution).

Q5 a) The sample mean is in the middle of the confidence interval, so it is halfway between 19.14 and 21.46. So $\bar{x} = 20.3$ kg.

b) The upper limit of the confidence interval is $\bar{x} + \frac{s}{\sqrt{n}}t_{(n-1)} = 21.46$.

You know that $n = 12$, so you need to look up $t_{(11)}$ for $p = 0.975$. This gives $t_{(11)} = 2.201$.

So $20.3 + \frac{s}{\sqrt{n}}(2.201) = 21.46$

$$\Rightarrow \frac{s}{\sqrt{n}} = \frac{21.46 - 20.3}{2.201}$$

$$= 0.5270... = 0.527\ (3\text{ d.p.})$$

c) $\frac{s}{\sqrt{n}} = 0.5270... \Rightarrow \frac{s^2}{n} = (0.5270...)^2$

$\Rightarrow s^2 = 12 \times (0.5270...)^2 = 3.333\ (3\text{ d.p.})$

d) You have everything you need already from the previous parts except for the value of $t_{(11)}$.
You're after $t_{(11)}$ when $p = 0.995$ so $t_{(11)} = 3.106$.

Substitute in the numbers:

$$\left(\bar{x} - \frac{s}{\sqrt{n}}t_{(n-1)},\ \bar{x} + \frac{s}{\sqrt{n}}t_{(n-1)}\right)$$

$$= (20.3 - 0.5270... \times 3.106,\ 20.3 + 0.5270... \times 3.106)$$

$$= (18.66, 21.94)\ (2\text{ d.p.})$$

e) The confidence interval has a width of $21.0183 - 19.5817 = 1.4366$.
So

$$2\frac{s}{\sqrt{n}}t_{(11)} = 1.4366 \Rightarrow (2 \times 0.5270...)t_{(11)} = 1.4366$$

$$\Rightarrow t_{(11)} = 1.363\ (\text{to } 3\text{ d.p.})$$

In the t-tables, $t_{(11)}$ is 1.363 when $p = 0.9$.
So $P(X \le 1.363) = 0.9$ and so the percentage confidence level is 80%.

2. Hypothesis Testing

Exercise 2.1 — Null and alternative hypotheses

Q1 a) Meryl is investigating the mean length, μ cm, of the croissants in her bakery cooked by the new pastry chef.

b) The null hypothesis assumes that the length of croissants has not decreased: $H_0: \mu = 12$.

c) The alternative hypothesis is what Meryl wants to get evidence for — that the croissant length has decreased: $H_1: \mu < 12$.

d) This is a one-tailed test.

Q2 a) The quantity being investigated is the mean number of hours per subject that this year's students at the school spend revising before an exam, μ.

b) The null hypothesis assumes the average is the same as usual: $H_0: \mu = 65.7$.

c) The alternative hypothesis is that the average has increased: $H_1: \mu > 65.7$.

d) This is a one-tailed test.

Q3 a) The quantity being investigated is the mean queuing time, μ hours, for entry into the theme park after the recent changes.

b) $H_0: \mu = 0.45$.
The managers are interested in either an increase or a decrease, so $H_1: \mu \neq 0.45$.

c) This test is two-tailed.

Q4 a) The quantity being investigated is the mean weight, μ kg, of lobster meat that Layton sells on his fish counter each day.

b) $H_0: \mu = 2.5$.
Layton thinks he'll sell more lobster meat so $H_1: \mu > 2.5$.

c) This is a one-tailed test.

Q5 Let the mean time Jules takes to play 18 holes be μ hours. Jules is unsure whether the time she needs to play 18 holes will be more than or less than the current mean, so $H_0: \mu = 3.7$ and $H_1: \mu \neq 3.7$.

Q6 Let the mean time that Katie's new toaster takes to toast a slice of bread be μ seconds.
Then $H_0: \mu = 33.2$ and $H_1: \mu \neq 33.2$.

3. Hypothesis Tests of the Mean of a Population

Exercise 3.1 — Hypothesis tests of a population mean — normal population with known variance

Q1 a) Let the mean weight in grams of all plums from the tree this year be μ.
Then H_0: $\mu = 42$ and H_1: $\mu > 42$. The significance level is $\alpha = 0.05$ and it is a one-tailed test.
Let $\overline{X}$ be the sample mean of the weight of plums in grams. Then under H_0, $X \sim N(42, 16)$,
so $\overline{X} \sim N\left(42, \frac{16}{25}\right) = N(42, 0.64)$.

So under H_0, $Z = \frac{\overline{X} - 42}{\sqrt{0.64}} \sim N(0, 1)$.

Now $\overline{x} = 43.5$, so $z = \frac{43.5 - 42}{\sqrt{0.64}} = 1.875$

You're interested in the higher end of the distribution, so find the critical value, z, such that $P(Z > z) = 0.05$, i.e. $P(Z < z) = 0.95$. This gives a critical value of 1.6449. So the critical region is $Z > 1.6449$. Since $1.875 > 1.6449$, the result lies in the critical region and is significant. There is significant evidence at the 5% level to reject H_0 in favour of the alternative hypothesis that the weight of plums from the tree has increased.

b) At the 1% level, you'll have a different critical region, but everything else is the same. So you're looking for a critical value, z, such that $P(Z > z) = 0.01$, i.e. $P(Z < z) = 0.99$. This gives a critical value of 2.3263. So the critical region is $Z > 2.3263$. Since $1.875 < 2.3263$, the result is not significant. There is insufficient evidence at the 1% level to reject H_0.

Q2 Let the mean of all the weekly winnings after the new person joins the games be £μ.
Then H_0: $\mu = 24$ and H_1: $\mu \neq 24$. The significance level is $\alpha = 0.01$, and it is a two-tailed test.
Let $\overline{X}$ be the sample mean of Bree's winnings.
Then under H_0, $X \sim N(24, 4)$,
so $\overline{X} \sim N\left(24, \frac{4}{12}\right) = N\left(24, \frac{1}{3}\right)$.

So under H_0, $Z = \frac{\overline{X} - 24}{\sqrt{1/3}} \sim N(0, 1)$.

Now $\overline{x} = 22.5$, so $z = \frac{22.5 - 24}{\sqrt{1/3}} = -2.5981$ (4 d.p.)

This is a two-tailed test, so the critical region will be split. You want to find critical values, $\pm z$, such that $P(Z > z) = \frac{\alpha}{2} = 0.005$, i.e. $P(Z < z) = 0.995$.
This gives a critical value of 2.5758. The other critical value will be -2.5758. So the critical region is $Z < -2.5758$ or $Z > 2.5758$.

Since $z = -2.5981 < -2.5758$, the result lies in the critical region and is significant. There is significant evidence at the 1% level to reject H_0 in favour of the alternative hypothesis that Bree's mean winnings have changed.

Q3 a) Let the mean mark of all the students in the city's schools be μ.
Then H_0: $\mu = 70$ and H_1: $\mu < 70$. The significance level is $\alpha = 0.05$, and it is a one-tailed test.
Let $\overline{X}$ be the sample mean of the scores.
Then under H_0, $X \sim N(70, 64)$,
so $\overline{X} \sim N\left(70, \frac{64}{40}\right) = N(70, 1.6)$.

So under H_0, $Z = \frac{\overline{X} - 70}{\sqrt{1.6}} \sim N(0, 1)$.

$\overline{x} = 67.7$, so $z = \frac{67.7 - 70}{\sqrt{1.6}} = -1.8183$ (4 d.p.)

You're interested in the lower end of the distribution, so find the critical value, z, such that $P(Z < z) = 0.05$, i.e. $P(Z < -z) = 0.95$.
This gives $z = -1.6449$. So the critical region is $Z < -1.6449$. Since $-1.8183 < -1.6449$, the result lies in the critical region and is significant. There is significant evidence at the 5% level to reject H_0 in favour of the alternative hypothesis that the mean score this year is lower.

b) The null hypothesis has been incorrectly rejected, so it is a Type I error.

Q4 a) Let the mean weight in grams of all the pigeons in the city centre this year be μ. Then H_0: $\mu = 300$ and H_1: $\mu > 300$.

b) This is a one-tailed test.

c) Let $\overline{X}$ be the sample mean of the pigeon weights.
Then under H_0, $X \sim N(300, 45^2)$,
so $\overline{X} \sim N\left(300, \frac{45^2}{25}\right) = N(300, 81)$.

So under H_0, $Z = \frac{\overline{X} - 300}{\sqrt{81}} \sim N(0, 1)$.

$\overline{x} = 314$, so $z = \frac{314 - 300}{\sqrt{81}} = 1.5556$ (4 d.p.)

You're interested in the higher end of the distribution, so find the critical value, z, such that $P(Z > z) = 0.01$, i.e. $P(Z < z) = 0.99$.
This gives a critical value of 2.3263.
So the critical region is $Z > 2.3263$.
Since $1.5556 < 2.3263$, the result does not lie in the critical region and is not significant. There is insufficient evidence at the 1% level to reject H_0 in favour of the alternative hypothesis that the mean pigeon weight has gone up.

d) The null hypothesis was not rejected when in fact it was incorrect, so this is a Type II error.

Q5 Let the mean number of hours that Kyle has spent building his time machine each week this year be μ.
Then H_0: $\mu = 32$ and H_1: $\mu > 32$. This is a one-tailed test.

Let $\overline{X}$ be the sample mean number of hours.
Then under H_0, $X \sim N(32, 5^2)$,
so $\overline{X} \sim N\left(32, \frac{5^2}{20}\right) = N(32, 1.25)$.

So under H_0, $Z = \frac{\overline{X} - 32}{\sqrt{1.25}} \sim N(0, 1)$.

$\overline{x} = 34$, so $z = \frac{34 - 32}{\sqrt{1.25}} = 1.7889$ (4 d.p.)

First test at the 5% level:
You're interested in the higher end of the distribution, so find the critical value, z, such that $P(Z > z) = 0.05$, i.e. $P(Z < z) = 0.95$.
This gives a critical value of 1.6449.
So the critical region is $Z > 1.6449$.
Since $1.7889 > 1.6449$, the result lies in the critical region and is significant. There is significant evidence at the 5% level to reject H_0 in favour of the alternative hypothesis that the mean amount of time spent building the time machine has gone up.

Now test at the 1% level:

Again, you're interested in the higher end of the distribution, so find the critical value, z, such that $P(Z > z) = 0.01$, i.e. $P(Z < z) = 0.99$.
This gives a critical value of 2.3263.
So the critical region is $Z > 2.3263$.
$1.7889 < 2.3263$, so the result does not lie in the critical region and is not significant. There is insufficient evidence at the 1% level to reject H_0 in favour of the alternative hypothesis that the mean amount of time spent building the time machine has gone up.

So the null hypothesis can be rejected at the 5% level, but not at the 1% level.

Exercise 3.2 — Hypothesis tests for a large sample

Q1 Let the mean lifetime of the whole 'population' of light bulbs be μ hours. Then $H_0: \mu = 1400$ and $H_1: \mu \neq 1400$. The significance level is $\alpha = 0.05$ and it is a two-tailed test.
Let $\overline{X}$ be the sample mean lifetime. The sample size is large (> 30), so using the Central Limit Theorem you can assume that under H_0
$\overline{X} \sim N\left(1400, \frac{80^2}{100}\right) = N(1400, 64)$.

So under H_0, $Z = \frac{\overline{X} - 1400}{\sqrt{64}} \sim N(0,1)$.

Now $\overline{x} = 1380$, so $z = \frac{1380 - 1400}{\sqrt{64}} = -2.5$

This is a two-tailed test so the critical region will be split. You want to find critical values, $\pm z$, such that $P(Z > z) = \frac{\alpha}{2} = 0.025$, i.e. $P(Z < z) = 0.975$.
This gives critical values of ± 1.96.
So the critical region is $Z < -1.96$ or $Z > 1.96$.
Since $-2.5 < -1.96$, the result lies in the critical region and so is significant.

There is significant evidence at the 5% level to reject H_0 in favour of the alternative hypothesis that the mean lifetime of a light bulb is different from 1400 hours.

Q2 **a)** Let the mean breaking strength of all new cables be μ kg.
Then $H_0: \mu = 700$ and $H_1: \mu > 700$.
The significance level is $\alpha = 0.05$ and it is a one-tailed test.
Let $\overline{X}$ be the sample mean of the breaking strengths.

The sample size is large so you can use the Central Limit Theorem to say that under H_0
$\overline{X} \sim N\left(700, \frac{6400}{40}\right) = N(700, 160)$.

So under H_0, $Z = \frac{\overline{X} - 700}{\sqrt{160}} \sim N(0,1)$.

Now $\overline{x} = 725$, so $z = \frac{725 - 700}{\sqrt{160}} = 1.9764$ (4 d.p.).

You're interested in the higher end of the distribution, so find the critical value, z, such that $P(Z > z) = 0.05$, i.e. $P(Z < z) = 0.95$. This gives a critical value of 1.6449. So the critical region is $Z > 1.6449$.

Since $1.9764 > 1.6449$, the result lies in the critical region and is significant. There is significant evidence at the 5% level to reject H_0 in favour of the alternative hypothesis that the mean breaking strength of the cables is greater.

b) At the 1% level, everything is the same except the critical region.

Again, you're interested in the higher end of the distribution, so the critical value, z, is such that $P(Z > z) = 0.01$, i.e. $P(Z < z) = 0.99$. This gives a critical value of 2.3263. So the critical region is $Z > 2.3263$. Since $1.9764 < 2.3263$, the result does not lie in the critical region and is not significant. There is insufficient evidence at the 1% level to reject H_0 in favour of the alternative hypothesis that the mean breaking strength of the cables is greater.

Q3 **a)** $s^2 = \frac{\sum(x - \overline{x})^2}{n - 1} = \frac{351}{39} = 9$

b) Let the mean score with a set of darts be μ.
Then $H_0: \mu = 57$ and $H_1: \mu > 57$.
Let $\overline{X}$ be the sample mean score.
The sample size is large (> 30) so you can use the Central Limit Theorem to say that under H_0

$\overline{X} \sim N\left(57, \frac{9}{40}\right) = N(57, 0.225)$.

So under H_0, $Z = \frac{\overline{X} - 57}{\sqrt{0.225}} \sim N(0,1)$.

$\overline{x} = \frac{\sum x}{n} = \frac{2316}{40} = 57.9$

so $z = \frac{57.9 - 57}{\sqrt{0.225}} = 1.8974$ (4 d.p.)

You're interested in the higher end of the distribution, so find the critical value, z, such that $P(Z > z) = 0.05$, i.e. $P(Z < z) = 0.95$.
This gives a critical value of 1.6449.
So the critical region is $Z > 1.6449$.
Since $1.8974 > 1.6449$, the result lies in the critical region and is significant. There is significant evidence at the 5% level to reject H_0 in favour of the alternative hypothesis that Tiger's mean score has gone up.

Q4 a) $s^2 = \frac{\sum(t-\bar{t})^2}{n-1} = \frac{34.51}{34} = 1.015$

b) Let the mean time that the robot takes to cover 100 m be μ seconds.
Then H_0: $\mu = 10.1$ and H_1: $\mu < 10.1$.
The significance level is $\alpha = 0.01$ and it is a one-tailed test.

Let $\overline{T}$ be the sample mean time.
The sample size is large so you can use the Central Limit Theorem to say that under H_0
$\overline{T} \sim N\left(10.1, \frac{1.015}{35}\right) = N(10.1, 0.029)$.
So under H_0, $Z = \frac{\overline{T} - 10.1}{\sqrt{0.029}} \sim N(0,1)$.

Now $\bar{t} = \frac{\sum t}{n} = \frac{346.5}{35} = 9.9$,
so $z = \frac{9.9 - 10.1}{\sqrt{0.029}} = -1.1744$ (4 d.p.)
You're interested in the lower end of the distribution, so find the critical value, z, such that $P(Z < z) = 0.01$. This gives a critical value of -2.3263. So the critical region is $Z < -2.3263$.

Since $-1.1744 > -2.3263$, the result does not lie in the critical region and is not significant. There is insufficient evidence at the 1% level to reject H_0 in favour of the alternative hypothesis that the mean time has decreased.

c) The null hypothesis was not rejected when it was in fact incorrect, so this is a Type II error.

Exercise 3.3 — Hypothesis tests of a population mean — normal population / unknown σ^2 / small n

Q1 a) $\sum x = 218$ and $\sum x^2 = 7942$.
So the sample mean is
$\bar{x} = \frac{\sum x}{n} = \frac{218}{6} = \frac{109}{3} = 36.33$ (2 d.p.)
And the sample variance is
$s^2 = \frac{6}{5}\left[\frac{7942}{6} - \left(\frac{218}{6}\right)^2\right] = \frac{64}{15} = 4.27$ (2 d.p.)

b) Let the mean time for an aerial fitting be μ mins.
Then H_0: $\mu = 35$ and H_1: $\mu > 35$.
The significance level is $\alpha = 0.05$ and it is a one-tailed test. σ^2 is unknown and $n = 6$, so you need to use a t-test.

Let $\overline{X}$ be the sample mean. Since X is assumed to be normally distributed and $n = 6$,
$T = \frac{\overline{X} - \mu}{s/\sqrt{n}} \sim t_{(n-1)}$
$\Rightarrow T = \frac{\overline{X} - 35}{\sqrt{\frac{64/15}{6}}} \sim t_{(5)}$

Now $\bar{x} = \frac{109}{3}$, so $t = \frac{\frac{109}{3} - 35}{\sqrt{\frac{64/15}{6}}} = 1.581$ (3 d.p.)

You're interested in the higher end of the distribution, so find the critical value, $t_{(5)}$, such that $P(T > t_{(5)}) = 0.05$, i.e. $P(T < t_{(5)}) = 0.95$. This gives a critical value of 2.015. So the critical region is $Z > 2.015$.

Since $1.581 < 2.015$, the result is not in the critical region and is not significant.
So there is not significant evidence at the 5% level to reject H_0 in favour of the alternative hypothesis that the mean fitting time is longer than 35 minutes.

Q2 a) Let the mean length of a jelly worm be μ cm.
Then H_0: $\mu = 12$ and H_1: $\mu < 12$.
The significance level is $\alpha = 0.05$ and it is a one-tailed test. σ^2 is unknown and $n = 6$ so you need to use a t-test.

You need to find the sample mean and estimate the population variance.
Using the data, $\sum x = 67.9$ and $\sum x^2 = 770.01$.
So $\bar{x} = \frac{67.9}{6} = \frac{679}{60} = 11.32$ (2 d.p.)
And an estimate of the population variance is
$s^2 = \frac{6}{5}\left[\frac{770.01}{6} - \left(\frac{67.9}{6}\right)^2\right] = 0.3216...$
Let $\overline{X}$ be the sample mean of the lengths of jelly worms. Then X is assumed to be normally distributed and $n = 6$, so $T = \frac{\overline{X} - \mu}{s/\sqrt{n}} \sim t_{(n-1)}$,
i.e. $T = \frac{\overline{X} - 12}{\sqrt{\frac{0.3216...}{6}}} \sim t_{(5)}$

Now $\bar{x} = \frac{679}{60}$

so $t = \frac{\frac{679}{60} - 12}{\sqrt{\frac{0.3216...}{6}}} = -2.951$ (3 d.p.)
You're interested in the lower end of the distribution, so find the critical value, $t_{(5)}$, such that $P(T < t_{(5)}) = 0.05$ — this gives a critical value of -2.015. So the critical region is $T < -2.015$.

Since $-2.951 < -2.015$, the result lies in the critical region and is significant. So there is significant evidence at the 5% level to reject H_0 in favour of the alternative hypothesis that the jelly worms are shorter.

b) Again, H_0: $\mu = 12$ and H_1: $\mu < 12$.
The significance level is $\alpha = 0.05$ and it is a one-tailed test. σ^2 is unknown and $n = 20$ so you need to use a t-test.

You need to find the sample mean and estimate the population variance.
$\bar{x} = \frac{\sum x}{n} = \frac{236}{20} = 11.8$
And an estimate of the population variance is
$s^2 = \frac{\sum(x-\bar{x})^2}{n-1} = \frac{5.1}{19} = 0.2684...$

Let $\overline{X}$ be the sample mean length of jelly worms. Then X is assumed to be normally distributed and $n = 20$, so $T = \frac{\overline{X} - \mu}{s/\sqrt{n}} \sim t_{(n-1)}$,

i.e. $T = \frac{\overline{X} - 12}{\sqrt{\frac{0.2684...}{20}}} \sim t_{(19)}$

Now $\overline{x} = 11.8$,

so $t = \frac{11.8 - 12}{\sqrt{\frac{0.2684...}{20}}} = -1.726$ (3 d.p.)

You're interested in the lower end of the distribution, so find the critical value, $t_{(19)}$, such that $P(T < t_{(19)}) = 0.05$ — this gives a critical value of -1.729. So the critical region is $Z < -1.729$. Since $-1.726 > -1.729$, the result does not lie in the critical region and is not significant. So there is insufficient evidence at the 5% level to reject H_0 in favour of the alternative hypothesis that the jelly worms are shorter.

Review Exercise — Chapter 4

Q1 a) He needs to make the assumption that the population follows a normal distribution.

b) $\left(\overline{X} - \frac{S}{\sqrt{n}} t_{(n-1)},\ \overline{X} + \frac{S}{\sqrt{n}} t_{(n-1)}\right)$

c) $n = 12$, so for $p = 0.975$, $t_{(11)} = 2.201$.
So 95% confidence interval

$= \left(50 - \frac{\sqrt{0.7}}{\sqrt{12}} \times 2.201, 50 + \frac{\sqrt{0.7}}{\sqrt{12}} \times 2.201\right)$

$= (49.5, 50.5)$ (to 3 sig.fig.)

Q2 9 lies outside this confidence interval, so there is evidence to doubt the claim.

Q3 a) i) One-tailed — Salma is only interested in whether the average height is greater than 160 cm.

ii) Two-tailed — Joy is interested in either an increase or a decrease in the mean diameter.

b) i) H_0: $\mu = 160$ cm and H_1: $\mu > 160$ cm

ii) H_0: $\mu = 2.2$ cm and H_1: $\mu \neq 2.2$ cm

Q4 A type I error — he rejects H_0 when it's actually true.

Q5 You'd use a t-test when the population follows a normal distribution, the population variance is unknown and the sample size is small.

Q6 H_0: $\mu = 45$, H_1: $\mu < 45$, $\alpha = 0.05$ and $\sigma^2 = 9$.
Under H_0,

$\overline{X} \sim N\left(45, \frac{9}{16}\right)$ and $Z = \frac{42 - 45}{3/4} = -4$

Critical region is $Z < -1.6449$.
$-4 < -1.6449$, so there is evidence to reject H_0 at the 5% level.

Q7 a) $\overline{x} = \frac{\sum x}{n} = \frac{197.8}{10} = 19.78$

$s^2 = \frac{n}{n-1}\left[\frac{\sum x^2}{n} - \left(\frac{\sum x}{n}\right)^2\right]$

$= \frac{10}{9}\left[\frac{3919.78}{10} - 19.78^2\right]$

$= \frac{10}{9} \times 0.7296 = 0.8106... = 0.811$ (3 s.f.)

b) H_0: $\mu = 20$ and H_1: $\mu < 20$. $\alpha = 0.05$.
The variance is unknown and $n = 10$, so you need to use a t-test with 9 degrees of freedom.

Under H_0, $T = \frac{\overline{X} - 20}{\sqrt{\frac{0.8106...}{10}}} \sim t_{(9)}$

$\overline{x} = 19.78 \Rightarrow t = \frac{19.78 - 20}{\sqrt{\frac{0.8106}{10}}} = -0.773$ (3 s.f.)

The critical value is t such that $P(T < t) = 0.05$. By symmetry, it's $-t$, where $P(T > t) = 0.05$, i.e. where $P(T < t) = 0.95$. $P(T < 1.833) = 0.95$, so the critical value is -1.833, and the critical region is $T < -1.833$.
$-0.733 > -1.833$, so the result is not significant at this level. There is no evidence at the 5% level to suggest that $\mu < 20$.

Exam-Style Questions — Chapter 4

Q1 Let μ = mean time taken to travel to work.
Then H_0: $\mu = 17$ and H_1: $\mu < 17$ ***[1 mark for both]***
n is large so you can estimate σ^2 with s^2 and use the Central Limit Theorem ***[1 mark]*** to say that $\overline{X} \sim N\left(\mu, \frac{\sigma^2}{n}\right)$. So $\overline{X} \sim N\left(17, \frac{2.3}{45}\right) = N(17, 0.0511...)$.

$\overline{x} = 16.55$,

so $z = \frac{16.55 - 17}{\sqrt{0.0511...}} = -1.9905$ (4 d.p.) ***[1 mark]***.

For a one-tailed test at a 5% significance level where the significant values are at the lower end of the distribution, you need a critical value, z, such that $P(Z < z) = 0.05$. This gives a critical value of -1.6449, so the critical region is $Z < -1.6449$ ***[1 mark]***.
Since $-1.9905 < -1.6449$, the result is significant and there is significant evidence at the 5% level to reject H_0 ***[1 mark]*** and support Samir's claim that the mean time taken to travel to work by the employees is less that 17 minutes ***[1 mark]***.

Q2 a) (i) The sample mean is the midpoint of the confidence interval so

$\overline{x} = \frac{1}{2}(49.20 + 50.20) = 49.70$ ***[1 mark]***.

(ii) The sample size is large, so use the confidence interval formula involving z.
To find the percentage confidence level of the interval, you need to find the value of z that was used and find p with $P(-z \le Z \le z) = p$.

The confidence interval is given by

$\left(\overline{X} - z\frac{s}{\sqrt{n}},\ \overline{X} + z\frac{s}{\sqrt{n}}\right)$ ***[1 mark]***

Taking the lower limit and substituting in what you know:

$$49.70 - z\frac{1.52982}{\sqrt{36}} = 49.20$$

$\Rightarrow z = 1.96$ (to 2 d.p.) ***[1 mark]***

Looking up $z = 1.96$ in the tables you get $p = 0.975$, so the confidence interval has a confidence level of 95% ***[1 mark]***.

Or you could use the fact that the width of the confidence interval is $\frac{2s}{\sqrt{n}}z$.

(iii) This is a reasonable claim ***[1 mark]***, as the claimed mean lies within the confidence interval ***[1 mark]***.

b) (i) $\overline{x} = \frac{395}{8} = 49.375$ kg ***[1 mark]***

$$s^2 = \frac{n}{n-1}\left[\frac{\sum x^2}{n} - \left(\frac{\sum x}{n}\right)^2\right]$$

$$= \frac{8}{7}\left[\frac{19503.4}{8} - \left(\frac{395}{8}\right)^2\right] = 0.03928...$$

[1 mark]

The population variance is unknown and the sample size is small, so you need to use a t-distribution ***[1 mark]***.

The confidence interval for the population mean is given by

$\left(\overline{X} - \frac{s}{\sqrt{n}}t_{(n-1)},\ \overline{X} + \frac{s}{\sqrt{n}}t_{(n-1)}\right)$.

This is a 99% confidence interval with $n = 8$, so you're looking for the value of $t_{(7)}$ such that $P(T < t_{(7)}) = 0.995$.

This gives $t_{(7)} = 3.499$ ***[1 mark]***.

So the 99% confidence interval is

$$\left(49.375 - \frac{\sqrt{0.03928...}}{\sqrt{8}} \times 3.499,\quad 49.375 + \frac{\sqrt{0.03928...}}{\sqrt{8}} \times 3.499\right)$$

[1 mark]

= (49.13, 49.62) (2 d.p.) ***[1 mark]***

(ii) This value does not lie in the above 99% confidence interval for the mean ***[1 mark]***. Based on this sample, there is evidence to doubt the claim that the mean volume of the bags is 50 litres ***[1 mark]***.

Q3 a) You need to make the assumption that the journey times follow a normal distribution ***[1 mark]***.

$\overline{x} = \frac{\sum x}{n} = \frac{324}{20} = 16.2$ mins ***[1 mark]***

$s^2 = \frac{\sum(x-\overline{x})^2}{n-1} = \frac{19.2}{19} \Rightarrow s = 1.005$ ***[1 mark]***

$n = 20$, so you need to look up $t_{(19)}$ in the tables.
And it's a 95% confidence interval, so read across to $p = 0.975$ to get $t_{(19)} = 2.093$ ***[1 mark]***.

The interval is given by:

$$\left(\overline{x} - \frac{s}{\sqrt{n}}t_{(n-1)},\ \overline{x} + \frac{s}{\sqrt{n}}t_{(n-1)}\right)$$

$$= \left(16.2 - \frac{1.005}{\sqrt{20}} \times 2.093,\quad 16.2 + \frac{1.005}{\sqrt{20}} \times 2.093\right)$$ ***[1 mark]***

$= (16.2 - 0.47, 16.2 + 0.47)$ ***[1 mark]***

$= (15.7, 16.7)$ (to 3 s.f.) ***[1 mark]***

b) Joe's claimed time of 15 minutes lies outside the 95% confidence interval, so there is evidence to doubt this claim. ***[1 mark]***

Q4 a) $\overline{x} = \frac{\sum x}{n} = \frac{490}{100} = 4.9$ m ***[1 mark]***

$$s^2 = \frac{n}{n-1}\left[\frac{\sum x^2}{n} - \left(\frac{\sum x}{n}\right)^2\right]$$

$= \frac{100}{99}\left[\frac{2421}{100} - 4.9^2\right]$ ***[1 mark]***

$= \frac{20}{99} = 0.202$ (to 3 d.p.) ***[1 mark]***

b) Let μ = mean height of trees in 2nd area.
$H_0: \mu = 5.1$ and $H_1: \mu \ne 5.1$ ***[1 mark]***

Under H_0, $\overline{X} \sim N\left(5.1, \frac{20/99}{100}\right)$ ***[1 mark]***

So $\overline{X} \sim N\left(5.1, \frac{1}{495}\right)$

$Z = \frac{4.9 - 5.1}{\sqrt{1/495}}$ ***[1 mark]*** $= -4.45$ ***[1 mark]***

This is a two-tailed test at the 1% level, so the critical values you need are z such that $P(Z < z) = 0.005$ and $P(Z > z) = 0.005$. Looking these up in the normal tables you get critical values of -2.5758 and 2.5758 ***[1 mark]***. Since $-4.45 < -2.576$, the result is significant. There is evidence to reject H_0 and to suggest that the trees in the second area have a different mean height ***[1 mark]***.

Q5 a) (i) $\sum x = 255$ and $\sum x^2 = 7291$.

$\overline{x} = \frac{255}{9} = \frac{85}{3} = 28.333$ (3 d.p.) ***[1 mark]***

$$s^2 = \frac{n}{n-1}\left[\frac{\sum x^2}{n} - \left(\frac{\sum x}{n}\right)^2\right]$$

$= \frac{9}{8}\left[\frac{7291}{9} - \left(\frac{255}{9}\right)^2\right] = 8.25$ ***[1 mark]***

The population variance is unknown and the sample size is small, so you need to use the t-distribution. This means you need to assume that the weights of the jars are normally distributed ***[1 mark]***.

The confidence interval for the population mean is given by $\left(\overline{X} - \frac{s}{\sqrt{n}}t_{(n-1)}, \overline{X} + \frac{s}{\sqrt{n}}t_{(n-1)}\right)$.

This is a 99% confidence interval with $n = 9$, so you're looking for the value of $t_{(8)}$ such that $P(T < t_{(8)}) = 0.995$.
This gives $t_{(8)} = 3.355$ ***[1 mark]***.

So the 99% confidence interval is

$$\left(\frac{85}{3} - \frac{\sqrt{8.25}}{\sqrt{9}}(3.355), \frac{85}{3} + \frac{\sqrt{8.25}}{\sqrt{9}}(3.355)\right)$$ ***[1 mark]***

= (25.12, 31.55) (2 d.p.) ***[1 mark]***

(ii) Ceara's claim is reasonable ***[1 mark]***, as 26 lies within the 99% confidence interval for the mean ***[1 mark]***.

b) Let μ = mean weight of jars of chilli flakes.
Then $H_0: \mu = 26$ and $H_1: \mu > 26$ ***[1 mark]***
n is small and the population variance of the weights of the jars of chilli flakes is unknown, so you need to estimate σ^2 with s^2 and use a t-test.

The assumption that you need to make is that the weights of the jars are normally distributed ***[1 mark]***.

Let $\overline{X}$ be the sample mean of the weights of jars.
Then under H_0, $T = \frac{\overline{X} - \mu}{s/\sqrt{n}} \sim t_{(n-1)}$,

i.e. $T = \frac{\overline{X} - 26}{\sqrt{\frac{8.25}{9}}} \sim t_{(8)}$

Now $\overline{x} = \frac{85}{3}$, so $t = \frac{\frac{85}{3} - 26}{\sqrt{\frac{8.25}{9}}}$ ***[1 mark]***

= 2.437 (3 d.p.) ***[1 mark]***

To test at a 5% significance level, you need the critical value $t_{(8)}$ such that $P(T > t_{(8)}) = 0.05$, i.e. $P(T < t_{(8)}) = 0.95$.

This gives a critical value of 1.86, so the critical region is $T > 1.86$ ***[1 mark]***.

2.437 > 1.86, so the result is significant and there is significant evidence at the 5% level to reject H_0 ***[1 mark]*** and support Megan's claim that the mean weight of the jars of chilli flakes is more than 26 g ***[1 mark]***.

c) The null hypothesis has been rejected when it was in fact true ***[1 mark]***, so this is a Type I error ***[1 mark]***.

Chapter 5: Chi-Squared Contingency Table Tests

1. Chi-Squared Contingency Table Tests

Exercise 1.1 — Contingency tables

Q1 For each observed frequency, you find the corresponding expected frequency using the formula $E_{ij} = \frac{R_i \times C_j}{T}$, i.e. you multiply the total frequency in its row by the total frequency in its column, and divide by the total number of observations. You get the following table:

	House value < £100 000	House value ≥ £100 000	Total
< 100 books	19.5	10.5	30
≥ 100 books	45.5	24.5	70
Total	65	35	100

Q2 First add row and column totals to the table:

		Maths grades			
		High	Medium	Low	Total
English grades	High	20	15	5	40
	Medium	16	19	15	50
	Low	12	9	14	35
	Total	48	43	34	125

Then, using the formula $E_{ij} = \frac{R_i \times C_j}{T}$, you get the following expected frequencies:

		Maths grades			
		High	Medium	Low	Total
English grades	High	15.36	13.76	10.88	40
	Medium	19.2	17.2	13.6	50
	Low	13.44	12.04	9.52	35
	Total	48	43	34	125

Q3 a) To make a contingency table, you need to change the percentages to frequencies. Use the percentages shown to work out how many of the 80 male and 120 female students choose each sport:

0.5 × 80 = 40 males choose table tennis,
0.35 × 80 = 28 males choose snooker,
and 0.15 × 80 = 12 males choose badminton.

0.4 × 120 = 48 females choose table tennis,
0.2 × 120 = 24 females choose snooker,
and 0.4 × 120 = 48 females choose badminton.

And include the row and column totals:

	Table tennis	Snooker	Badminton	Total
Male	40	28	12	80
Female	48	24	48	120
Total	88	52	60	200

b) Using the formula $E_{ij} = \frac{R_i \times C_j}{T}$, you get the following expected frequencies:

	Table tennis	Snooker	Badminton	Total
Male	35.2	20.8	24	80
Female	52.8	31.2	36	120
Total	88	52	60	200

Exercise 1.2 — Chi-squared (χ^2) contingency table tests

Q1 a) First add row and column totals to the table:

Age of resident		In favour of plan	Against plan	Total
	16-21	4	10	14
	22-49	7	23	30
	50-64	93	87	180
	65 or over	17	14	31
	Total	121	134	255

Now you can calculate the expected frequencies using the formula $E_{ij} = \frac{R_i \times C_j}{T}$, and draw the following table:

Observed frequency (O_i)	Expected Frequency (E_i)
4	6.64
7	14.24
93	85.41
17	14.71
10	7.36
23	15.76
87	94.59
14	16.29
255	255

b) The test statistic is $X^2 = \sum \frac{(O_i - E_i)^2}{E_i}$, so add a column to your table showing the values of $\frac{(O_i - E_i)^2}{E_i}$:

Observed frequency (O_i)	Expected Frequency (E_i)	$\frac{(O_i - E_i)^2}{E_i}$
4	6.64	1.0496
7	14.24	3.6810
93	85.41	0.6745
17	14.71	0.3565
10	7.36	0.9470
23	15.76	3.3260
87	94.59	0.6090
14	16.29	0.3219
255	255	10.966

So $X^2 = \sum \frac{(O_i - E_i)^2}{E_i} = 10.966$.

Q2 a) The 5% point of $\chi^2_{(3)} = x$ where $P(X \le x) = 0.95$. So the critical value = 7.815. 7.213 < 7.815, so there is no evidence of an association at the 5% level of significance.

b) The 1% point of $\chi^2_{(6)} = x$ where $P(X \le x) = 0.99$. So the critical value = 16.812. 18.147 > 16.812, so there is evidence to suggest an association at the 1% level of significance.

c) The 10% point of $\chi^2_{(9)} = x$ where $P(X \le x) = 0.9$. So the critical value = 14.684. 15.655 > 14.684, so there is evidence to suggest an association at the 10% level of significance.

Q3 First define the hypotheses:
H_0: no association between performance in piano and performance in violin, and
H_1: an association between performance in piano and performance in violin.

Next work out the expected frequencies under H_0 using the formula $E_{ij} = \frac{R_i \times C_j}{T}$, and list them in a table with the observed frequencies.

Observed frequency (O_i)	Expected Frequency (E_i)
32	18.88
24	31.78
17	22.34
54	48.09
98	80.98
34	56.93
12	31.03
43	52.24
65	36.73
379	379

Calculate the values of $\frac{(O_i - E_i)^2}{E_i}$, and sum them to find the value of the test statistic X^2:

Observed frequency (O_i)	Expected Frequency (E_i)	$\frac{(O_i - E_i)^2}{E_i}$
32	18.88	9.1173
24	31.78	1.9046
17	22.34	1.2764
54	48.09	0.7263
98	80.98	3.5772
34	56.93	9.2356
12	31.03	11.6707
43	52.24	1.6343
65	36.73	21.7586
379	379	60.901

So $X^2 = \sum \frac{(O_i - E_i)^2}{E_i} = 60.901$.

Under H_0, the sampling distribution of X^2 is approximately $\chi^2_{(\nu)}$, where $\nu = (3 - 1) \times (3 - 1) = 4$. So X^2 approximately follows a $\chi^2_{(4)}$ distribution.

The significance level is 1%, so look up the 1% point of $\chi^2_{(4)}$ in the table. $P(X \le x) = 0.99$ for $x = 13.277$, so the critical value is 13.277.

Since 60.901 > 13.277, the data is significant at the 1% level. So there is evidence to reject H_0 and to suggest that there is an association between performance in piano and performance in violin.

Q4 a) First add row and column totals to the table:

Age of member		In favour of longer hours	Against longer hours	Total
	16-20	3	8	11
	21-25	9	26	35
	26-30	72	87	159
	31-45	31	37	68
	46 or over	4	2	6
	Total	119	160	279

Then, using the formula $E_{ij} = \frac{R_i \times C_j}{T}$, you get the following expected frequencies:

Age of member		In favour of longer hours	Against longer hours	Total
	16-20	4.69	6.31	11
	21-25	14.93	20.07	35
	26-30	67.82	91.18	159
	31-45	29.00	39.00	68
	46 or over	2.56	3.44	6
	Total	119	160	279

b) Three of the expected frequencies are less than 5, which means the χ^2 approximation may not be valid. Grouping the age categories will ensure that every expected frequency is greater than 5 and so the χ^2 approximation should be valid.

Grouping the first two categories and the last two categories gives the following table:

Age of member		In favour of longer hours	Against longer hours	Total
	16-25	12	34	46
	26-30	72	87	159
	31 or over	35	39	74
	Total	119	160	279

c) First define the hypotheses:
H_0: no association between age and attitude to longer opening hours, and
H_1: an association between age and attitude to longer opening hours.

Next work out the expected frequencies under H_0 using the formula $E_{ij} = \frac{R_i \times C_j}{T}$, and list them in a table with the observed frequencies.

Observed frequency (O_i)	Expected Frequency (E_i)
12	19.62
72	67.82
35	31.56
34	26.38
87	91.18
39	42.44
279	279

Calculate the values of $\frac{(O_i - E_i)^2}{E_i}$, and sum them to find the value of the test statistic X^2:

Observed frequency (O_i)	Expected Frequency (E_i)	$\frac{(O_i - E_i)^2}{E_i}$
12	19.62	2.9594
72	67.82	0.2576
35	31.56	0.3750
34	26.38	2.2011
87	91.18	0.1916
39	42.44	0.2788
279	279	6.264

So $X^2 = \sum\frac{(O_i - E_i)^2}{E_i} = 6.264$.

Under H_0, the sampling distribution of X^2 is approximately $\chi^2_{(\nu)}$, where $\nu = (3 - 1) \times (2 - 1) = 2$. So X^2 approximately follows a $\chi^2_{(2)}$ distribution.

The significance level is 5%, so look up the 5% point of $\chi^2_{(2)}$ in the table. $P(X \leq x) = 0.95$ for $x = 5.991$, so the critical value is 5.991.

Since $6.264 > 5.991$, the data is significant at the 5% level. So there is evidence to reject H_0 and to suggest that there is an association between age and attitude to longer opening hours.

d) There are more people aged 26-30 in favour of longer opening hours than expected under H_0, and fewer people aged 26-30 against longer opening hours than expected.

Exercise 1.3 — 2 × 2 contingency tables

Q1 a) First add row and column totals to the contingency table:

		Obedience		
		Pass	Fail	Total
Agility	Pass	103	44	147
	Fail	22	31	53
	Total	125	75	200

Now you can calculate the expected frequencies using the formula $E_{ij} = \frac{R_i \times C_j}{T}$, and draw the following table:

Observed frequency (O_i)	Expected Frequency (E_i)
103	91.875
22	33.125
44	55.125
31	19.875
200	200

b) The test statistic is $X^2 = \sum\frac{(|O_i - E_i| - 0.5)^2}{E_i}$, so add a column to your table showing the values of $\frac{(|O_i - E_i| - 0.5)^2}{E_i}$:

Observed frequency (O_i)	Expected Frequency (E_i)	$\frac{(|O_i - E_i| - 0.5)^2}{E_i}$
103	91.875	1.2287
22	33.125	3.4080
44	55.125	2.0479
31	19.875	5.6800
200	200	12.365

So $X^2 = \sum\frac{(|O_i - E_i| - 0.5)^2}{E_i} = 12.365$.

Q2 a) Use the categories: 'Men', 'Women', 'Vegetarian' and 'Not vegetarian', and include the totals in your table:

	Vegetarian	Not vegetarian	Total
Men	12	35	47
Women	22	21	43
Total	34	56	90

b) Calculate the expected frequencies using the formula $E_{ij} = \frac{R_i \times C_j}{T}$, and draw the following table:

Observed frequency (O_i)	Expected Frequency (E_i)
12	17.76
22	16.24
35	29.24
21	26.76
90	90

Since the contingency table is a 2 × 2 table, the test statistic is $X^2 = \sum \frac{(|O_i - E_i| - 0.5)^2}{E_i}$. So add a column to your table showing the values of $\frac{(|O_i - E_i| - 0.5)^2}{E_i}$:

Observed frequency (O_i)	Expected Frequency (E_i)	$\frac{(\lvert O_i - E_i\rvert - 0.5)^2}{E_i}$
12	17.76	1.5579
22	16.24	1.7037
35	29.24	0.9462
21	26.76	1.0339
90	90	5.242

So $X^2 = \sum \frac{(|O_i - E_i| - 0.5)^2}{E_i} = 5.242$.

Q3 First define the hypotheses:
H_0: no association between height of gymnast and score on vault, and
H_1: an association between height of gymnast and score on vault.

Next work out the expected frequencies under H_0 using the formula $E_{ij} = \frac{R_i \times C_j}{T}$, and list them in a table with the observed frequencies.

Observed frequency (O_i)	Expected Frequency (E_i)
16	15.12
20	20.88
26	26.88
38	37.12
100	100

Since this is a 2 × 2 table, you need to calculate the values of $\frac{(|O_i - E_i| - 0.5)^2}{E_i}$, then sum them to find the value of the test statistic X^2:

Observed frequency (O_i)	Expected Frequency (E_i)	$\frac{(\lvert O_i - E_i\rvert - 0.5)^2}{E_i}$
16	15.12	0.0096
20	20.88	0.0069
26	26.88	0.0054
38	37.12	0.0039
100	100	0.026

So $X^2 = \sum \frac{(|O_i - E_i| - 0.5)^2}{E_i} = 0.026$.

Under H_0, the sampling distribution of X^2 is approximately $\chi^2_{(\nu)}$, where $\nu = (2 - 1) \times (2 - 1) = 1$. So X^2 approximately follows a $\chi^2_{(1)}$ distribution.

The significance level is 1%, so look up the 1% point of $\chi^2_{(1)}$ in the table. $P(X \le x) = 0.99$ for $x = 6.635$, so the critical value is 6.635.

Since 0.026 < 6.635, the data is not significant at the 1% level. So there is no evidence to reject H_0 and to support the coach's claim that there is an association between the height of a gymnast and their score on vault.

Q4 a) First define the hypotheses:
H_0: no association between doing the exercise programme and quality of sleep, and
H_1: an association between doing the exercise programme and quality of sleep.

Add row and column totals to the table:

	Good sleep	Poor sleep	Total
Did exercise programme	58	22	80
Didn't do exercise programme	43	37	80
Total	101	59	160

Next work out the expected frequencies under H_0 using the formula $E_{ij} = \frac{R_i \times C_j}{T}$, and list them in a table with the observed frequencies.

Observed frequency (O_i)	Expected Frequency (E_i)
58	50.5
43	50.5
22	29.5
37	29.5
160	160

Since this is a 2 × 2 table, you need to calculate the values of $\frac{(|O_i - E_i| - 0.5)^2}{E_i}$, then sum them to find the value of the test statistic X^2:

Observed frequency (O_i)	Expected Frequency (E_i)	$\frac{(\lvert O_i - E_i\rvert - 0.5)^2}{E_i}$
58	50.5	0.9703
43	50.5	0.9703
22	29.5	1.6610
37	29.5	1.6610
160	160	5.263

So $X^2 = \sum \frac{(|O_i - E_i| - 0.5)^2}{E_i} = 5.263$.

Under H_0, the sampling distribution of X^2 is approximately $\chi^2_{(\nu)}$, where $\nu = (2 - 1) \times (2 - 1) = 1$. So X^2 approximately follows a $\chi^2_{(1)}$ distribution.

The significance level is 5%, so look up the 5% point of $\chi^2_{(1)}$ in the table. $P(X \le x) = 0.95$ for $x = 3.841$, so the critical value is 3.841.

Since 5.263 > 3.841, the data is significant at the 5% level. So there is evidence to reject H_0 and to suggest that there is an association between doing the exercise programme and quality of sleep.

b) There were fewer people who didn't do the exercise programme and had good sleep than expected under H_0.

c) $P(X \le x) = 0.99$ for $x = 6.635$, so the critical value for a test at the 1% level of significance is 6.635. Since 5.263 < 6.635, the data is not significant at the 1% level. So if you tested at the 1% level you would come to a different conclusion — you would conclude that there is no evidence at this level to reject H_0 and to suggest that there is an association between doing the exercise programme and quality of sleep.

Review Exercise — Chapter 5

Q1 Assuming the variables are independent, the expected frequencies are given by $E_{ij} = \frac{R_i \times C_j}{T}$.

a)

	Result of first driving test		
	Pass	Fail	Total
Male	25.6	14.4	40
Female	38.4	21.6	60
Total	64	36	100

b) First add row and column totals to the table:

		Colour of cat			
		Black	White	Tabby	Total
Length of tail	Long	14	15	31	60
	Short	19	11	10	40
	Total	33	26	41	100

Then calculate the expected frequencies:

		Colour of cat			
		Black	White	Tabby	Total
Length of tail	Long	19.8	15.6	24.6	60
	Short	13.2	10.4	16.4	40
	Total	33	26	41	100

Q2 a) Since every expected frequency is greater than 5, a χ^2 test should be valid.

The test statistic is $X^2 = \sum\frac{(O_i - E_i)^2}{E_i}$, so add a column to the table showing the values of $\frac{(O_i - E_i)^2}{E_i}$:

Observed frequency (O_i)	Expected Frequency (E_i)	$\frac{(O_i - E_i)^2}{E_i}$
12	12	0
18	18	0
7	9.2	0.5261
16	13.8	0.3507
21	18.8	0.2574
26	28.2	0.1716
100	100	1.306

So $X^2 = \sum\frac{(O_i - E_i)^2}{E_i} = 1.306$.

b) One of the expected frequencies is less than 5, so a χ^2 test may not be valid.

c) Since every expected frequency is greater than 5, a χ^2 test should be valid.

There are 4 pairs of frequencies, which means the contingency table is a 2 × 2 table. That means the test statistic is $X^2 = \sum\frac{(|O_i - E_i| - 0.5)^2}{E_i}$, so add a column to your table showing the values of $\frac{(|O_i - E_i| - 0.5)^2}{E_i}$:

Observed frequency (O_i)	Expected Frequency (E_i)	$\frac{(\lvert O_i - E_i\rvert - 0.5)^2}{E_i}$
45	49.8	0.3713
38	33.2	0.5569
75	70.2	0.2634
42	46.8	0.3951
200	200	1.587

So $X^2 = \sum\frac{(|O_i - E_i| - 0.5)^2}{E_i} = 1.587$.

Q3 The 1% point of $\chi^2_{(4)} = x$ where $P(X \le x) = 0.99$. $P(X \le x) = 0.99$ for $x = 13.277$, so the critical value is 13.277. 8.3 < 13.277, so there is no evidence, at the 1% level, of an association between the variables.

Q4 a) Assuming no association, the expected frequencies are given by $E_{ij} = \frac{R_i \times C_j}{T}$, which gives you the following table:

Observed frequency (O_i)	Expected Frequency (E_i)
22	14.4
14	21.6
26	22.4
30	33.6
12	23.2
46	34.8
150	150

b) The test statistic is $X^2 = \sum \frac{(O_i - E_i)^2}{E_i}$, so add a column to the table showing the values of $\frac{(O_i - E_i)^2}{E_i}$:

Observed frequency (O_i)	Expected Frequency (E_i)	$\frac{(O_i - E_i)^2}{E_i}$
22	14.4	4.0111
14	21.6	2.6741
26	22.4	0.5786
30	33.6	0.3857
12	23.2	5.4069
46	34.8	3.6046
150	150	16.661

So $X^2 = \sum \frac{(O_i - E_i)^2}{E_i} = 16.661$.

c) H_0: there is no difference in potato yield between the two fields, and
H_1: there is a difference in potato yield between the two fields.
I.e. H_0 is that potato yield is independent of the field a plant is grown in.

Under H_0, the sampling distribution of X^2 is approximately $\chi^2_{(\nu)}$, where $\nu = (2 - 1) \times (3 - 1) = 2$. So X^2 approximately follows a $\chi^2_{(2)}$ distribution.

The significance level is 10%, so look up the 10% point of $\chi^2_{(2)}$ in the table. $P(X \leq x) = 0.9$ for $x = 4.605$, so the critical value is 4.605.

Since $16.661 > 4.605$, the data is significant at the 10% level. So there is evidence to reject H_0 and to suggest that there is a difference in potato yield between the two fields.

Q5 Define the hypotheses:
H_0: no association between gender and liking olives, and
H_1: an association between gender and liking olives.
Add row and column totals to the table:

	Likes olives	Dislikes olives	Total
Male	22	18	40
Female	30	30	60
Total	52	48	100

Next work out the expected frequencies under H_0 using the formula $E_{ij} = \frac{R_i \times C_j}{T}$, and list them in a table with the observed frequencies.

Observed frequency (O_i)	Expected Frequency (E_i)
22	20.8
30	31.2
18	19.2
30	28.8
100	100

Since this is a 2 × 2 table, you need to calculate the values of $\frac{(|O_i - E_i| - 0.5)^2}{E_i}$, then sum them to find the value of the test statistic X^2:

Observed frequency (O_i)	Expected Frequency (E_i)	$\frac{(|O_i - E_i| - 0.5)^2}{E_i}$
22	20.8	0.0236
30	31.2	0.0157
18	19.2	0.0255
30	28.8	0.0170
100	100	0.082

So $X^2 = \sum \frac{(|O_i - E_i| - 0.5)^2}{E_i} = 0.082$.
Under H_0, the sampling distribution of X^2 is approximately $\chi^2_{(\nu)}$, where $\nu = (2 - 1) \times (2 - 1) = 1$. So X^2 approximately follows a $\chi^2_{(1)}$ distribution.

The significance level is 5%, so look up the 5% point of $\chi^2_{(1)}$ in the table. $P(X \leq x) = 0.95$ for $x = 3.841$, so the critical value is 3.841.

Since $0.082 < 3.841$, the data is not significant at the 5% level. So there is no evidence to reject H_0 and to suggest that there is an association between gender and liking olives.

Exam-Style Questions — Chapter 5

1 Define the hypotheses:
H_0: no association between age and favourite flavour of ice cream, and
H_1: an association between age and favourite flavour of ice cream ***[1 mark for both hypotheses correct].***

Work out the expected frequencies under H_0 using the formula $E_{ij} = \frac{R_i \times C_j}{T}$, and list them in a table with the observed frequencies.

Observed frequency (O_i)	Expected Frequency (E_i)
10	11.52
24	24
7	5.28
7	7.2
14	12.48
26	26
4	5.72
8	7.8
100	100

[1 mark for using row and column totals to find the expected frequencies and 1 mark for all values of E_i correct.]

The test statistic is $X^2 = \sum \frac{(O_i - E_i)^2}{E_i}$, so add a column to the table showing the values of $\frac{(O_i - E_i)^2}{E_i}$:

Observed frequency (O_i)	Expected Frequency (E_i)	$\frac{(O_i - E_i)^2}{E_i}$
10	11.52	0.2006
24	24	0
7	5.28	0.5603
7	7.2	0.0056
14	12.48	0.1851
26	26	0
4	5.72	0.5172
8	7.8	0.0051
100	100	1.474

[1 mark for the formula $(O_i - E_i)^2 / E_i$ and 1 mark for all values of $(O_i - E_i)^2 / E_i$ correct.]

So $X^2 = \sum \frac{(O_i - E_i)^2}{E_i} = 1.474$ ***[1 mark].***

Under H_0, the sampling distribution of X^2 is approximately $\chi^2_{(\nu)}$, where $\nu = (4 - 1) \times (2 - 1) = 3$ ***[1 mark].*** So X^2 approximately follows a $\chi^2_{(3)}$ distribution.

The significance level is 5%, so look up the 5% point of $\chi^2_{(3)}$ in the table. $P(X \leq x) = 0.95$ for $x = 7.815$, so the critical value is 7.815 ***[1 mark].***

Since $1.474 < 7.815$, the data is not significant at the 5% level. So there is no evidence to reject H_0 and to suggest that there is an association between age and favourite flavour of ice cream ***[1 mark].***

2 **a)** Define the hypotheses:
H_0: no association between train arriving on time and station, and
H_1: an association between train arriving on time and station ***[1 mark for both hypotheses correct].***

Work out the expected frequencies under H_0 using the formula $E_{ij} = \frac{R_i \times C_j}{T}$, and list them in a table with the observed frequencies.

Observed frequency (O_i)	Expected Frequency (E_i)
40	36
56	45
24	39
20	24
19	30
41	26
200	200

[1 mark for using row and column totals to find the expected frequencies and 1 mark for all values of E_i correct.]

The test statistic is $X^2 = \sum \frac{(O_i - E_i)^2}{E_i}$, so add a column to the table showing the values of $\frac{(O_i - E_i)^2}{E_i}$:

Observed frequency (O_i)	Expected Frequency (E_i)	$\frac{(O_i - E_i)^2}{E_i}$
40	36	0.4444
56	45	2.6889
24	39	5.7692
20	24	0.6667
19	30	4.0333
41	26	8.6538
200	200	22.256

[1 mark for the formula $(O_i - E_i)^2/E_i$ and 1 mark for all values of $(O_i - E_i)^2/E_i$ correct.]

So $X^2 = \sum \frac{(O_i - E_i)^2}{E_i} = 22.256$ ***[1 mark].***

Under H_0, the sampling distribution of X^2 is approximately $\chi^2_{(\nu)}$, where $\nu = (3 - 1) \times (2 - 1) = 2$ ***[1 mark].*** So X^2 approximately follows a $\chi^2_{(2)}$ distribution.

The significance level is 1%, so look up the 1% point of $\chi^2_{(2)}$ in the table. $P(X \leq x) = 0.99$ for $x = 9.210$, so the critical value is 9.210 ***[1 mark].***

Since $22.256 > 9.210$, the data is significant at the 1% level. So there is evidence to reject H_0 and to suggest that there is an association between a train arriving on time and the station it arrives at ***[1 mark].***

b) There are fewer trains arriving on time than expected under H_0 at Station 3 ***[1 mark]***, and more trains arriving late than expected at Station 3 ***[1 mark].***

3 a) To make a contingency table, you need to change the percentages to frequencies. Use the percentages shown to work out how many of each group gave each rating:

$0.56 \times 200 = 112$ club members said 'enjoyable', and $0.44 \times 200 = 88$ club members said 'not enjoyable'.
$0.64 \times 200 = 128$ of the other people said 'enjoyable', and $0.36 \times 200 = 72$ of the other people said 'not enjoyable'.

And include the row and column totals:

	Film rating		
	Enjoyable	Not enjoyable	Total
Club members	112	88	200
Others	128	72	200
Total	240	160	400

[1 mark for both 'enjoyable' values correct and 1 mark for both 'not enjoyable' values correct.]

b) Define the hypotheses:
H_0: film rating is independent of belonging to the film club, and
H_1: film rating is not independent of belonging to the film club
[1 mark for both hypotheses correct].

Work out the expected frequencies under H_0 using the formula $E_{ij} = \frac{R_i \times C_j}{T}$, and list them in a table with the observed frequencies.

Observed frequency (O_i)	Expected Frequency (E_i)
112	120
128	120
88	80
72	80
400	400

[1 mark for using row and column totals to find the expected frequencies and 1 mark for all values of E_i correct.]

Since this is a 2×2 table, you need to calculate the values of $\frac{(|O_i - E_i| - 0.5)^2}{E_i}$, then sum them to find the value of the test statistic X^2:

Observed frequency (O_i)	Expected Frequency (E_i)	$\frac{(\|O_i - E_i\| - 0.5)^2}{E_i}$
112	120	0.4688
128	120	0.4688
88	80	0.7031
72	80	0.7031
400	400	2.344

[1 mark for the formula $(|O_i - E_i| - 0.5)^2 / E_i$ and 1 mark for all values of $(|O_i - E_i| - 0.5)^2 / E_i$ correct.]

So $X^2 = \sum \frac{(|O_i - E_i| - 0.5)^2}{E_i} = 2.344$ ***[1 mark]***

Under H_0, the sampling distribution of X^2 is approximately $\chi^2_{(\nu)}$, where $\nu = (2 - 1) \times (2 - 1) = 1$ ***[1 mark]***. So X^2 approximately follows a $\chi^2_{(1)}$ distribution.

The significance level is 5%, so look up the 5% point of $\chi^2_{(1)}$ in the table. $P(X \leq x) = 0.95$ for $x = 3.841$, so the critical value is 3.841 ***[1 mark]***.

Since $2.344 < 3.841$, the data is not significant at the 5% level. So there is no evidence to reject H_0 and to suggest that there is an association between the film rating given and whether or not a person belongs to the film club ***[1 mark]***.

c) There were slightly fewer people belonging to the film club who rated the film as 'enjoyable' than expected under H_0 ***[1 mark]***.

4 a) Define the hypotheses:
H_0: no association between proportion of this species of bumblebee and location of conservation area, and
H_1: an association between proportion of this species of bumblebee and location of conservation area
[1 mark for both hypotheses correct].

Work out the expected frequencies under H_0 using the formula $E_{ij} = \frac{R_i \times C_j}{T}$, and list them in a table with the observed frequencies.

Observed frequency (O_i)	Expected Frequency (E_i)
115	105
75	70
60	75
305	315
205	210
240	225
1000	1000

[1 mark for using row and column totals to find the expected frequencies and 1 mark for all values of E_i correct.]

The test statistic is $X^2 = \sum \frac{(O_i - E_i)^2}{E_i}$, so add a column to the table showing the values of $\frac{(O_i - E_i)^2}{E_i}$:

Observed frequency (O_i)	Expected Frequency (E_i)	$\frac{(O_i - E_i)^2}{E_i}$
115	105	0.9524
75	70	0.3571
60	75	3
305	315	0.3175
205	210	0.1190
240	225	1
1000	1000	5.746

[1 mark for the formula $(O_i - E_i)^2/E_i$ and 1 mark for all values of $(O_i - E_i)^2/E_i$ correct.]

So $X^2 = \sum\frac{(O_i - E_i)^2}{E_i} = 5.746$ ***[1 mark]***.

Under H_0, the sampling distribution of X^2 is approximately $\chi^2_{(\nu)}$, where $\nu = (3 - 1) \times (2 - 1) = 2$ ***[1 mark]***. So X^2 approximately follows a $\chi^2_{(2)}$ distribution.

The significance level is 10%, so look up the 10% point of $\chi^2_{(2)}$ in the table. $P(X \leq x) = 0.9$ for $x = 4.605$, so the critical value is 4.605 ***[1 mark]***.

Since 5.746 > 4.605, the data is significant at the 10% level. So there is evidence to reject H_0 and to suggest that there is an association between the proportion of this species of bumblebee and the location of the conservation area ***[1 mark]***.

b) There were fewer bumblebees of the species being studied observed in Yorkshire than expected under H_0 ***[1 mark]***.

c) Look up the 5% point of $\chi^2_{(2)}$ in the table. $P(X \leq x) = 0.95$ for $x = 5.991$, so the critical value is 5.991 ***[1 mark]***.

Since 5.746 < 5.991, the data is not significant at the 5% level. So there is no evidence to reject H_0 and to suggest that there is an association between the proportion of this species of bumblebee and the location of the conservation area ***[1 mark]***.

Glossary

Alternative hypothesis
The statement that you will accept instead if you decide to reject the **null hypothesis** in a **hypothesis test.** It gives a range of values for the **parameter** and is usually written H_1.

Association
An association between two variables means that they change together in some way.

Chi-squared test
A **hypothesis test** used to determine whether there is an **association** between two variables.

Confidence interval
A range of values, calculated from sample data, with a specified probability of containing a **population parameter**.

Contingency table
A two-way table showing the numbers of observations fitting particular combinations of categories.

Continuous random variable
A **random variable** which is measured on a continuous scale. It may take any value in a given range (i.e. with no 'gaps' between possible values).

Critical region
In a **hypothesis test**, the set of all values of the **test statistic** that would cause you to reject the **null hypothesis**.

Cumulative distribution function
A function, F(x), giving the probability that a **random variable**, X, will be less than or equal to a particular value, x.

Discrete random variable
A **random variable** with 'gaps' between its possible values.

E

Expected frequency
In a **chi-squared test**, an expected frequency is the number of observations that would fit a particular combination of categories in a **contingency table** if there is no **association** between the two variables.

Expected value
The expected value of a **random variable** is the 'expected' mean of a large number of readings.

Hypothesis
A statement or claim that you want to test.

Hypothesis test
A method of testing a **hypothesis** using observed sample data.

Independence
Two variables are independent if there is no **association** between them.

Lower quartile of a continuous random variable
The value that a **random variable** is less than or equal to with probability 0.25. Often written Q_1.

Mean of a random variable
The 'expected' mean of a large number of readings.
Also known as the **expected value**.

Median of a continuous random variable
The value that a **random variable** is less than or equal to with probability 0.5. Often written Q_2.

Normal distribution
A 'bell-shaped' continuous **probability distribution** where the further from the mean a value is, the less likely it is to occur.

Null hypothesis
Usually written H_0, a null hypothesis is a statement to be tested during a **hypothesis test**. In a test of the value of a **population parameter**, the null hypothesis gives a specific value to the parameter. In a **chi-squared test**, the null hypothesis is that there is no **association** between the two variables.

One-tailed test
A **hypothesis test** is 'one-tailed' if the values of the **test statistic** that favour the **alternative hypothesis** are at only one end of that test statistic's **sampling distribution**. E.g. it says $p < a$ or $p > a$ for a **parameter** p and constant a.

Parameter
A quantity that describes a characteristic of a **population**.

Percentiles of a continuous random variable
Percentiles divide a **probability distribution** into 100 parts. The nth percentile is the value that a **random variable** is less than or equal to with probability $\frac{n}{100}$. Often written P_n.

Piecewise function
A function f(x) which is defined by different formulas for different ranges of x.

Poisson distribution
A discrete **probability distribution** which models the probability that x events occur in a period of time or space.

Population
The whole group that you want to investigate, consisting of every single person/item/animal.

Probability density function (p.d.f.)
A function f(x) whose integral over a certain range gives the probability of a **continuous random variable** taking a value in that range.

Probability distribution
A description of the possible values a **random variable** can take, along with a way to find the probability of those values (e.g. a **probability function** or a **p.d.f.**).

Probability function
A function that generates the probabilities of a **discrete random variable** taking each of its possible values.

R

Random variable
A variable taking different values with specific probabilities.

Rectangular distribution
A continuous **probability distribution** where all values in a given range are equally likely.

Sample mean
A **statistic** used to estimate the mean of a **population**. It's the sum of the observed values in a sample divided by the sample size.

Sampling distribution
The **probability distribution** of a **statistic** — giving all the possible values that the statistic can take, along with their probabilities.

Significance level (α)
Determines how unlikely the observed value of the **test statistic** needs to be (under H_0) before rejecting the **null hypothesis** in a **hypothesis test**.

Significant result
The observed value of a **test statistic** is significant if, under H_0, it has a probability lower than the **significance level**.

Standard deviation of a random variable
The 'expected' standard deviation of a large number of readings. Found by taking the square root of the variance.

Standard error
The standard deviation of the **sampling distribution** of a **statistic**.

Standard normal variable, Z
A **random variable** that follows a **normal distribution** with mean 0 and variance 1.

Statistic
A quantity that is calculated using only observations from a sample.

Test statistic
A **statistic** calculated from sample data which is used to decide whether or not to reject the **null hypothesis** in a **hypothesis test**.

Two-tailed test
A **hypothesis test** is 'two-tailed' if the values of the **test statistic** that favour the **alternative hypothesis** are at both ends of that test statistic's **sampling distribution**. E.g. it says $p \neq a$ for a **parameter** p and constant a.

Upper quartile of a continuous random variable
The value that a **random variable** is less than or equal to with probability 0.75. Often written Q_3.

Variance of a random variable
The 'expected' variance of a large number of readings.

Y

Yates' continuity correction
An adjustment made to the **test statistic** in a **chi-squared test** when you have a 2 × 2 **contingency table**.

***Z*-tables**
Tables relating to the **standard normal variable** (Z) — such as the **cumulative distribution function** $\Phi(z)$, and the percentage-points table.

Index

S2 Formula Sheet

The formulas below will be included in the formula book for your exams — make sure you know exactly **when you need them** and **how to use them.**

Discrete Distributions

For a discrete random variable X taking values x_i with probabilities p_i:

Expectation (mean): $E(X) = \mu = \Sigma x_i p_i$

Variance: $Var(X) = \sigma^2 = \Sigma(x_i - \mu)^2 p_i = \Sigma x_i^2 p_i - \mu^2 = E(X^2) - \mu^2$

For a function g(X): $E(g(X)) = \Sigma\, g(x_i)\, p_i$

Standard discrete distribution:

Distribution of X	$P(X = x)$	Mean	Variance
Poisson $Po(\lambda)$	$e^{-\lambda}\frac{\lambda^x}{x!}$	λ	λ

Continuous Distributions

For a continuous random variable X having probability density function (p.d.f.) $f(x)$:

Expectation (mean): $E(X) = \mu = \int x\, f(x)\, dx$

Variance: $Var(X) = \sigma^2 = \int (x - \mu)^2 f(x)\, dx = \int x^2 f(x)\, dx - \mu^2 = E(X^2) - \mu^2$

For a function g(X): $E(g(X)) = \int g(x)\, f(x)\, dx$

Cumulative distribution function: $F(x) = P(X \leq x) = \int_{-\infty}^{x} f(t)\, dt$

Standard continuous distribution:

Distribution of X	p.d.f.	Mean	Variance
Uniform (rectangular) on $[a, b]$	$\frac{1}{b - a}$	$\frac{1}{2}(a + b)$	$\frac{1}{12}(b - a)^2$

Sampling Distributions

For a random sample of n observations from $N(\mu, \sigma^2)$:

$$\frac{\overline{X} - \mu}{\frac{\sigma}{\sqrt{n}}} \sim N(0, 1) \qquad \frac{\overline{X} - \mu}{\frac{S}{\sqrt{n}}} \sim t_{n-1}$$

Distribution-free Tests

χ^2 contingency table tests:

$$\sum \frac{(O_i - E_i)^2}{E_i} \text{ is approximately distributed as } \chi^2$$

MAS2T61